Government
and Agriculture

Government

and Agriculture:

ECONOMIC POLICY

IN A DEMOCRATIC SOCIETY

Dale E. Hathaway

PROFESSOR OF AGRICULTURAL ECONOMICS

MICHIGAN STATE UNIVERSITY

THE MACMILLAN COMPANY, NEW YORK

COLLIER-MACMILLAN LIMITED, LONDON

Library of Congress catalog card number: 63–11797

The Macmillan Company, New York
Collier-Macmillan Canada, Ltd., Toronto, Ontario

Printed in the United States of America

Preface

This is not a book on the history of agricultural policy in the United States. This is not to imply that history is unimportant or that it is unnecessary in the understanding of current events. The opposite will be obvious, for at certain points it becomes necessary to understand the evolution of institutions and events in order to grasp the current situation. But history is used in this book only to further our understanding of the current scene, and no claim is made that the history considered relevant for this task is in any sense comprehensive or inclusive.

Neither is it intended as a book on what United States agricultural policy ought to be, either at present or in the future. What policy *ought* to be is a function of beliefs, values, facts, and weights attached to them at a particular time. I am inherently suspicious of blanket policy prescriptions for a variety of reasons. Underlying values change, society's goals for agriculture change, the economic situation or reality changes, the political forces that formulate policies change, and with such changes what should be considered the "best" policy for agriculture should change.

This is intended to be a book *about* agricultural policy in the United States since World War II. It is done with the belief that policy can be understood only if one understands the forces that underlie it and the processes that produce it. Thus, the book attempts to deal with those aspects of United States agricultural policy as well as with the usual economic background and consequences of various policy proposals.

Even though the broad term "government and agriculture" is used in the title and throughout the text, no attempt has been made to encompass all of the public action pertaining to agricul-

v

ture. This book concentrates upon the public action generally termed "price-and-income" policy and generally ignores many important and long-standing public policies affecting agriculture, including some which have major indirect effects upon farm income.

In many ways, federal government intervention in agriculture is greater than in perhaps any other sector of the economy. This is puzzling and alarming to many persons who regard farming as the remaining outpost of free enterprise in an economy increasingly dominated by big business, big labor, and big government. It is hoped that this book will indicate why the government intervention has occurred, why it has persisted, and what future directions it may follow.

Pressures are great on one hand to return agriculture to its historical free market position, while other pressures push for an extension of government activity in agriculture. Either move will mark a major change in our social, economic, and political structure. It is hoped that this book will provide a benchmark from which to measure these changes and suggest points where such changes will bring economic and political stress. It also may point the direction that future policy may take if certain political or economic conditions change.

The intellectual debts implicit in this manuscript are numerous and, where possible, I have tried to make them obvious by noting published material upon which I have depended heavily. Beyond that, I have received valuable comments from W. Keith Bryant and George Brandow on the entire manuscript, and from Glenn L. Johnson on certain parts. Equally important to the development of my ideas has been the stimulation of capable colleagues over the years at Michigan State University, in the government, and at the University of Chicago, where most of the writing was done. Special thanks are due to: Mrs. Josephine Guemple who typed numerous versions of the manuscript; Mrs. Lou Ritchie who helped with the manuscript editing; my family who tolerated South Chicago with me; the University of Chicago which supported us while we were there; and those who "minded the store" while I was away.

DALE E. HATHAWAY
East Lansing, Michigan

Table of Contents

                                                               vii

Introduction

Public economic policy is a part of our daily lives in a complex modern society, and an important determinant of the course taken by our economy. Yet not many of us stop to consider it carefully, let alone attempt to understand all of its complexities. This is a discussion of public policy in one area—government policy for United States agriculture. However, even this would be too much for one book and, therefore, it concentrates upon a single set of policies which are generally termed "income policies."

The term *public policy* carries implications which need to be considered. First, the concept of policy implies an action or course of conduct. Second, the idea of public implies some sort of group action, in this case group action taken via the mechanism of the federal government.

When these elements are introduced and combined with the term *economic*, we have produced something that tends to be a complex blend of its various parts. There is a tendency to look at public economic policies (at least at agricultural policy) in terms of only one of its parts and, failing to recognize the reasons for a given direction, to dismiss it as a subject not worthy of further examination.

When the idea of courses or lines of action is introduced, it becomes necessary to consider three elements: ideas of what people want from and for the economy, ideas as to where and how things are proceeding at present, and facts and principles as to the forces that will move us in various directions. These ideas about what the various people want are called *values*. Ideas about where we are and how things are proceeding are *beliefs*. When people find that things *are* different in the world than they believe they *ought to be,* they will attempt to take actions which will bring them closer to where they want to be. Facts and principles enable us to understand the forces that will help or hinder in reaching a particular situation.

One of the ways which modern democratic society has devised to help bring people closer to the aspirations held by a majority of the members of the society, is governmental action. This is the "public" portion of public economic policy. However, we soon find that in most areas different individuals have somewhat different aspirations and that the achievement of the aspirations of some will diminish the achievement of someone else's. Or, in some cases, circumstances are such that the achievement of one aspiration (even if everyone shares it) will diminish the achievement of another one shared by all. This means that public policy has to make some choices and, in a democratic society, these choices are made via the political processes. Thus, a second part of public economic policy is the politics of that policy for, as we shall see, who is elected influences the use of government power and, therefore, the course of the economy.

The third element in the discussion of public economic policy is the "economic" aspects of the policies under discussion. These are the most widely discussed and probably the best understood facets of farm policy. The primary reason for this is that a great deal of attention has been given to this phase of policy by economists, just as specialists in engineering and map reading have developed these phases of navigation into careful analyses of how to get to a given point.

There is a good deal of controversy as to whether economists should be involved in determining where we should go or whether they should just determine the best way to get there once the ending point has been decided. This leads many lay people and some economists to one of two extreme positions, neither of which is tenable. Some assert that economics is the whole of public economic policy and that the other elements are merely capricious deviations which thwart the steering of the "correct" policy. On the other side are those who feel that economics is the application of stale theories which are irrelevant to the solution of the problems of the real world and, therefore, have no contribution to make to the formulation of public policy.

The first position leads to such statements as, "Good (sound) economics is the best politics." What usually is meant by such a statement is that the speaker believes the economic concepts such as "efficiency" and "growth" are of such importance to most people that programs which have these values as their major objective will gather strong political support.

The second position is often expressed as, "Those issues may be important in theory, but they really are not important in practice." Such persons often mean that they either doubt that some economic facts and principles even exist, or that their importance is great enough to be considered. These are the "Damn the torpedoes—full speed ahead!" group.

The Relevant Variables in Farm Policy

The understanding of public economic policy is not helped particularly by the discussion of "good" and 'bad" values or "good" and "bad" politics or "good" and "bad" economic principles and theories. A more appropriate terminology might be "relevant" and "irrelevant" values, politics, and economic facts, principles, and theories.

The determination of the relevant variables in a given policy is, of course, a matter of judgment and is dependent upon the criteria used to determine relevancy. The major criterion used in this case is whether or not the variable helps to explain the course taken. Admittedly, there is a good deal of room for disagreement as to whether the particular variables chosen actually are the valid ones, but the advance of knowledge about such matters comes largely from a discussion of these points.

This means that in the case of beliefs and values that underlie farm policy, those that are discussed are those apparently held by society, not those held by the author on these subjects. It seems to me that the relevant beliefs and values are those of people influential in the formulation of on-going policies, regardless of how much one may admire or abhor the particular set of values and beliefs of certain individuals or groups. This happens to be a difficult business because the determination of people's values is not an especially well-developed science, and it is not uncommon for one to confuse an individual's or group's current goals for the values and beliefs that underlie these current goals. Some of this difficulty and the distinctions are covered later.

The relevant economics for a discussion of farm policy are the economic facts, principles, and theories that enable one to understand the agricultural industry in the United States. Although some policy makers may find it disconcerting, certain facts relating to the elasticity of demand for farm products, the output behavior of farm firms, and the markets for productive factors all affect the outcome of a given policy action. They are, therefore, relevant. Conversely, even though they have the appealing simplicity of a flat world, I do not believe that the concept of a backward-bending supply curve is relevant, nor do I believe that the usual static competitive theory of the firm is adequate to understand the economics of farm policy. These matters, of course, are discussed at some length throughout the book.

The politics of a public policy also need to be relevant. A discussion of how democratic government ought to work is fine, but the issue of importance is how do those responsible for political decisions in farm policy actually operate? Whose interests do they weight and how much? These also are difficult issues to determine. About all that can be done is to attempt to describe that portion of the mechanism that is visible and infer from it some of what has taken place.

Putting the Elements Together

It is rather common for a discussion of farm policy to start with a discussion of the "goals" of farm policy. Commonly, there is a discussion of "parity" and "family farm," "food for peace," and "supply management." This tends to be misleading because it gives the uninitiated the mistaken impression that these concepts are aspired to for themselves. If you asked a group of young men what their goal is, they might answer, "To make a million dollars." However, hardly any of them would want the money for its own sake; instead they would want it for travel, to educate their children, to build a home, or to buy other things. A casual observer might think that making money was the most important thing in many people's lives, unless he realized that for most people money was merely a goal which they believed would enable them to achieve their basic aspirations. Actually, as we shall see later, most of the slogans often called "goals" of policy are concepts which have evolved to obtain political support for programs. To achieve support, these offer attainment of different aspirations of many people, or many aspirations of some people, such as "making money" tends to.

Therefore, an understanding of a public economic policy must begin with an understanding of the basic values of aspirations that people hold regarding the issue—in other words, by looking at how people think things ought to be.

Having considered where we (or they) want to go, it is necessary to determine where we are at the present time. In farm policy, this requires some evaluation of the state of affairs that exists. By comparing where we are with where people want to be, we can get some idea of the distance involved in getting there, and some idea of the actual or potential demands to move in one direction or another.

Once these things are in mind we can look at the events that got us where we are, the economic forces that led to the present situation and those which will be at work in the future. In farm policy, this includes the ideas of supply, demand, elasticity, and the economic structure of the industry with which we are concerned.

Given all of these things, together with the political processes by which policy choices are made, we can understand better the policies being followed; and we can understand better why it is that some other policy—which may look more desirable to us— was not chosen.

Government
and Agriculture

PART ONE

THE PRESSURES FOR
PUBLIC ACTION

DESPITE its campaign promises to reduce the federal budget and "to get the government out of agriculture," the administration in office for the eight years 1953–60 incurred budget expenditures for agriculture in excess of $40 billion. About $25 billion of these expenditures were for programs to maintain or improve the income of farmers. The administration in power during the 1960's will be fortunate to avoid a substantially higher rate of expenditure.

It is an understatement to suggest that budget expenditures of this magnitude are made reluctantly, at least by some of the persons involved in the decisions. Whereas in other areas of public policy every administration can point with some pride to its achievements, albeit they are not always justified, in agricultural policy claims of achievement usually are in terms of having avoided even greater misfortunes than those that occurred.

Virtually every group or individual concerned with United States farm policy is dissatisfied with some or all of it. Persons not intimately concerned with farm policy find it

1

difficult to understand the basis for its continuation, given this widespread dissatisfaction. Some are prone to believe that it is continued via some capricious reoccurring mistake in the processes of democratic government. It is necessary, therefore, to begin an examination of recent United States farm policy by observing the underlying situation that provides the continuing pressures for public action, even though it is public action which completely pleases no one.

Chapter 1

Beliefs and Values Underlying United States Farm Policy

Why do we have farm policies? Presumably, they are a method of achieving some things that people desire. What is desired and who desires it? Why do they believe that what they desire will be achieved by government policy?

One cannot understand United States farm policy, presently or in the future, without understanding the answers to the above questions. Our government policies in agriculture represent an attempt to achieve, via government, certain widely-shared aspirations or values in our society.

Public policy is a special kind of group action designed to achieve certain aspirations held by members of the society. Group action is common in a complex society via labor unions, cooperatives, corporations, and other groups. However, *public* policy is a special kind of group action in that it involves the use of the special powers of government in order to achieve the desired ends.

In order to understand fully the nature of the public policies, it is necessary to understand the ends that are sought via such actions or the aspirations that underlie them. This is particularly true in agricultural policy, for, as we shall see, these aspirations relate to fundamental issues regarding how society should be

3

organized and the desirable relationships between men. Many of these aspirations are deeply rooted in our history. Some are common to most of Western civilization, whereas others are unique to the American scene and can only be understood in light of our particular experience.

The underlying drive for our farm policies arise from a complex set of "beliefs" and "values" that exist regarding our society and the role of agriculture in it. These must be our starting point.

A belief is an opinion as to how things are and how they relate to an existing state of affairs or relationships. Beliefs may pertain to factual matters or they may pertain to normative matters. Thus, there can be a belief that farm prices are declining relative to other prices or there can be a belief that justice is not being done.

A value may be described as a concept of what is good or bad. It has been variously described as "pattern principles that guide human action," "patterns of belief and action," "societal norms," and "sentiments." However defined, there is little question that people do have preferences and attitudes regarding what is good or desirable. These values are an important criterion by which situations and potential situations are judged.[1]

This discussion of American agricultural policy assumes values exist, that they are important, and that, to a limited extent at least, they can be recognized, studied, and developed for use in policy pronouncements and in taking actions. In fact, starting the discussion of policy with a discussion of values and beliefs implies that one can neither understand the demands for policy action nor the goals and policies that are involved, without an understanding of these deep-rooted pervasive concepts.

Many of the values that underlie or influence farm policy are those that influence the content and style of our whole society. Therefore, they essentially are similar to those which have been identified by others as influencing our entire societal pattern and are not unique to agriculture. They are unique in that these values, together with certain beliefs regarding agriculture, in combination produce ideas regarding agriculture that provide the

---

[1] For a discussion of the different concepts of values and their presumed role in social action, see Charles P. Loomis and Zona K. Loomis, *Modern Social Theories* (Princeton: Van Nostrand, 1961).

basis of much of our farm policy. This chapter attempts to isolate some of the values and beliefs that are important in this regard and which produce the basic drive for a public policy in agriculture.

There are an almost infinite number of beliefs and values that might be cited as having some effect upon agricultural policy. Some are widely shared by both farm and nonfarm people; others are held less widely but by groups which play an important role in policy formation.

What follows is an attempt to identify the most important beliefs and values that underlie our agricultural policy and to indicate some of the different beliefs and values that appear to exist on certain issues.

Political and Social Stability

There can be little doubt that the United States society values social and political stability. Put in other terms, it may be said that we value orderly and democratic methods of achieving social and political change. The evidence that this is true is widespread.

One evidence is the often repeated desire of the United States to carry out international affairs by some "rule of law." This is in direct contrast to the obvious willingness of some other world powers to achieve their international goals by terror, trickery, or the overt use of military power—changing the rules as the occasion demands. In the United States, we want to bring about changes according to the "rules" and, moreover, we want an orderly, organized process to bring about desirable changes in the rules.

The high value placed upon social and political stability and orderly processes of change is reflected in our general unwillingness to condone violations of these processes even to achieve other strongly-held values. The high value placed upon orderly processes has caused many Northern liberals to question "sit-ins" and "freedom rides" as instruments to achieve racial integration in the South. Conversely, the same value has caused many conservative Southerners to permit school integration rather than incur violence.

Political and social stability is a value strongly held by the farm population in the United States, at least in modern times. Since the desperate days of the 1930's, there are few instances of the strike as a weapon in the farmers' quest for better prices. Moreover, where the strike has been used by farmers, an outbreak of physical violence has usually been a signal for most farmers to disclaim any further support for the strike, however much they value its potential gains. It is probable that this value on the part of farmers accounts in part for the suspicion that farmers often have of labor unions, where strikes and violence were not uncommon in the past and are not unknown today.

Thus, our people generally appear to value political and social stability highly and they desire orderly processes of change. Much evidence suggests that this value is even stronger among farm people than among many of their nonfarm counterparts. This, together with certain beliefs about who contributes most to the achievement of the desired values, plays an important part in United States farm policy.

The value placed upon political and social stability is related to beliefs regarding the contribution of farm people to a stable political and social order. Going back in our history, at least to Thomas Jefferson, there has been a belief that freeholder farmers constitute a basic source of a country's political and social stability.[2] This belief apparently was shared by Marx, who suggested that the rural population was a conservative group which would resist the revolution.[3]

Even today, it appears that many persons hold the belief that somehow farm people are "better citizens" than are persons living in or raised in cities. The important and influential persons who express such beliefs are illustrated by this introduction to a special message to the United States Congress in 1956:

To the Congress of the United States:

In this session no problem before the Congress demands more urgent attention that the paradox facing our farm families. Although

---

[2] See A. Whitney Griswold, *Farming and Democracy* (New Haven: Yale University Press, 1952), for a discussion of the origin of this idea.

[3] See "The Communist Manifesto" in Max Eastman (ed.), *Capital, The Communist Manifesto, and Other Writings by Karl Marx* (New York: Modern Library, 1932), especially pp. 325 and 332.

agriculture is our basic industry, they find their prices and incomes depressed amid the Nation's greatest prosperity. For 5 years, their economy has declined. Unless corrected, these economic reversals are a direct threat to the well-being of all our people.

But more than prices and incomes are involved. In America, agriculture is more than an industry; it is a way of life. *Throughout our history the family farm has given strength and vitality to our entire social order.* We must keep it healthy and vigorous.[4] (Italics mine.)

Some may argue that in modern governments speeches and messages by the President are not a reflection of his personal values and beliefs, but are merely designed to project a desirable "image" in an advertising sense. Even if this were true, it would not remove the point. The fact that the drafters of the message felt an expression of such beliefs (and values) was the *desirable* image suggests they thought that others shared the same beliefs.[5] In an administration not noted for its vigorous departures from popular views, this is even more likely to hold.

Apparently this belief has been fairly widely shared. A Cornell University report covering the attitudes of 3,429 persons with varying backgrounds, experiences, and wide geographic dispersion reports:

If the reactions of the six chief groupings and 30 subgroupings we have studied are fairly representative of the population in this country, then we can conclude that there is today a general attitude among American people that still emphasizes the values in rural living.[6]

The presumed influence of rural living on developing good citizens seemed to be present, since virtually every group in the study rated the rural environment highest as a good place to raise children.[7]

4 Special message to the Congress of the United States from President Dwight D. Eisenhower (transmitted Jan. 9, 1956).

5 Actually, the author was employed in the Executive Office of the President at the time and concluded that the beliefs and values expressed by this statement were held by people very influential with the President, and perhaps the President himself, and were not merely to project an image.

6 W. A. Anderson, "Cornell University Agricultural Experiment Station, Rural Sociology Publication," No. 34, *A Study of the Values of Rural Living, Part VII, Summary of Findings* (Ithaca: Oct. 1952), p. 9.

7 *Ibid.*, p. 11.

Whether or not these beliefs about the unique contribution of farm people to social and political stability are borne out by the facts is a subject for research for sociologists and political scientists. Such research will require a more careful and precise definition of terms than is usually found in either the political statements or research that is currently available. However, as long as major portions of our population continue to hold such beliefs, people are likely to react accordingly. Given the value placed upon political and social stability and the belief that farm people make a special contribution to it, there is likely to be concern regarding the continuing diminution of the farm population and pressure to maintain people in farming.

It is interesting to note that President John F. Kennedy, in his first special message on agriculture,[8] did not mention this belief or value. Whether this was due to the age and background of the new President, or to his failure to win a majority in rural areas outside the South in the 1960 Presidential election, is unknown.

Economic Stability

Since the great depression of the 1930's, the United States public has placed a high value on maintaining general economic stability. This value was instrumental in the passage of the Employment Act of 1946, and its importance is illustrated by the emphasis put upon employment and income levels in political campaigns.

Coupled with the value placed upon general economic stability is the widely-held belief that agriculture plays an important role in maintaining general economic stability in the nonfarm economy. The opening paragraph of the Eisenhower message quoted earlier contains an expression of this belief. On this count, Mr. Kennedy did not differ from his predecessor. In his first message on agriculture he said: [9]

Farming remains our largest industry. . . . It employs 12 times as many people as work in steel and 9 times as many as in the automobile

8 March 16, 1961.
9 *Ibid.,* pp. 1 and 2.

industry. . . . The farmer is a consumer as well as a producer, and other economic groups are affected by the continued drop in farm purchasing power. . . . It is deeply in the interest of all Americans that our agriculture be not only progressive but prosperous.

A more extreme position was taken by the Committee on Appropriations in 1958.[10] Their view was:

A review of economic history of the United States will show that every economic recession in this country has started on the farm. Every recession has been preceded by a period of reduced income to the agricultural segment of our population. Since agriculture is the principal segment of our economy which generates new wealth, it is inevitable that a prolonged depression in agriculture will eventually reflect itself in more aggravated economic distress throughout the rest of the economy.

Much of the support by labor leaders for agricultural price and income measures appears to rest largely upon their belief that agricultural prosperity is a crucial factor in achieving and maintaining full employment. Farm leaders and farm spokesmen in Congress further this belief to justify support for agricultural legislation to other members of Congress and to the community at large.

Presumably, this belief is verifiable, given our present knowledge and theories of the business cycle. However, it would be inappropriate at this point to divert our attention to what we know on this matter. It is sufficient to note that these beliefs and values have played a major role in determining the goals of farm policy and in gathering support for legislative programs to achieve these goals.

Economic Organization

There are several closely-related values held in American society regarding the way in which our economic system should be organized. The importance of these values in the determination

[10] *Department of Agriculture and Farm Credit Appropriation Bill*, Report No. 1584, House of Representatives, 85th Congress, 2nd Session (Mar. 28, 1958), p. 5.

of public policies varies in different sectors of the economy, but they are important in agricultural policy.

In economic terms these values might be considered as being concerned with efficiency, distribution, and control. Brewster has characterized them somewhat differently by referring to them as the *work ethic, democratic creed,* and *enterprise creed.*[11]

Whether one attributes the value placed upon efficiency by our society to early religious history as does Brewster, or whether one concludes that it serves as an instrumental value to achieve the higher value placed on increases in real wealth, seems largely immaterial insofar as policy implications are concerned. What is important for our purposes however, is to recognize that, all other things equal, we prefer the production of more goods and services to less. Therefore, it follows that we aspire to use our resources in a fashion that will produce the maximum total output.

Growing directly out of our value regarding the desirability of maximum total output is the judgment that an individual's contribution to society ought to be measured by his individual contribution to production. This leads directly to the judgment that the worth of one's individual contribution ought to be related to his output. Thus, the value is expressed—each *should share* according to his productivity or contribution to the total production of goods and services.

While the above values allow for different individual contributions to output and, therefore, do not say that men should be treated as equals in the marketplace, there is another value which says that people should be considered equal before their God. In the United States, this has been extended in the political sphere to, "all men are created equal" and, therefore, that some individuals should not exercise political power over others. Moreover, this concept of equal worth leads to the judgment that all men should have *equal* opportunity to develop their productive abilities to the fullest extent.

The value that one individual should not have control over another is also extended to the economic sphere to say that the

---

11 John M. Brewster, "Technological Advance and the Future of the Family Farm," *Journal of Farm Economics,* **40** (Dec. 1958), pp. 1957–99.

individual proprietor should have exclusive right to control his enterprise. This is extended to say: (1) that government should not intervene in the operation of individual enterprise and (2) that economic power should not be distributed in such a way that an individual enterprise (or economic group) has the market power to control decisions or outcomes within other enterprises.

There may be some doubt that these complex value systems actually exist among farm people or, more important, that they really have anything to do with farm policy. Fortunately, this doubt can be resolved by a referral to recent annual resolutions of the major farm organizations.

The introduction to the 1960 Resolutions of the American Farm Bureau Federation said in part: [12]

We, as Farm Bureau members believe:
. . . In the right of every man to choose his own occupation; to be rewarded according to his productive contribution to society; and to save, invest, and spend, or to convey to his heirs, his earnings as he chooses.
. . . In government by law, impartially administered, without special privilege.

Other farm organizations are somewhat less explicit in their values that rewards *should be* related to productive contribution, but this value is certainly implicit in their statements. Virtually all farm groups are explicit in expressing their values relating to the undesirability of unequal distribution of political or economic power. Thus, the National Grange resolutions stated: [13] "The Grange believes that farmers are entitled to bargaining power comparable to that enjoyed by 'labor' and 'business.' "

Coupled with the values relating to how economic rewards (income) and political and economic power ought to be distrib-

12 *Farm Bureau Policies for 1960.* (Chicago: American Farm Bureau Federation, Dec. 17, 1959), p. 6. While these are stated as beliefs, they are actually statements as to how things ought to be rather than statements as to how things are and, therefore, are values by my definition.

13 *1960 Summary of the Legislative Policies and Programs of the National Grange.* (Washington, D. C.: The National Grange, 1960), p. 9.

uted and that high productivity is desirable are various beliefs regarding these issues. Perhaps the most important of these has its foundations in economics.

Classical economics and its successors, usually termed *competitive price theory,* have provided a framework of beliefs which interact significantly with the values just discussed. These economic theories say that the market, under competitive conditions, will allocate resources such as to: (1) maximize total output and (2) reward each person in society according to his contribution of productive resources. Conversely, these theories hold that government intervention in the market will either reduce total ouput or distort the relationship between individual contribution and reward, or both. They also say that concentrations of economic power (monopolies) will alter the functioning of the market such that total output from a given set of resources is reduced or that income is not determined by an individual's contribution.

The resolutions of the American Farm Bureau clearly express a belief in the ability of the competitive market to achieve the desired values. They said: "The principles of our competitive enterprise system derives from, and are consistent with, our religious values and the highest goals that mankind seeks." [14]

Under direct government payments. . . . "Inevitably, farm income would be distributed on the basis of 'the politics of equal shares' *instead of by the market on the basis of each individual's economic contribution to society."* [15] (Italics mine.)

Thus, the resolutions of the Farm Bureau suggest its members believe that the competitive market *would* produce the most desirable income distribution and the highest total product or standard of living, if it were allowed to operate. While the other major farm organizations generally indicate a value judgment in favor of maximum output and for rewards according to contribution, they do not express the belief that the competitive market will produce the desired results. Therefore, while the Farm Bureau presses for a return to "free" markets, the National Grange and the National Farmers Union are not averse to government intervention in the markets to achieve the desired level of rewards

14 *Op. cit.,* p. 5.
15 *Op. cit.,* p. 10.

from the market. The position of these organizations thus appears to depend less upon differences in values than upon sharp differences in beliefs about the way in which the market system operates without government intervention.

Another belief that differs substantially from one farm organization to another relates to the distribution of political power in government. The Farm Bureau resolutions imply the belief that the federal government tends to be controlled by a relatively few persons and that the use of government programs will give some individuals political and economic control over others.[16] The Grange states a different belief quite bluntly: "Government is the creation and servant of all the people, not any one class or group." [17]

It is worth noting that beliefs regarding the distribution of political power vary both as to the branch of government in question and the level of government, that is, federal, state, or local. The belief that rural interests are more powerful in state governments than in federal government is, of course, shared by nonfarm people and by political scientists. This underlies attempts by urban residents to either reapportion state legislatures or push matters of importance to the national level. Conversely, some farm organizations tend to push for state and local programs wherever possible. Within the federal government the Farm Bureau tends to believe its political power is greatest in the legislative branch and least in the executive branch. We shall examine the factual basis for these beliefs in the third section of this book.

On another issue, the distribution of economic power, the farm organizations tend to share some beliefs and not others. There appears to be a widespread belief among farmers that other groups in society have economic power not now possessed by farmers and that this power generally is used to the disadvantage of farmers. There also appears to be agreement that the possession and exercise of this power is dependent upon the acquiescence of government. However, widely differing beliefs are apparent as to the extent of this power held by different groups in the economy and as to its existing or potential effects upon the market system.

16 *Op. cit.*, see especially pp. 6, 36, 45.
17 *Op. cit.*, p. 8.

The Grange indicates a belief that greater bargaining power possessed by both "labor" and "business" causes the markets to work to the disadvantage of farmers.[18]

The Farmers Union expresses the belief that economic power possessed by business is the primary factor in preventing the market from functioning properly.[19] The Farm Bureau states the belief that the "most dangerous" monopoly power is that of government and that the economic power of labor unions is used to the disadvantage of farmers.[20] The Farm Bureau resolutions suggest that the declining number of buyers of farm products *increases the opportunity* for undue exercise of economic power by these groups, but there is no belief expressed that such power is actually being used.

Thus, it can be shown that the values and beliefs held by farm people regarding efficiency, economic rewards, and the distribution of economic and political power are important in the determination of the goals of United States farm policy. Further implications of these complex systems of beliefs and values will be sketched in a later chapter.

Economic Growth

There can be little question, even in the mind of the casual observer, as to the high value that United States society places on economic growth. The fact that growth rates were a political issue, however unprecisely expressed, in the recent Presidential campaigns is one evidence.

The value placed upon economic progress might be termed the value that more material goods are better than fewer. In recent years, this value has taken a different turn, perhaps because we have resented the charge of being gross materialists. In any case, economic growth has taken on the role of an instrumental value, instrumental in that it is necessary in order to compete with Russia and thus preserve "our way of life." Fundamentally, this last expression is not different from the first, since we could

18 *Op. cit.*, p. 9.
19 *The National Farmers Union Official Program for 1960*, pp. 10–11.
20 *Op. cit.*, pp. 36 and 37.

compete, at least in short-run armaments, without growth, by merely reducing personal consumption levels to buy more "hardware." However, since the competition hopefully is more than military and extends to the long-run ability of two economic and political systems to produce the greatest output of consumer satisfactions, growth becomes necessary.

Concurrent with the high value placed upon growth, there is a widely-held value that the benefits of growth should be widely shared in our economy and especially that *those sectors which contribute to growth in output should benefit* by their contribution. Moreover, the value is increasingly expressed, which is something more than the reverse of the above, that no group should be made substantially worse off by the process of growth, even if they make no direct contribution to the growth.

Whereas the discussion of values regarding economic rewards and contribution to output is related to a given point in time, the values regarding rewards and contribution to progress are concerned with changes over time. Thus, there are values which say that economic rewards should be related to current contribution to output and that changes in rewards due to growth should be distributed among those contributing to growth. However, there also is a value that increased rewards from growth for certain groups should not be allowed to adversely affect others. The possible inconsistency between these first two values and the third does not alter their existence. It does, however, mean that the process of policy formulation must consider these conflicts where they arise.

Turning to beliefs about economic growth, there are several which can be identified, most of which are based on recent findings or statements of economists. First, it is generally accepted that the agricultural industry has made a contribution to economic growth as measured in the United States. This point has been repeatedly made by a number of prominent economists and has been generally accepted by the public or at least by economic policy makers.[21] The reasoning usually says that general economic

21 As examples, see Theodore W. Schultz, "A Policy to Redistribute Losses from Economic Progress," *Journal of Farm Economics*, 43 (Aug. 1961) and Edward F. Denison, *The Sources of Economic Growth in the United States and the Alterna-*

growth is increased by the provision of an abundant food supply *at stable or declining relative prices* and without resort to the use of increased total resources.[22] Growth is dependent upon the economy's ability to produce more food and more of other things simultaneously.

Second, it is believed that in recent years farmers have not shared in the gains from growth in the economy, even though they have contributed to it. The evidence for this belief will be examined in the next chapter. Finally, there is the growing acceptance of the belief that economic growth makes farmers worse off in an absolute as well as a relative sense.

These values and beliefs regarding economic growth, the distribution of its benefits, and the incidence of its costs are becoming increasingly important in United States agricultural policy. Part of the increasing importance may be due to the general increase in attention being given to the problems of growth in other areas of the world or the change may be due to increased availability of economic "facts" about the sources, costs, and benefits of growth. Whatever the reason, they are important and their importance is likely to increase rather than diminish with time.

Equal Opportunity

Going back, perhaps, to our religious ethics, there are several value concepts of importance to farm policy relating to the concept that each individual should have "equal opportunity." [23]

Sometimes this value is expressed as "everyone should have equal opportunity to develop his abilities to the utmost of his ca-

---

tives Before Us (New York: Committee for Economic Development, 1962). In a paper before a joint session of the Econometrics Society and the American Farm Economic Association in St. Louis, Missouri, Dec. 30, 1960, George R. Tolley and Seymour Smidt reported an attempt to measure agriculture's contribution to total growth.

[22] It is interesting to note that while classical economic theory has been widely accepted as a relevant tool to analyze policies for achieving values relating to maximizing output and distributing income, it is not widely accepted as such in dealing with policies regarding growth and agriculture's role in it.

[23] Brewster, *op. cit.,* traces this concept to our religious background.

pacity." This led earlier to the establishment of free public schools and land-grant colleges where the sons and daughters of farmers and working men could obtain access to higher learning with little regard to social or economic background. The concept of equal opportunity led to the establishment of Rural Free Delivery (RFD) and clear-channel radio stations, so that farm people could have equal opportunities to obtain information and literature.

Another value concept related to equal opportunity might be termed a *welfare concept*. Thus, in United States society, there is widespread acceptance of the judgment that the consumption opportunities of individuals ought to be, if not equal, at least not below certain levels.[24]

In a society such as the United States, which is relatively free of sharp social or caste systems which limit equal opportunity, the most important limitation upon equal opportunity appears to be an economic limitation. Thus, it is generally believed that the main barrier to equal opportunities, in either sense of the word, is income level and that aspirations in this area will largely be achieved by the achievement of improved incomes for farm people.

Farmers and farm organizations also express certain beliefs about the concept of *equal opportunity*. The Farm Bureau statement expresses a belief about progress and opportunity: "Americans' unparalleled progress is based on the freedom and dignity of the individual, initiative, *and equal opportunity*, sustained by our faith in God and our basic moral and ethical values." (Italics mine.)[25]

The Grange statement clearly puts the emphasis upon economic matters and suggests a belief that the opportunity for economic equality for farmers is lacking in the absence of government intervention: "We seek development of farm programs which would, while assuring the American people the abundance

[24] It is interesting to note the statement "equal opportunity to develop one's abilities to the limit of his capacity" implies that there are differences in individual capacities, whereas the concept of equal consumption opportunities implies equal capacities for receiving satisfaction from consumption.

[25] *Op. cit.,* p. 5.

needed in a rising standard of living, *offer to farmers an oppor-*
tunity to achieve economic equality with other segments of our
economy." (Italics mine.) [26]

While the above statement implies a belief that government
programs are a way of achieving equal economic opportunity,
some farm people hold the belief that government intervention
will reduce or prohibit the achievement of economic opportunity.
Thus, the Farm Bureau says: ". . . in his quest for 'security,' the
individual must oppose policies leading to the curtailing of individual freedom and opportunity.[27] Payment limitations . . .
would place a ceiling on opportunity and level individual farm
incomes downward." [28]

Therefore, there are several different and conflicting beliefs
held by farm people regarding the achievement of equal opportunity via government action.

Nearly all farm people appear to believe that the desired
equal opportunity cannot be achieved without "equal" income
and thus, the resolutions of farm organizations express a concern
for equal opportunity to achieve incomes comparable with the
other segments of the economy. Some believe that government
programs can help farmers achieve this opportunity, whereas
others express the belief that many government programs prohibit rather than further its achievement.

Part of this difference in beliefs regarding the role of government in the achievement of equal opportunity may be due to the
subtle distinction, mentioned earlier, between "equal opportunity
to develop to the limit of one's capacities" and "equal opportunity to enjoy a high standard of living." Whatever the basis for
the difference in beliefs, these differences do appear to exist and
as such influence both the direction and content of United States
agricultural policy.

Sharing United States Abundance

Despite the Communist claims of ulterior imperialistic mo-
tives, people in the United States generally hold the value that

26 *Op. cit.*, p. 8.
27 *Op. cit.*, p. 6.
28 *Ibid.*, p. 10.

one who has been "fortunate" and blessed with an abundance of material goods should share his good fortune with his less fortunate neighbors. This value is deeply rooted in both our rural and urban society and was widely applied both privately and publicly long before the atomic age made national survival a matter of some doubt.

The judgment that we should share our abundance was extended to an international scale during and immediately after World War I, and its scale was extended even further following World War II. The sharing of food supplies has always been a major issue in this regard, perhaps because of the vital and immediate relationship between food and life itself. This value now has been extended to cover nearly all persons at all times. Whereas it was earlier restricted to times of unusual shortages or famine, it has been broadened to say that we *should* share food with people, both at home and abroad whose diets are below some defined minimum standard.

The importance of this value has been strengthened by our desire to speed economic growth in underdeveloped areas, partially as an extension of our general desire to share our abundance, and partially as an extension of our struggle for international political stability.

There are several important beliefs that are closely related. One is that the United States has a relatively greater abundance of food than other countries. This is widely held and, given certain criteria as a measurement, is probably a demonstrable fact, although our per capita daily calorie intake is not the world's highest. There is also the belief that food plays a crucial role, not held by any other commodities, in economic development and that adequate food supplies are an essential element in underdeveloped countries.

Of greater importance is the growing acceptance of the belief that donations of food abroad are different than the donations of purchasing power (money) or of other goods and services. This belief is related to another, that somehow the production of food in the United States for distribution abroad involves "free" resources, whereas the production of food elsewhere in the world involves "scarce" resources. This particular set of assertions has been made by a number of "economists" and politicians (sometimes as the same person) and has been widely accepted by farm people, farm organizations, and by makers of farm policy.

Whereas our earlier beliefs and values regarding the sharing of our food supplies with other nations dealt with existing stocks or supplies, our present beliefs and values go much beyond the sharing of existing output and stocks. Increasingly, these beliefs and values are leading to the formulation of *production policies* rather than distribution policies for United States farm products. The accuracy of these beliefs will be discussed in a later chapter.

Public Action and Value Achievement

It might be suggested that the values that have been suggested as underlying United States farm policy are not unique to the United States or to farm people. To a large extent this is true, but there is one set of values and beliefs underlying farm policy that is of special significance because it leads to *public or group action*.

The value is held by many farm people that if the situation that exists in the absence of public action is not in line with their values, then a situation which is more in line with desires *should be attained* by group or public action. This value is one that is widely, but not universally, held by other persons in Western society. Individuals in some societies accept a view that if their desires are not attained, this is because it was not meant to be so. Not so American farmers!

Closely allied with the above is the belief that even if certain situations are not attainable by individual action, they are attainable by group action, that is, the group is more powerful than the sum of its individuals. Moreover, in the United States, this has usually been extended to the belief that even if private action will not attain a desired situation, it *always* can be attained via government.

Admittedly, the latter belief is not universally held by all farmers and their organizations, but it is held by a large number of farm and nonfarm people. Thus, regardless of the problem, it is asserted that government action should and can solve it. Hence, when gaps arise between reality and value aspirations in and for agriculture, the problem tends to push into the sphere of public policy.

Individuals who reject the assumption that government action *can* solve their problems generally cling to the assumption that group action can. Thus, farmers who argue that the government is unable to give farmers "equal bargaining power" often claim that group action through farmer cooperatives can achieve it. To nearly all involved in farm policy, the power of the group is assumed unlimited if you merely define the proper group.

The Resolution of Conflicts in Beliefs and Values

This attempt to summarize the important beliefs and values underlying United States farm policy illustrates major problems arising in policy formation. Individuals may hold values that are inconsistent or conflicting in that both cannot logically represent "goods" within the same system of logic. In addition, individuals may have values which are competing, in that it is impossible in a given situation to attain additional satisfaction of one value without losing the satisfaction of another. Individuals also may have conflicting or inconsistent beliefs in that they believe two or more things to be true, all of which cannot be true. Individuals may also have beliefs and values which conflict with those of other individuals.

In a later chapter, it will be pointed out that pressure groups in policy generally consist of individuals whose value systems are quite similar. As in the case of individuals, a group may hold values which conflict with those held by other groups, and a group may hold values which are competing. Groups also may share beliefs which are inconsistent both with other beliefs within the group and/or with beliefs of other groups.

The task of policy formation thus involves at least three functions. First, it involves the resolution, if possible, among conflicting beliefs. Second, it involves choosing among conflicting values expressed by individuals or groups. Third, where a given policy involves competing values, it requires some weighing of these values to arrive at a policy which will provide the maximum satisfaction for the individuals involved.

An apparently satisfactory method for dealing with conflicting beliefs about factual matters has been developed. Thus, the validity of beliefs can be judged by their consistency with other accepted factual concepts, by their workability or ability to predict, and by their clarity and understandability. Thus, the problem of inconsistent beliefs on factual matters is settled by the acceptance of one set of beliefs or facts as valid and the rejection of another.

Views regarding how value conflicts are resolved are more divergent because they depend upon one's view as to the nature of values. Some persons regard value concepts as meaningless in a scientific sense and claim that value concepts cannot be verified in the fashion applicable to factual matters.[29]

Another position is that values are not essentially different than factual concepts and that the same tests of validity can be applied as are accepted for factual matters. This position must lead to the conclusion that the resolution of conflicts requires an ordering of values and the rejection of some in favor of others.[30] This view suggests that value conflicts are settled by one party's acceptance of different values or by a different ordering of values.

A solution to the problem of the nature of values, the problem of handling them in social science research, and the problem as to how conflicts are resolved is neither possible nor appropriate in this volume on the nature of policy. While an acceptable solution(s) might ease the policy-making process, it does not appear to be available in a readily adaptable form at present.

Where values are competing, it appears possible to handle them much in the same fashion that we attempt to maximize the satisfaction from the consumption of competing goods in eco-

[29] For a discussion of different views as to the nature of values, see G. L. Johnson and Lewis K. Zerby, "Values in the Solution of Credit Problems," in *Capital and Credit Needs in a Changing Agriculture*, E. L. Baum, Howard G. Diesslin and Earl O. Heady (eds.), (Ames: Iowa State University Press, 1961).

[30] The latter is the position taken by Johnson and Zerby in the paper cited above. Gunnar Myrdal in *An American Dilemma* (New York: Harper, 1944), Appendix I and II, arrives at the same method of resolving conflicts from a different view as to the nature of values.

nomics.[31] This framework will help solve one of the major problems of handling values in policy formation, but it leaves the others untouched.

[31] See D. E. Hathaway, "Farmers' Freedom and Agricultural Policy: A Theoretical Framework," *Journal of Farm Economics,* **35** (Nov. 1953).

Chapter 2

The Gap Between
Desires and Reality

Some who feel uneasy when dealing with aspirations or values are much more at ease when they turn to a discussion of reality or "what is." But in the area of farm policy, as we shall see, "reality" is sometimes as difficult to pin down as are the values involved. Moreover, it often turns out to be difficult to even sort out which of several possible "realities" is relevant. This is especially true when attempting to answer the question of whether there is a significant gap between the values held by and for farm people and the situation that currently exists.

Much of the confusion over the relevant reality hinges on the particular way that we view agriculture in the United States. There is still the tendency to view farming as "a way of life." Thus, many consider the agricultural industry, the farm firms in the industry, the managers of these firms, the persons who provide labor inputs to farm firms, and people who live on "places" classified as farms, as all one and the same. It is doubtful that such a situation ever existed, but if it did, it has long since passed in the United States. Therefore, it is necessary to discuss these various concepts and their interrelationships before we can decide what is relevant to measure the gaps, if any, between the desires and realities of United States farm policy.

24

The Agricultural Industry and the Firms in It

The Census of Agriculture was taken in late 1959 and the Census of Population in the spring of 1960. Therefore, these years will be used as base years in our description of the agricultural industry and the people in it.

In 1959, the agricultural industry marketed products with an estimated value of $33.5 billion. In addition, it received *direct* government payments [1] of $682 million, consumed an estimated $1,328 million of home-produced farm products by the families of farmers, and used farm dwellings with an estimated rental value of $1,957 million. These items produced a realized gross farm income of $37.5 billion in 1959.

In that same year, production expenses (including depreciation) were estimated at $22.1 billion, leaving $15.4 billion as national income originating in agriculture. However, out of this, farm operators paid $3 billion to farm workers, $.6 billion interest on mortgage debt, and $1 billion net rent to nonfarm landlords, leaving $11.4 billion as the net farm income of farm operators. This figure (net income of farm operators from farming) is the one often used to measure changes in the welfare of farm people, although it is not the net total income of the operators of farm firms, nor is it the net income of the owners of productive resources in agriculture.

In 1959, the Census of Agriculture counted 3.7 million places as farm firms, using the newly-adopted definition.[2] This was the

---

[1] These are direct payments to the industry. The level of cash receipts also was affected by government purchases of farm products, but the figure for government payments does not include this. The estimated government payments to agriculture *are not* government payments to farm people in the form of pensions, social security, etc. These are presumed to be captured in another set of accounts.

[2] In 1959, all places of 10 acres or more were counted as farms if the estimated sales of farm products for the year amounted to at least $50 or if they could normally be expected to produce agricultural products sufficient to meet the requirements. Places of less than 10 acres were counted as farms if the estimated sales for the year amounted to at least $250 or if they could normally be expected to produce enough agricultural products to meet this requirement.

In the 1954 Census of Agriculture, places of 3 acres or more were counted as farms if the value of farm products, whether for home use or sale (exclusive of smallest number of firms counted in the industry since 1870, and the decline in the number of farms from 1954 to 1959 was the most rapid ever recorded. About one-fourth of the total decline of 1,079,000 farms from 1954 to 1959 was the result of the change in definition, and the rest was the result of the disappearance of farms by consolidation or abandonment.

Despite the tighter definition and the continued commercialization of United States agriculture, there are still great diversities between the units classified as farms in 1959. On one end of the scale were 1,200 farm units each selling one-half million or more dollars of farm products annually. At the same time, there were still 1.64 million farms (44 per cent of the total) which each sold less than $2,500 of farm products annually.

About 95 per cent of the total annual sales of farm products is from farms selling more than $2,500. Even though the total number of farm firms has been decreasing rapidly, especially during the 1950's, the number of farms with annual sales exceeding this amount (adjusted for changes in prices) has remained remarkably stable (Table 1). However, the statistics do indicate a marked shift within this group of farms toward farms with higher annual output.

Who were the managers or operators of these 3.7 million farm firms? The Census of Agriculture only allows one farm operator per farm unit, thus by its count there were also 3.7 million farm operators. The person defined by the Census as the farm operator may be the owner, a member of the owner's household, a hired manager, a tenant, renter, or sharecropper. If he rents land to others or has land worked on shares by others, he is the operator only on the land retained for his operation. Thus, a farm operator may or may not do the work on the farm he operates, may or may not own it, and may or may not even be responsible for most of the decisions made regarding the firm's operation.

---

gardens) amounted to $150 or more. Places of less than 3 acres were counted as farms only if annual *sales* amounted to $150 or more. A few places were also counted as farms if they normally could have been expected to meet the minimum value or sales criteria.

Thus, the "reality" of the number of farms depends in part upon the definition used.

Given this fuzziness of definition, very little can be said precisely regarding those who make the decisions regarding the operation of farms. Certain facts are available regarding persons defined as farm operators. In 1959, only 21 per cent of the farm operators were tenants and 79 per cent of all farm operators owned part or all of the farm they operated. The number of sharecroppers declined to 121 thousand in 1959, less than one-sixth the number of sharecroppers three decades earlier. Concurrently, the number of nonwhite operators declined to 286 thousand, less than one-third the level of 1930.

Table 1

Number of Farms by Selected Economic Size Classes, 1939–59

Value of Farm Products Sold (in 1954 dollars)	1939	1949	1954	1959 *
	(Thousands)			
$10,000 and over	312	484	583	794
5,000 to 9,999	585	721	707	654
2,500 to 4,999	1,015	882	812	618
Total 2,500 and over	1,912	2,087	2,102	2,066

* Using the 1954 definition of a farm. The change in definition did not materially affect the number of farms selling over $2,500 of products.

Source: For 1939, 1950 and 1954, Jackson V. McElvenn, *Family Farms in a Changing Economy*, U. S. Department of Agriculture, Agricultural Information Bulletin No. 171. (Washington: U. S. Govt. Printing Office, March 1957), Table 4, p. 19. For 1959 the actual number of farms as reported in the *1959 Census of Agriculture-Preliminary*, U. S. Dept. of Commerce, Bureau of the Census, Series AC 59-1. (Washington: U. S. Govt. Printing Office, January 1961), was used without adjustment. Since the index of prices received by farmers in 1959 was 240 and in 1954 was 246, the adjustment for price change would have been too small to be meaningful.

In 1959, 16.7 per cent of the farm operators were 65 years old or over. This was the highest percentage ever recorded, and it was approximately double the percentage recorded in 1910.

While the Census of Agriculture gives us a reasonably accurate picture of farm firms, it tells us relatively little about the persons who make the economic decisions regarding these firms. The illusion that farms, farmers, and farm people are one and the same thus clouds the picture of who does what and for how much in agriculture.

The Labor Force in Agriculture

Presumably, we are interested primarily in the welfare of people, not in the welfare of farms or producing units. Therefore, if they are different, we should look at the persons comprising the labor force in agriculture. However, not only is it difficult to define a farm or a farm operator, but it also turns out to be at least as difficult to define and identify the persons who do the work that produces farm products.

There are several sources of information regarding the persons who do the work in agriculture. One source is in the Census of Agriculture. It shows, for the week prior to the Census, that there were 3 million farm operators working 1 or more hours on their farm in the week; 1.7 million unpaid family members working 15 hours or more in the week; and 689 thousand regular hired workers employed (150 or more days). Since the week was different for different farms and the criteria for employment varied sharply for each class of worker, we know very little from such statistics other than that not all farm operators put in as much as one hour of work during the survey week on the farm they operated.

The United States Department of Agriculture publishes a series on farm employment.[3] It includes separate estimates for family workers and for hired workers. It counts all of the persons employed as farm operators if they work one hour or more in the survey week, unpaid family labor if they work 15 hours or more, and hired labor if they work one hour or more. It samples farms so that individuals can be counted as working on more than one farm. Thus, the United States Department of Agriculture employment series measures all people employed in agriculture, paid or unpaid, on a part- or full-time basis. A simple average of this monthly series showed 7.4 million persons in the farm labor force for 1959.

[3] A complete description of how these estimates are derived and comparisons between these estimates and those of the Department of Commerce is contained in *Farm Population, Employment, and Levels of Living, Vol. 7, Major Statistical Series of the United States Department of Agriculture: How They Are Constructed and Used.* U. S. Department of Agriculture, Agriculture Handbook No. 118 (Washington: U. S. Government Printing Office, Sept. 1957).

The Bureau of the Census of the United States Department of Commerce also issues employment estimates for agriculture. These estimates are based upon sample surveys of households, and persons are classified as employed if they worked for pay at all or if they worked in an unpaid status for 15 hours or more. However, the industry of their employment is that industry in which the individual worked the most hours—one man, one job—so that persons shown as working in agriculture either spent more hours there than elsewhere or had no other job. Conversely, farmers working more hours off the farm than on the farm during the survey period are classified in the nonfarm industry in which they are working.

The Census statistics for 1959 show 5.8 million persons employed in agriculture, of which 4.9 million were white and 908 thousand were nonwhite. These 5.8 million were composed of 1.7 million wage and salary workers, 3 million self-employed workers, and 1.1 million unpaid family workers other than the operators. Most of the wage and salary workers were males (four-fifths), and most of the self-employed workers were males (96 per cent), whereas slightly over one-half of the unpaid family workers were women.

Any illusion that these statistics measure the people actually working in agriculture is quickly dispelled by studies of multiple job-holding in December 1959 and December 1960.[4] In December 1959, about 3 million people held two or more jobs, and 970 thousand of them were persons with a primary or secondary job in agriculture. A December 1960 survey showed about the same result and stated: [5] "Farmers and professional and technical workers are two-job holders to a greater extent than persons employed in other occupation groups."

Thus, it turns out that neither estimate of farm employment gives an accurate measure of the labor input in agriculture, either in terms of man-hours or in terms of equivalent full-time em-

[4] "Multiple Job Holders in December 1959," *Special Labor Force Report No. 9, Monthly Labor Review* (Washington: U. S. Dept. of Labor, Bureau of Labor Statistics, Oct. 1960); "Multiple Job Holders in December 1960," *Special Labor Force Report No. 18, Monthly Labor Review* (Washington: U. S. Dept. of Labor, Bureau of Labor Statistics, Oct. 1960).

[5] *Special Labor Force Report No. 18, op. cit.,* p. 4.

ployed persons. The Department of Agriculture series consistently overestimates the persons working in agriculture by counting everyone, almost without regard to contribution. The Census figures underestimate by failing to count persons who contribute to the farm labor force, although they work more hours elsewhere.[6]

The Department of Agriculture does publish a figure entitled *Man-hours Used in Agriculture*. This is an estimate derived from multiplying output of various farm products by the *estimated man-hours* that are believed to be required to produce them. While this series moves roughly parallel with the other two, it provides a very weak basis for welfare comparisons in agriculture and should not be subject to the common misuse of dividing it into the total farm income to obtain the earnings per hour in agriculture.

Farmers and Farm People

For many years it was assumed that people who lived in the country lived on farms and were farmers. Thus, our Census of Population included two residence categories, urban and rural. With time, it became increasingly clear that people who lived in the country were not all engaged in farming, so that in the 1930 Census of Population the rural population was divided into rural farm and rural nonfarm components.[7] It was generally assumed that the rural farm population could be identified by asking people if the place they lived on was a farm. If they answered, "yes," they were placed in the rural farm population.

We have already seen the problems of deciding what is a farm unit. So, in 1959 and 1960, the Census decided to find out what would happen if they applied the definition of a farm used in the

[6] For a fuller discussion of these differences and problems, see D. Gale Johnson, "A Critical Analysis of Farm Employment Estimates," *Journal of the American Statistical Association,* 46 (June 1950), pp. 191–205.

[7] Actually, a monograph on the farm population based on the 1920 Census used the rural farm, rural nonfarm break. For the history of the development of this classification, see Leon E. Truesdell, "The Development of the Urban-Rural Classification in the United States: 1874 to 1949," *Current Population Reports* Series P-23, No. 1. (Washington: Bureau of the Census, Aug. 5, 1949).

1959 Census of Agriculture to the places rural people lived, rather than letting people define a farm themselves.

The results were astonishing, to say the least. In April 1960, the farm population, using the new definition, was about 15.6 million people, whereas under the definition previously in use, it was 19.8 million! [8] Thus, precisely defining a farm reduced the estimated farm population by 4.2 million—which was the result of removing 5.4 million people that would have been counted as farm population and adding 1.2 million to it that wouldn't have been counted before.

These new statistics simultaneously cleared the air and created confusion. They cleared the air because the new statistics removed from the farm population persons who live in rural areas but who are neither dependent upon nor contributing to the agricultural industry. The farm population under the new definition only reduced persons employed in agriculture 120,000 or 3 per cent, but it deleted a million, or one-third, of the previously reported nonagricultural workers from the farm population. Even so, of the 6 million employed persons in the newly-defined farm population in April 1960, only two-thirds of them were employed in agriculture by the Census definition of employment.

The endless confusion arises because many of the statistical series used for policy purposes in agriculture are based upon the farm population, and the shifts in base will make historical comparisons impossible. Thus, we shall face the question: Did per capita income improve because income rose, or because the same income was divided by fewer estimated people?

Leaving aside historical comparisons, we can say certain things about the farm population in 1960. In April 1960, there were an estimated 15.6 million persons living on places that met the Census definition of a farm. About 6 million of the persons living on farms were employed, with two-thirds of them working wholly or principally in agriculture. During the same month there were an estimated 5.4 million employed persons whose major employment was agriculture. Thus, during that month about one-fourth

8 "Effect of Definition Changes on Size and Composition of the Rural Farm Population, April 1960 and 1959," *Farm Population* Series Census, AMS P27, No. 28 (April 17, 1961).

of the persons counted as primarily employed in agriculture apparently did not live on places that qualified as farms.

The old illusion should be dispelled. In 1960, people who live on farms do not necessarily farm for a living, and those who farm for a living do not always live on farms.

Income Aspirations and Reality in Agriculture

With different values held by various groups as to what income in agriculture ought to be vis-à-vis other groups, and with the difficulty of defining precisely the incomes which are included as agricultural incomes, there is understandable confusion as to the appropriate income measure. Therefore, it is necessary to review several measures, their relevance, and their implications. Despite their frequency, most income comparisons between different groups in the population rest upon shaky assumptions and are of doubtful validity. This is not to imply that income comparisons should not be made, but more attention is needed to what really is involved.

Presumably, income comparisons should be in real terms, taking into account differences in cost of living as well as differences in measured income levels. Moreover, certain occupations carry with them certain real income advantages, in that the occupation enables one to obtain certain goods and services at lower cost than can other groups. Thus, presumably, doctors' families pay less for medical care and farmers pay less for home-produced food. Since farms usually have a house as part of the farm buildings, allowance should be made for rental value of the housing that is used by the owner-operator.

Department of Agriculture statistics on farm income do include the value of home-produced food consumed by farm families and the rental value of housing on farms. Thus, while these statistics attempt to account for both money and nonmoney income flows, they do not take into account the other factors which may determine the level of real income of farm people.

Koffsky[9] examined differences in farm and urban purchasing

[9] Nathan Koffsky, "Farms and Urban Purchasing Power," *Studies in Income and Wealth*, 11 (New York: National Bureau of Economic Research, 1949), pp. 153–78.

power in 1941 and concluded that city prices were 27 per cent higher than prices paid by farmers for similar goods. However, much of this difference was because farmers produced much of their own food. In Koffsky's index, this food was priced at farm prices, which substantially reduced living costs to farmers.[10] The cost of purchased foods alone was about 10 per cent higher in cities.[11]

Times have changed substantially since 1941. Farms have become more specialized, and most food processing occurs off the farm. Consequently, farmers now produce less of their own food. In 1955, farm families relied upon their own farms for about 40 per cent of their food compared to nearly 60 per cent in 1941.[12]

Under present circumstances it would appear better, in making income comparisons, to divide the differences in living costs into two elements—differences in purchasing power of money income due to differences in prices for comparable items in urban and rural areas and differences in real income accruing to farmers from having part of their income in kind or priced at lower prices than nonfarmers can obtain these items.

A recent United States Department of Agriculture study gives us an indication of the differences in real income arising from price differences between the farm and nonfarm sectors. It said: [13]

> With the differential in food purchasing power between the farm and nonfarm segments of the economy estimated at about 6 per cent and the purchasing power differential of nonfood items (excluding medical care, housing, and clothing) estimated to be about 1 per cent, a purchasing power approximately 2 or 3 per cent higher for the farm segment as compared with the nonfarm segment is indicated for 1955.

However, it also pointed out that: [14]

10 *Ibid.*, p. 160.

11 *Ibid.*, p. 161.

12 Mollie Orshansky, "Changes in Farm Family Food Patterns," *Farm Family Spending in the United States.* Agricultural Information Bulletin No. 192 (Washington: U. S. D. A., June 1958), p. 7. The percentage is based upon retail prices of all items.

13 Horace L. Puterbaugh, "Purchasing Power of Urban, Rural Non-farm and Rural Farm Income, 1955," *Agricultural Economics Research,* **13** (July 1961), pp. 89–95.

14 *Ibid.*, p. 90.

If the results of this study are used to develop a purchasing power adjustment factor to be applied to ratios of incomes among the various urbanization groups, care must be taken to insure comparability between procedures used for treating nonpurchased food in this study and in the income ratio calculation. For example, agricultural income would need to include nonpurchased food valued at retail prices.

An adjustment of this kind can be obtained by pricing the farm-produced-food portion of the income of the farm population at the retail level. A rough adjustment of this kind for 1959 suggests that the total income of the farm population from all sources, as reported by the United States Department of Agriculture, needs to be adjusted upward by about 6 per cent to compensate for the fact that farmers got their home-produced food at farm rather than retail prices.[15]

D. Gale Johnson has stated that in order to measure whether farm people are receiving comparable incomes for comparable labor, farm income ought to be adjusted for differences in sex and age composition of the labor force, labor capacity, dependency, income tax payments, the relative share of labor income, as well as for purchasing power.[16] He did this and suggested that per capita incomes in agriculture would represent equivalent labor incomes if farm per capita income averaged about 70 per cent of the nonfarm figure.

However, recent data suggest that Johnson's figure must be revised upward. As mentioned, the difference between prices paid by farmers and nonfarmers has declined, so that the purchasing

[15] This was computed as follows: The total income of the farm population in 1959 from all sources was $19.0 billion; of this, $1.3 billion was income from home-produced food consumed by farmers, and $17.7 billion was from other sources.

However, about three-fourths of the food produced at home consists of meat, milk, poultry, and eggs (Orshansky, *op. cit.*, p. 8). The marketing margin for these products is lower than for all food.

Assuming that the marketing margin on these items was 50 per cent, the approximate retail value of home-consumed food was $2.6 billion. This retail value, added to the $17.7 billion from other sources, meant the net income of the farm population was equivalent to $20.3 billion of nonfarm income. The $20.3 divided by the reported $19.0 gives 106 per cent.

[16] D. Gale Johnson, "Labor Mobility and Agricultural Adjustment," E. O. Heady et al. (Eds.), *Agricultural Adjustment Problems in a Growing Economy.* (Ames: Iowa State College Press, 1958), pp. 163–72.

power of money income is closer and, even if the adjustment for pricing home-consumed farm products is added, the real income differences are much less than in 1941. Moreover, the participation of farm population in the labor force has risen from 1950 to 1960. These changes are shown in Table 2, and they suggest that the average per capita income on farms would have to be about 88 per cent of nonfarm levels to represent comparable labor earnings for the farm population.

Table 2

Adjustments to Determine When Per Capita Income Estimates in Agriculture Reflect Labor Returns in Agriculture Comparable to Those in the Nonfarm Economy

1. Sex composition *	.97
2. Age composition †	1.08
3. Labor capacity †	1.10
4. Labor force participation ‡	.98
5. Relative share of labor earnings †	.86
6. Purchasing power of money income **	1.03
7. Income tax payments †	1.07
8. Value of home-produced food at retail prices ††	1.06
Product	1.14
Reciprocal	87.70

* In April 1960, the labor force of the rural farm population consisted of 75.7 per cent men and 24.3 per cent women (*Farm Population, Series Census*, AMS P-27, No. 29, April 18, 1961). For the nonfarm population the labor force was 68.8 per cent men and 31.2 per cent women (computed from the above and *Labor Force and Employment in 1960*, Special Labor Force Report No. 14 (U. S. Dept. of Labor, 1961). During 1960 the median income of year-round full-time working females was 60.6 per cent of males ("Income of Families and Persons in the United States: 1960," *Current Population Reports*, Series P-60, No. 37, Bureau of the Census (Jan. 17, 1962).

† Values developed by D. Gale Johnson, *op. cit.* Data from 1960 Census not yet available. Johnson's figure for labor capacity adjusted down slightly to allow for the reduction in negroes in farm labor force.

‡ The labor force participation of the farm population calculated at 39.5 per cent and for the nonfarm population 38.8 per cent. Calculations from data cited in (*) above.

** Taken from Puterbaugh, *op. cit.*

†† Calculated by determining the increase in total income of the farm population that would result from pricing farm-produced foods consumed on farms at retail prices rather than farm prices.

Taking the above qualifications into account, we can examine the per capita income comparisons between farm and nonfarm people as shown by recent estimates (Table 3). These statistics include allowances for home-produced food and the rental value of farm housing, and they include income from all sources, not just farming. Even so, they suggest that the average per capita income

in agriculture would have to be substantially higher for it to represent comparable real labor earnings.

FAMILY INCOME OF THE FARM POPULATION

The figures on per capita income leave one uneasy. They are aggregate figures, dependent upon gross estimates of income, ex-

Table 3

Per Capita Income of the Farm and Nonfarm Population

Year	Farm	Nonfarm	% Farm Was of Nonfarm
1934	$ 166	$ 512	32.4
1935	240	552	43.5
1936	227	636	35.7
1937	287	666	43.1
1938	232	621	37.4
1939	240	655	36.6
1940	250	699	35.8
1941	334	835	40.0
1942	484	1,034	46.8
1943	623	1,222	51.0
1944	665	1,314	50.6
1945	700	1,334	52.5
1946	790	1,373	57.5
1947	814	1,442	56.4
1948	963	1,529	63.0
1949	787	1,514	52.0
1950	884	1,618	54.6
1951	1,043	1,765	59.1
1952	1,024	1,854	55.2
1953	1,008	1,919	52.5
1954	999	1,889	52.9
1955	960	1,997	48.1
1956	993	2,103	47.2
1957	1,066	2,166	49.2
1958	1,197	2,165	55.3
1959	1,144	2,276	50.3
1960	1,255	2,309	54.4
1961	1,373	2,345	58.6

Source: *Farm Income Situation*, Economic Research Service, U.S.D.A., No. 187 (July 1962).

penses, and farm population. As we have seen, such gross estimates sometimes are subject to substantial revisions.

There are, however, other independent estimates of the comparative income position of the farm population. These are the Consumer Income Surveys of the Bureau of the Census and the income data from the decennial Census of Population. These data differ from the United States Department of Agriculture estimates of per capita incomes in several ways. First, the data are based upon household surveys (or Census) and as such are subject to some sampling error. Second, the data pertain to *money* income, which differs from the total realized income concept used by Agriculture.

Money income does not take into account the value of home-produced food or the rental value of farm housing. (Neither does it take into account the imputed value of owner-occupied nonfarm housing on the other side.) Thus, money income tends to understate the total real income of farmers.

Therefore, to compare family income statistics, two additional adjustments are needed to improve the comparability of the two sets of data. First, the income figures for farmers need to be adjusted to include the total value of home-produced food; and secondly, differences in family size need to be taken into account. These two adjustments indicate that the returns for comparable labor would be about equal if the median incomes of farm families were 86 per cent of nonfarm families (Table 4).[17]

The median money income reported by farm and nonfarm families in the Census Survey, by regions, is shown for 1960 in Table 5. It shows that the median farm family income in the United States was 49 per cent of the median urban family income, not greatly different than the 54 per cent for average per capita income and consistent with the difference in concepts.

It can be seen from Table 5 that the relationship of farm and nonfarm income differs substantially by color and region of the country. However, even in the west, with few nonwhite farmers

---

[17] One can also make welfare comparisons by different adjustments, also shown in Table 4. They suggest that farm families would have the same level of welfare if incomes were 86 per cent of nonfarm families. It is a coincidence that the two figures are the same.

and few low-production farms, the gap between farm and nonfarm family incomes still is wide.[18]

Table 4

Adjustments to Determine When Money Income of Rural Farm Families Reflect Welfare Levels and Labor Returns Comparable to Those of Nonfarm Families

1. Sex composition of the labor force *	.97
2. Age composition of the labor force *	1.08
3. Labor capacity *	1.10
4. Labor force participation *	.98
5. Relative share of labor earnings *	.86
6. Purchasing power of money income *	1.03
7. Income tax payments *	1.07
8. Value of home-produced food †	1.16
9. Family size ‡	.91
10. Proportion of population over 14 years of age ‡	1.03

	Product of 1 through 10	1.16
Comparable labor returns:	Reciprocal	.86
Comparable welfare or	Product of 6, 7, 8, 9	1.16
purchasing power:	Reciprocal	.86

* Same as Table 2.

† The retail value of home-produced food consumed by farmers was $2.6 billion in 1959, and the gross rental value of farm dwellings was $2.0 billion (*Farm Income Situation*, Econ. Res. Service, U.S.D.A. (July 1962), p. 44). The income of the farm population from other sources than these items was $15.7 billion. Thus, money income should be adjusted by a factor of 1.16 to account for the value of home-produced food (18.3/15.7).

‡ The average family in the rural farm population consisted of 4.19 persons, and the average nonfarm family 3.67 in 1961. However, 68.1 per cent of the farm population was over 14, whereas 70.4 per cent of the nonfarm population was in this group.

Therefore, on the basis of this evidence, it appears that the people who live on places classified as farms (the farm population) have average incomes well below their rural nonfarm neighbors and the urban population. Even if one makes adjustments for differences in labor force capacity and composition, the income differences remain large, indicating that labor returns in agriculture are low and that the welfare level of many farm families also is low.

[18] The figure to obtain comparable labor returns differs markedly from region to region. In the South, 47 per cent of the food consumed by farm families was home-produced, whereas in the West, 36 per cent was home-produced. Education, racial composition, family size, etc. differ substantially from region to region. Data are not now available to make these computations.

Table 5

Median Money Income of Farm and Nonfarm Families by Region and Color, 1960

	MEDIAN INCOME			RURAL FARM INCOME	
				(as a % of)	
	Urban	Rural Nonfarm	Rural Farm	Urban	Rural Nonfarm
U. S. Total	$5,911	$5,620	$2,875	48.6	51.2
White	6,163	5,779	3,194	51.8	55.3
Nonwhite	3,894	2,021	1,168	30.0	57.8
Northeast	6,089	6,125	4,077	67.0	66.6
North Central	6,150	5,893	3,109	50.6	52.8
South, Total	4,885	4,505	2,059	42.1	45.7
White	5,377	4,905	2,668	49.6	54.4
Nonwhite	2,773	1,707	1,154	41.6	67.6
West	6,564	6,735	5,242	79.9	77.8

Source: "Consumer Income," *Current Population Reports*, Bureau of the Census, Series P-60, No. 37 (Jan. 17, 1962), Table 16, p. 35.

THE RELATIONSHIP BETWEEN THE FARM FIRM AND FAMILY INCOME

The Census of Agriculture generally gathers detailed information about farm firms and little about farm people, while the Census of Population gathers vast detail about the people without regard to the farm upon which they are located. Only rarely are the data for both the farms and the total income of the operators' families available together.

Table 6 shows such data from a sample survey for 1959. It contains some very striking figures. First, it shows that the average income of farm operator families on farms selling over $10,000 of products annually is not low—averaging close to $10,000 from all sources. Second, it shows that the average family income of those on part-time farms is not especially low, largely because of good off-farm earnings.

The question arises, are these data compatible with other estimates of farm income from the other sources cited? Examination of the aggregate totals implicit in the table suggests that it is

Table 6 Average Net Income of Farm Operator Families, 1959

	NUMBER OF FARMS 1959			AVERAGE NET INCOME OF FARM OPERATOR FAMILIES			
	Total	Per cent of total	Per cent of sales of farm products	Net cash farm income *	Off-farm income	Total cash income	Total income including nonmoney income from farm food and housing
	(000)	(Per cent)	(Per cent)	(Dollars)	(Dollars)	(Dollars)	(Dollars)
Commercial							
Farms with sales							
$10,000 and over	795	21.5	71.9	6,636	1,978	8,614	9,960
$5,000 to $9,999	654	17.6	15.4	2,165	1,567	3,732	5,018
$2,500 to $4,999	618	16.7	7.4	1,288	2,077	3,365	4,572
$50 to $2,499	349	9.4	1.5	438	525	963	1,476
Other farms							
Part-time †	888	23.9	2.7	176	4,283	4,459	4,890
Part-retirement ‡	404	10.9	1.1	116	1,846	1,962	2,363
Farms with sales $5,000 and over	1,449	39.1	87.3	4,618	1,826	6,444	7,763
Farms with sales of less than $5,000	2,259	60.9	12.7	510	2,589	3,099	3,750
All farms	3,708	100.0	100.0	....	....	....	....

* Cash receipts from farm marketings plus government payments less production expenses.
† Value of sales less than $2,500, operator under 65 years of age and either worked off farm 100 days or more or income of family from nonfarm sources greater than value of products sold.
‡ Value of sales less than $2,500, operator 65 years or older.

Source: *An Agricultural Program for the 1960's* (Washington: U.S.D.A., January 1962), Table 5, p. 50.

consistent. The realized net income of farm operators from farming, implicit in Table 6, amounts to $11.3 billion, the same as the global estimate.

The data also are roughly consistent with the Consumer Income data for 1959 which show the median income of rural farm families to be $2,800. That estimate suggests that the 800 thousand families in the rural farm population with the highest income would have an average money income of $8,600—if you assume that those over $25,000 have an average income of $50,000 per family.

These data suggest that farm operator families living on that one-fifth of our farms which are most productive, in terms of sales of farm products, have family income levels exceeding the average nonfarm income level. This relatively good income level should not be construed as meaning that there are no economic problems relating to this portion of agriculture, however. These farms not only produce 72 per cent of all farm products, but they also include three-fourths or more of all capital assets in United States agriculture; and it is the returns on this large capital investment which account for a major portion of their income. Moreover, in 1959, their incomes were heavily dependent upon the government price-support programs.

INCOME BY OCCUPATION

It already has been noted that not everyone who lives on a farm works in agriculture and that nonfarm income looms large in the income of farm families. If we sorted out those who were mainly or largely dependent upon farming for their income (either as managers, operators, or workers), how does their income look? In other words, if we remove most of the people living on farms who are primarily dependent upon nonfarm income, how does the income of those largely dependent upon agriculture compare with other occupations and industries?

Table 7 shows that the money income of male full-time year-round workers who are either farmers, farm managers, or farm laborers is well below any other occupational group. It suggests that removing that portion of the farm population largely dependent upon working off the farm tends to remove persons whose

Table 7

Median Money Income in 1960 of Year-Round Full-Time Male
Workers 14 Years Old and Over, by Occupation

Occupation	Median Income
Total, United States	$5,435
Professional, technical and kindred workers	7,228
Farmers and farm managers	2,210
Managers, officials and proprietors, except farm	6,922
Clerical and kindred workers	5,328
Sales workers	5,938
Craftsmen, foremen and kindred workers	5,905
Operatives and kindred workers	5,030
Service workers, except household	4,209
Farm laborers and foremen	1,843
Laborers except farm and mine	3,956

Source: "Consumer Income," *op. cit.*, p. 43.

incomes are higher than are the incomes of full-time workers in agriculture.

Essentially the same picture is obtained when one looks at the money incomes of full-time workers by industry (Table 8). The median income in the agricultural industry is about one-half the next highest, which is personal services. Thus, viewed either by

Table 8

Median Money Income in 1960 of Year-Round Full-Time Male Workers
14 Years of Age and Over, by Major Industry

Industry	Median Income
Total	$5,455
Agriculture, forestry, and fisheries	2,242
Mining	5,953
Construction	5,664
Manufacturing	5,923
Transportation, communication and other public utilities	5,903
Wholesale trade	5,652
Retail trade	4,956
Finance, insurance, and real estate	6,170
Business and repair services	4,500
Personal services	4,022
Professional and related services	5,691
Public administration	5,636

Source: "Consumer Income," *op. cit.*, p. 45.

occupation or by industry, people that work in agriculture have much lower money incomes than workers in other industries or occupations.

It appears that two groups in the farm population have achieved income levels that are sufficient to enable them to have consumption levels comparable to nonfarm people. These are the farm families that live on the larger commercial farms and those that live on part-time farms where the income is largely from non-farm sources. A major portion of those largely or solely dependent upon agriculture clearly have incomes well below individuals in other industries and occupations. Given this wide gap between aspirations and reality, it is not difficult to understand why improvement of farm income stands high as a goal for United States farm policy.

OTHER MEASURES OF ECONOMIC WELL-BEING IN AGRICULTURE

Despite the observed low incomes in agriculture, it is not unusual to find that many farm people are about as well off in their later years as are their nonfarm counterparts whose annual incomes have been substantially higher. Part of this well-being can be attributed to frugal living and the tendency of farm families to put a high proportion of their current income into productive investment. An even greater part can be attributed to the very substantial capital gains that have occurred in agriculture as a result of increases in the price of physical assets owned by farmers.

Changes in the price of assets may arise from three sources: (1) changes in the general price level; (2) changes in the actual or expected income stream from the assets; or (3) changes in the rate at which expected income streams are discounted. The first change does not represent a gain in real wealth to the asset holder, whereas the latter two do.

Capital gains and losses in agriculture have been very large in some years and there have been capital gains in all but three of the years since 1940. Most of these capital gains have been due to a rise in the price of farm real estate. When they are compared with current income, there are a number of years in which the capital gain or loss has exceeded the current income.

Care should be exercised in interpreting these statistics. Book capital gains or losses are not always realized. However, these unrealized gains or losses affect the net equity position of farmers, and presumably over their lifetime most will be realized. Indications are that farmers regard these changes in net worth as the equivalent of income in determining well-being. One interviewer found that farmers compared their gains in net worth with those of nonfarm workers and felt they were as well or better off despite lower annual incomes.[19]

Unfortunately, these capital gains tend to be somewhat misleading to farmers. First, they represent money increases not increases in real wealth. Boyne found that the net gain in real wealth of the owners of farm real estate amounted to $29 billion from 1940 to 1960, whereas the book capital gains over that period amounted to about $90 billion.[20] Second, since the increases in asset prices appear to be due largely to changes in the discount rate rather than to current or expected increases in income, the assets must be sold in order for even these gains in real wealth to be realized.

The relative importance of these changes in asset prices highlights the importance of starting and quitting at the right time in order to be successful in agriculture. A person buying a farm in the period 1910–20 and selling it prior to the 1930's could hardly avoid failure. A person starting in the mid 1930's and selling his farm in the 1950's could hardly have avoided doing fairly well. Thus, for more than two decades it has been possible to typify agriculture as an industry "where you live poor and die rich."

Two additional points need to be made on this subject. First, it is difficult to believe that capital gains in agriculture can continue, especially in light of the prospective income stream to agriculture. Much of the postwar gain probably is due to the federal price and income support programs and would disappear if these were removed. Second, farmers tend to confuse capital gains with

[19] Samuel Lubell, " 'Sick' American Farms Have a Healthy Look," *Chicago Daily News* (April 6, 1962), p. 25.

[20] David H. Boyne, *Changes in the Real Wealth Position of Owners of Agricultural Assets, 1940–60*, unpublished Ph.D. dissertation (University of Chicago, 1962).

income, and this has probably contributed to the overcommitment of owner-operator labor to farming. Both farmers and economists should realize that other asset-holders in the economy also
have received major capital gains which are not measured in their
current incomes. Therefore, adding real or money gains in asset
values in agriculture to the current income of farmers is not a
valid comparison unless the same is done for other groups.

Income Stability

The desire of both farm and nonfarm people for income stability in agriculture has been mentioned. Among farm people, the
reasons for such desires are obvious. The reasons of merchants
who sell farm supplies or other goods to farm families are obvious.
Others support these aspirations because they believe agricultural
stability is necessary to achieve general economic stability.

Table 9 shows the variation in estimated income for certain
modal types of farms in the United States. It suggests that most
types of farms have been subject to a high degree of income variability during the past 30 years, but that during the past decade
there has been a substantial reduction in this year-to-year variability. Despite this reduction in income variability, the year-to-
year variation in income is still high for many types of farms,
especially those located in the Great Plains and Mountain regions.

Table 9

Income Instability by Type of Farm by Decades

| Type of Farm: | COEFFICIENT OF VARIATION | | |
| | 1930–39 | 1940–49 | 1950–60 |
		Per cent	
Corn Belt Farms:			
Hog—Dairy	64.2	36.9	15.8
Hog—Beef Raising	83.4	41.1	21.2
Hog—Beef Fattening	64.6	46.2	25.8
Cash Grain	58.6	35.5	14.6
Poultry Farms (New Jersey egg)	——*	49.8 ‡	85.8
N. C. Tobacco—Cotton	——*	34.2	17.7
N. C. Large Tobacco—Cotton	——*	33.8	20.2

Table 9—Continued

Income Instability by Type of Farm by Decades

Type of Farm:	COEFFICIENT OF VARIATION		
	1930–39	1940–49	1950–60
		Per cent	
Cotton Farms:			
High Plains Texas—nonirrigated	—— *	55.1	56.8
Delta—small	—— *	23.3 †	14.8
San Joaquin Valley—irrigated—large general	—— *	—— *	15.2
Southern Piedmont	39.5	36.0	22.0
Black Prairie, Texas	31.5	37.7	29.5
Cattle Ranches:			
Southern Plains	443.2	43.5	39.4
Intermountain	53.0	33.1	38.1
Southwest	—— *	54.1	85.8
Sheep Ranches:			
Northern Plains	52.0	29.7	49.8
Southwest	—— *	22.5	72.8
Dairy Farms:			
Central Northeast	33.3	38.8	10.3
Eastern Wisconsin	45.5	34.9	17.5
Dairy—Hog; Southeast Minnesota	50.1	34.0	11.1
Winter Wheat:			
Southern Plains wheat	101.2	54.0	39.9
Southern Plains wheat—sorghum	201.5	58.7	67.5
Pacific Northwest, wheat fallow	177.0	54.2	23.5
Spring Wheat:			
Northern Plains, wheat, small grain, livestock	513.6	47.2	32.4
Northern Plains, wheat, corn, livestock	201.5	44.2	39.0
Northern Plains, wheat, roughage, livestock	180.5	43.7	32.6

* Data not available.
† 1944–1949 only.
‡ 1945–1949 only.

Source: Computed from *Costs and Returns on Commercial Farms, Long-Term Study, 1930–57*, Statistical Bulletin No. 297, Farm Economics Division, Economic Research Service (Washington: U.S.D.A., Dec. 1961).

While the gap between aspirations regarding income stability and reality has been narrowed for most types of farms in the United States, much of the improvement has been due to public policy. Thus, the demand to continue such policies will persist as long as the characteristics of agriculture are such that they produce highly unstable incomes in the absence of such policies.

The Reality of Economic Organization

Dissatisfaction in this area is second only to that arising from the gap between income aspirations and reality for farm people. Moreover, while farmers are most concerned about the income gap, nonfarm groups are greatly concerned regarding the present use of resources and an "efficient" use of resources.

The ideal of efficient use of resources can be used in two contexts. First, it could relate to whether the maximum agricultural output was being obtained from the resources engaged in producing farm products. Second, it relates to whether total national output could be increased by shifting resources from producing farm products to producing other goods and services.

On the first count, efficient use of resources within agriculture, there is little complaint at present. The trend toward larger commercial farms with more capable managers, better methods of communicating new technology and organizational methods, and many other factors have contributed to increased agricultural output per unit of resource used in production. Of course, on some farms and in some areas, further gains could be achieved, but unlike many countries elsewhere in the world, the major problem of United States farms is not that too little output is obtained from agricultural resources.

There is a growing awareness among nonfarm people that there is a large gap between reality and aspirations regarding the total use of resources in the economy. Increasingly, it is becoming clear that our total national income and product might be higher if some people and resources now producing farm products were producing goods and services more highly valued by consumers.

There are several sources of evidence to substantiate the existence of a serious malallocation of resources in the economy. Assuming comparable resources, under conditions of "efficient" resource allocation the last unit (marginal) of labor and capital used in an industry should be earning the same as the last unit used to produce other goods and services. There is evidence that the marginal returns to labor in agriculture are well below estimated marginal returns to labor in other industries. One economist said, in summarizing a series of such studies: [21]

> The agricultural industry, as it has operated in recent years, can be typified as returning a low to modest earning for capital investments and submarginal returns to labor. These conclusions are substantiated by (1) the farm record analyses kept in departments of agricultural economics, (2) functional analyses and (3) the typical commercial farm studies of the USDA and (4) are consistent with the national agricultural accounts.

It should be kept in mind that the above statement was based on data obtained for years in which federal price-support programs were maintaining farm prices and incomes at levels substantially above the levels that would have prevailed in the absence of such programs. Therefore, marginal earnings of labor and capital in agriculture would have been even lower, at least in the shortrun, had it not been for government intervention, and the malallocation of resources would have appeared even greater.

This conclusion appears valid even for the 795 thousand farms shown in Table 6 upon which total family income appears good. The total market value of the productive assets (land, buildings, machinery, livestock, feed crops inventory, and working capital) in agriculture in 1959 was estimated at $155 billion. Those farms that produced 72 per cent of total output probably controlled at least three-fourths of these assets since the capital-man ratio on such farms is well above average. The total income of these farm families from farming amounted to about $6.4 billion, and if one allows a 5 per cent return on these productive assets involved, it amounts to $5.9 billion. Thus, even though total average incomes are good on such farms, they are not high enough to provide more than modest returns on both operator labor and capital values at market prices.

An Iowa study provides one piece of evidence as to the extent by which returns in agriculture are below those in other sectors

[21] Glenn L. Johnson, *The Surplus Trap in American Agriculture* (manuscript being prepared for publication), p. 22.

of the economy.[22] In the two years 1954–55, actual factor returns on a group of well-organized Iowa farms just covered alternative factor costs when the operator's labor was valued on the basis of a cooperative elevator manager's income. Factor returns were $1,300 below alternative factor costs when operator's services were valued on the basis of a farm supply manager's income, and they were $1,900 below alternative factor costs when the operator's services were valued on the basis of the average manufacturing foreman's income. When farm prices were adjusted to levels expected in the absence of price-support programs, estimated factor returns were $1,300, $3,200, and $3,800, respectively, below the three alternative factor opportunity costs. In other words, at 1954–55 prices total earnings on better-than-average Iowa farms were not large enough to provide returns equal to those earned by comparable resources elsewhere and, in the absence of price supports, the gap would have been substantially larger.

An estimate of the extent to which national product might be increased by reallocating resources (primarily labor) from the production of agricultural products to other products is provided by Denison.[23] He suggests that the "true" national product could be raised by 0.5 per cent ($2.5 billion in 1960) by different use of some resources now in farming. Moreover, he suggests that underemployment in agriculture costs us another .02 per cent of national product.[24] This is consistent with the earlier judgment that the major loss in efficiency is from the allocation of resources between farm products and other products, not from inefficient use of resources within the agricultural industry.

Despite the general agreement that resource earnings in farming are low and would be lower in the absence of government programs, it is sometimes argued that this does not represent inefficient use of resources as long as there is unemployment in the

[22] Don Kaldor, Raymond Beneke and Russell Bryant, *Comparison of Resource Returns of Well-Organized Iowa Farms with Selected Nonfarm Opportunities*, Research Bulletin 491 (Ames: Agricultural and Home Economics Experiment Station, Iowa State University, Mar. 1961).

[23] Edward F. Denison, *The Sources of Economic Growth in the United States and the Alternatives Before Us* (New York: Committee for Economic Development, 1962), p. 199.

[24] *Ibid.*, p. 210.

nonfarm economy. This argument, of course, can be used to justify any inefficient use of national resources, but it is another issue
entirely and should not be allowed to cloud the fact that the
present situation in agriculture means that our economy is falling
significantly short of obtaining the maximum output from our
available resources by having too many resources producing farm
products.

Income Distribution Within Agriculture

The desire to have individual income related to the individual's contribution has already been discussed. Here again, in certain respects we find a major difference between desires and
reality.

The difference arises because it is generally agreed that in recent years (since about 1952) the level of total farm income, and
thus of the income of individual farmers, has been heavily dependent upon government intervention in the market for farm
products. Estimates suggest that for several years total net farm
income would be one-third or more lower if the government price-
support activities were ended.[25]

These estimates, plus the multibillion dollar annual expenditures of the United States Department of Agriculture for farm
price supports, make it obvious to farmers and nonfarmers alike
that farm income is determined as much by government programs
as by the market value of agricultural output to the society. Those
who believe income should be determined in the market by the
value placed upon production are, therefore, not satisfied with
present conditions.

Within agriculture, income distribution between farm firms
is primarily based upon the amount of farm product produced.
Most past and current farm programs have manipulated market

25 *Report from the United States Department of Agriculture and a Statement
from the Land-Grant Colleges IRM-1 Advisory Committee on Farm Price and Income Projections 1960–65,* Senate Document No. 77, 86th Congress, 2nd Session
(Jan. 20, 1960) and *Economic Policies for Agriculture in the 1960's,* Materials Prepared for the Joint Economic Committee, Congress of the United States, 86th Congress, 2nd Session (Washington 1960), for different estimates of total net farm income
in the U. S. in the absence of government price-support programs.

price levels so that the individual farm incomes are dependent largely upon relative output. The few programs that did involve either payment limitations or other restrictions that allocated income without regard to total output have been strongly opposed by numerous groups because they distributed income other than in accordance with total output.

The fact that income within agriculture is distributed largely in accordance with production does not mean that there is widespread satisfaction with the income distribution that results. The available data on income distribution within agriculture shows that not only is the average low, but also it is obtained from a sharply-skewed income distribution (Table 10). Therefore, income distribution within agriculture, even though achieved by the desired methods, is not in accordance with the values relating to equal opportunity to enjoy minimum consumption levels.

Table 10

Distribution of Families Whose Heads Worked in Agriculture by
Total Money Income in 1960

Money Income	Total Employed Persons	Farmers and Farm Managers	Farm Laborers and Foremen
	Percentage of Total		
Under 500	1.8	11.2	4.9
500–999	1.5	8.0	10.1
1,000–1,499	2.2	9.6	12.7
1,500–1,999	2.5	8.5	10.8
2,000–2,499	3.2	7.5	11.9
2,500–2,999	3.4	8.6	7.7
3,000–3,499	4.4	7.4	9.1
3,500–3,999	4.7	7.0	8.9
4,000–4,499	5.1	4.8	2.1
4,500–4,999	5.4	4.4	3.0
5,000–5,999	14.0	6.7	5.6
6,000–6,999	12.0	3.8	3.7
7,000–7,999	10.1	4.1	1.9
8,000–9,999	13.0	3.6	4.2
10,000–14,999	12.3	3.6	3.0
15,000–24,999	3.4	1.0	——
over 25,000	1.1	0.2	0.2

Source: "Consumer Income," op. cit., p. 28.

Levels of Living

The low average income level and the highly-skewed income distribution in agriculture are reflected in the levels of living found in agriculture. The gap that still exists in parts of United States agriculture between desired and existing levels of living of farm people is illustrated by two studies of levels of living of young farm operator families in Mississippi in 1958.[26] Forty-six per cent of the 104 young white farm operators and 95 per cent of the 100 young Negro farm operators in the study samples had total family money incomes of less than $3,000 in 1957. All of the white families and 87 per cent of the Negro families had electricity in their houses. Eighty-two per cent of the whites and 18 per cent of the Negro families had water piped into the kitchen. Seventy-nine per cent of the white families and 6 per cent of the Negro families had water piped into the bathroom. Only 5 per cent of the houses occupied by the white families were classified as in poor condition, whereas 38 per cent of the houses occupied by the Negro families were classified as in poor condition. The average annual expenditures for recreation reported by the white families was $163 and by the Negro families was $83. Reported expenditures for education averaged $20 and $16 per family (the State furnishes books). Average expenditures per family for health and medical care were $265 for white families and $77 for Negro families.

Many will argue that these Mississippi statistics are misleading, but the scanty statistics from a national survey of farm operators in 1956 suggest they are less atypical than we would like to believe (Table 11). They show that many farm families live in houses lacking the items that are taken for granted as a part of the standard of living for most American families.

These statistics are not reported to give the impression that

[26] Dorothy Dickins, *Levels of Living of Young White Farm Operator Families in Mississippi.* Bulletin 579 (State College: Mississippi Agricultural Experiment Station, June 1959), and Dorothy Dickins, *Levels of Living of Young Negro Farm Operator Families in Mississippi.* Bulletin 580 (State College: Mississippi Agricultural Experiment Station, July 1959).

Table 11

Per Cent of Farm Operators' Residences Having Specified Facilities, for Eight Regions, North, South, West, and the United States: 1955

Item	UNITED STATES Total	North				South				West		
		Total	North-east *	East North Central	West North Central	Total	South Atlantic †	East South Central	West South Central	Total	Mount.	Pacific
						Per Cent						
Farm operators having:												
Running water in dwelling	64	73	90	77	63	50	52	39	61	89	78	98
Flush toilet in dwelling	50	61	74	66	51	34	34	24	46	81	67	91
Electric lighting in dwelling	94	97	98	97	97	91	92	87	94	97	96	99
Mechanical refrigerator	90	95	96	94	95	85	83	83	88	96	94	97
Home freezer	39	48	50	53	43	28	26	26	34	49	51	47
Washing machine	84	95	94	96	95	73	71	76	70	93	92	94
Television set	53	66	76	75	55	40	44	32	45	58	43	69

* Includes Maryland and Delaware.
† Excludes Maryland and Delaware.

Source: *Farmers' Expenditures in 1955 by Regions*, U.S.D.A. Statistical Bulletin No. 225 (April 1958), Table 53, p. 117.

all farm families have low levels of living. They are cited to destroy the widespread myth that one can and does live well and comfortably on a farm regardless of the level of cash income. Although all of the families in the Mississippi studies produced some food at home (the average value of the home-produced food exceeded the average value of purchased food for Negro families), it does not offset low cash income. Despite statements to the contrary, people who have low incomes generally live less well, and a disproportionate number of farm people have low money incomes.

Economic and Political Control

Another aspiration relating to economic organization is related to independent ownership—that no one should have economic control over the individual proprietor. In one sense, this aspiration may be nearer achievement in American agriculture than at any time in recent history. The 1959 Census of Agriculture shows the highest proportion of operators owning all or part of their farms (79 per cent) since 1880, and it shows the smallest proportion of tenants and sharecroppers ever recorded.

These statistics tell only part of the story. They do not tell how many owner-operated farms are under control or "vertically integrated" with marketing firms, with production and marketing decisions largely out of the hands of the operators. Nor do the statistics indicate the extent to which farm operators' decisions are controlled by government officials via acreage allotments, compulsory land retirement, and other programs. However, despite discussions of these and other infringements upon the freedom of decision of farm operators, it appears that relative to most businesses there is little outside control over the operators and operations of individual farms.

A similar conclusion must be drawn regarding the desire of farmers for political equality. There is little evidence that nonfarm groups exert more political influence than farm groups; in fact, the reverse appears to be true relative to the number of people involved. Moreover, all major farm programs involving production or marketing restrictions require the approval of participating farmers, but not the specific approval of affected consumers. While there is little indication that political power between agriculture in total and nonagricultural groups is distributed unfavorably against agriculture, there is strong evidence that the effective political power within agriculture is distributed unequally and in ways that strongly influence the kinds of farm programs that are developed.

Thus, it appears that farmers' aspirations regarding freedom from dominance by outside interests in individual economic and political decisions have been achieved reasonably well. The problem for farmers in the decade ahead probably will be to hold the position now attained rather than to improve significantly upon the present situation.

Sharing Our Abundance

A variety of programs tend to insure the possibility of a minimum level of food consumption to most citizens of the United States. First, there are a series of welfare and income transfer programs which tend to maintain incomes, thereby allowing the recipients to maintain a minimum level of food consumption if they so desire. In addition, there are a series of programs designed to increase the quality and quantity of food consumption among certain groups, especially low-income groups. These include school lunch programs, special school milk programs, direct distribution programs for agricultural commodities, and since mid-1961, food stamp programs for low-income families in selected areas of the country.

It is estimated that the domestic food distribution programs of the Department of Agriculture amounted to $341.7 million in fiscal year 1960.[27] While these are not large enough to provide every family in the United States with the quality of diet they might prefer, it does appear that the direct distribution programs together with the general welfare programs make it possible for most families to obtain adequate quantities of food. In other

[27] Lawrence W. Witt, "Potentials of New Markets for Agricultural Products," a manuscript prepared for the Committee for Economic Development (Michigan State University, Oct. 15, 1960).

words, incidences of malnutrition and hunger arising from inadequate income to buy the necessary food appears to be low in the United States.

The same conclusion cannot be reached regarding many other parts of the world. Indeed, all of the present stocks and potential output of United States agriculture could not bring the calorie intake of the total world population to the present United States levels. Hunger and malnutrition are common in many countries.

This causes many persons to feel that as long as there are hungry people we should use our surplus stocks and productive ability to feed them. We have made large quantities of farm products available in recent years via price concessions, foreign currency sales, and gifts to other countries. A December 1960 report on Public Law 480, under which most such transactions are carried out, shows that farm products costing our government $7.4 billion and having an export value of $5.2 billion had been sold for foreign currency since the inception of the program in 1954, and authorizations for famine relief and other assistance abroad were for products costing $771.3 million.[28] Thus, our total efforts to distribute food to needy persons abroad have not been small, even though they have not been large enough to prevent a sharp rise in stocks owned by the federal government.

Actually, the valid question to be asked is whether we are sharing enough of our total national income with poor nations. The Congress seems to feel that the answer is yes, although other government officials express contrary opinions. However, this question cannot be answered here. It has already been pointed out that we may be erroneously assuming that assistance in the form of United States farm products is the best assistance. As long as there is a reluctance to expand our total aid, there appears little reason to conclude that there is a gap between our desires and achievements regarding the sharing of our abundance of farm products.

[28] *The Thirteenth Semi-Annual Report on Activities Carried on Under Public Law 480, 83rd Congress, as amended.* House of Representatives Document No. 131, 87th Congress, 1st Session (Washington: U. S. Govt. Printing Office, 1961).

Sharing the Benefits of Economic Progress

Farm people believe that gains in agriculture have contributed to general economic progress, and they feel that as contributors they should benefit from this progress. Many farmers feel the gap between desires and reality in this area is perhaps the greatest of all, as they have seen incomes generally rise in the economy at a much faster rate than their own income.

However, as Table 12 indicates, relative rates of change in income depend upon which statistics are used and which base years are used for comparison. The United States Department of

Table 12

Comparative Income Changes for Farm and Nonfarm Groups

| | INCOME | | | |
| | Average Per Capita | | Median Family | |
Year	Farm	Nonfarm	Farm	Nonfarm
1945	$ 700	$1,334	$1,410	$2,857
1946	790	1,373	. . . .	2,981
1947	814	1,442	1,958	3,207
1948	963	1,529	2,034	3,391
1949	787	1,514	1,587	3,324
1950	884	1,618	1,970	3,497
1951	1,043	1,765	2,131	3,913
1952	1,024	1,854	2,226	4,111
1953	1,008	1,919	2,131	4,462
1954	999	1,889	1,968	4,406
1955	960	1,997	2,117	4,705
1956	993	2,103	2,375	5,061
1957	1,066	2,166	2,495	5,232
1958	1,197	2,165	2,738	5,331
1959	1,144	2,276	2,799 *	5,619 *
1960	1,255	2,304	2,876 *	5,813 *
1961	1,373	2,345	. . . .	. . . .
% change 1945–60	79	73	104	103
% change 1950–60	42	42	46	66

* Data not comparable to earlier years because of a change in definition.
Source: Same as for Tables 3 and 5.

Agriculture statistics on per capita income indicate a rise in farm income of 79 per cent from 1945 to 1960 while nonfarm per capita incomes increased by 73 per cent. If you use 1950 as the base year, per capita incomes of farmers rose at the same rates as nonfarm incomes.

On the other hand, if one used the Census figures on median family income, farmers' median family incomes rose 104 per cent from 1945 to 1958, while nonfarm families' rose 103 per cent. From 1950 to 1960 the respective median family incomes rose 46 and 66 per cent. Thus, depending on the base year, farm family incomes either increased faster, slower, or at the same rate as nonfarm families. You can prove that farmers have or haven't shared equitably in economic growth, depending upon the source of your statistics and your choice of base years.

Regardless of the statistics used, one conclusion is inescapable. During a period of rapid increase in the average income level in the economy, the wide gap between farm income and nonfarm income has not been reduced, in fact, it has increased in an absolute sense. Farm people believe that the increased productivity in agriculture has contributed to the general increase in incomes in the economy, and they feel that their contribution to growth has gone largely unrewarded. Thus, there is a widespread feeling among farmers that the gap is wide between desires and reality regarding the benefits of growth in the economy.

The Pressures for Public Action

The available evidence indicates that the gap between reality and the aspirations held by and for agriculture is wide, especially regarding certain matters. As a result of this gap, demands have arisen, among both farm and nonfarm people, that public action via the federal government must be taken to bring the existing situation closer to the desired situation.

The pressures for action are particularly acute in certain areas. They are: (1) to bring farm incomes more nearly in line with incomes in other occupations; (2) to make more efficient use of resources in the economy, thereby increasing total national product (often stated as reducing the surpluses); (3) to reduce year-

to-year variations in farm income; (4) to enable farmers to participate in the benefits of economic growth; and (5) to make the best
use of our agricultural abundance abroad. Thus, the pressures
are greatest for policies and programs that will bring reality closer
to aspirations in these areas.

The gap between aspirations and reality appears less in such
matters as: (1) ownership of farms by those who operate them; (2)
having income distributed within agriculture according to individual productivity; and (3) prevention of undue economic or
political control over farmers by other groups. At the present time,
there are few demands for positive actions to improve conditions
in these areas, although there may be vigorous opposition to policies which are regarded as retrogressions from the present position. The present battle cries are not so much to reduce tenancy
or to destroy the power of giant corporations as they are to preserve the family farm and prevent control over farmers by big
business, big labor, or big government.

Given the gap between aspirations and reality, the reasons for
pressures for public action can be understood. The next step is
to examine the way in which these gaps between aspirations and
achievements are translated into policy goals designed to achieve
support for various farm programs.

Chapter 3

The Translation
into Policy Goals

A number of values underlie farm policy in the United States, and farm policy is of concern to many people, both inside agriculture and out. Therefore, policies and programs which are to survive in the political process must be those which appear to be "right actions" in terms of the values and beliefs of our society.

Goals and values are often used as interchangeable terms. This, I believe, is a mistake, at least in discussing political policies and their goals, for it leads to fruitless discussions of ultimate and intermediate goals and values that add little or nothing to an understanding of the processes involved. Values may be conflicting, especially values held by different individuals. Values also may compete (probably this is more often the case), both for an individual and between different individuals. As every successful politician knows, the best policy is one that gives something wanted to everyone without making anyone less satisfied. Since this is difficult, the next best thing is a policy that offers the most of what many people want most strongly and irritates the fewest people possible.

Therefore, concepts that are put forth and persist as policy goals tend to be, in the crudest sense, things that promise some-

60

thing for almost everybody. It should be recognized that the "something" need not be in a material sense—for not all aspirations relate to material items. All that is required is that the policy moves toward a state of affairs which the person deems as desirable.

More precisely, a policy goal is a state of affairs which, if achieved, is conceived to be consistent with or contribute to the attainment of a number of values or aspirations of the group that adopts it. Thus, it is a state of affairs or situation, which is conceived by the group as being that which will provide them with attainment of the maximum possible satisfaction of their aspirations and values relating to the goal. Since a policy goal is by definition a goal that is a group goal, it is not necessary that it be either identical to or entirely consistent with all of the values of individual members of the group who subscribe to the policy goal.

A policy goal must meet three conditions: (1) It must offer simultaneous attainment of a number of individual ends or values; (2) It must be consistent with the other important norms or values of the group adopting it; (3) It must be able to meet the two preceding criteria for a significant portion of the group having political influence in the particular policy area. Policy goals which meet these three criteria will become important and will tend to persist. A failure to meet one or more of these criteria suggests the goal will be abandoned.

United States farm policy has long revolved around the goals of "parity," and "the family farm." In recent years, the ideas of "equality of bargaining power"—which is related closely to "supply management"—and "freedom" have been used as policy goals. It now appears that "sharing our agricultural abundance" is being put forth as a policy goal. Let us examine each of these concepts to see how it contributes to the attainment of previously discussed values and thus is considered to be a "right action."

The Family Farm As a Policy Goal

Few items of farm legislation pass the United States Congress that do not have as a stated goal the preservation, improvement, or maintenance of the family farm. The failure to distinguish between values and goals has led some authors to conclude that the concept of the family farm has become a value in and of itself.[1] It is then argued that it is an instrumental value contributing to the achievement of higher values or ends and, therefore, a doubtful policy goal. However, a more accurate appraisal suggests that the family farm has persisted as a major goal of United States farm policy not because it is a value in and of itself, but because people believe that the family farm will contribute substantially to the simultaneous achievement of several important values.

Because of our values regarding political and social stability, institutions which are believed to contribute to such stability are regarded highly. Mention was made in Chapter 1 of the belief that farm people made important contributions to that stability, but more important is the widespread belief that the owner-operated family farm is the major source of this stability.

This idea appears in the writings of Thomas Jefferson, who said: [2]

Generally speaking the proportion which the aggregate of the other classes of citizens bears in any state to that of its husbandmen, is the proportion of its unsound to its healthy parts and is a good enough barometer whereby to measure its degree of corruption.

These beliefs as to the importance of the family farm still are expressed frequently by political figures and by farm organizations. A 1956 report of a subcommittee of the House Committee on Agriculture said: [3]

[1] W. K. McPherson, "A Critical Appraisal of Family Farms as an Objective of Farm Policy," *Journal of Farm Economics,* **34** (Aug. 1952).

[2] Quoted from Jefferson's notes on Virginia by Paul H. Johnstone in "Old Ideals Versus New Ideas in Farm Life," *Farmers in a Changing World, 1940 Yearbook of Agriculture* (Washington: U. S. Govt. Printing Office, 1940), p. 117.

[3] *First Interim Report of the Subcommittee on Family Farms to the Committee on Agriculture,* House of Representatives, 84th Congress (March 31, 1956), p. 3. Even though the minority members of the committee could not agree with the majority of the committee on their policy recommendations, their minority views did contain the following statement: "We who endorse this minority report are in accord with the general statements setting forth the importance of the family farms to the general, economic, moral and spiritual health of our nation and we are paramountly aware of the contributions that rural America has in the past made to our national complex as we are aware of the important part it will play in a sound future." *Ibid.,* p. 28.

Moreover, this subcommittee by its intimate studies is persuaded that beyond all other notice and regard, the agricultural order in the family unit pattern must be considered especially for the spiritual, social and political vitality it has contributed to our civilization.

Recent resolutions of the National Grange and Farmers Union stated these beliefs: [4]

The Grange Farm policies and programs are predicated on the belief that family type farms are the basis for the best and most efficient kind of rural America. They are part of our heritage of equal opportunity, democratic society, individual respectability and stable political order.

The Farmers Union believes that (1) family farming (a) is the most efficient method of food and fiber production; (b) provides greatest protection for the consumer since family farmers ask only to be allowed to earn parity of income with other groups; (c) is essential to a truly democratic way of life. (2) The small business nature of farming is a strong bulwark against Communism or Fascism, but it leaves the family farmer without protection in the market place.

A second set of beliefs relate to economic organization and the role of the family farm in attaining the desired values, especially those of efficiency and individual control of enterprises. It is believed that the family farm is the most efficient form of organization in agriculture and that there are no economies of scale beyond the size attainable with typical family farms. This belief has been supported by a number of agricultural economists, and some have further shown that owner-operated family units are more efficient in resource allocation than are the same size units operating under different arrangements.[5]

It is also believed that the owner-operated family farm represents the epitome of freedom for an individual to manage his own enterprise. This belief was stated by the Subcommittee on Family Farms: [6]

[4] *1958 Legislative Programs and Policies of the National Grange,* p. 3, and Farmers Union Policy Leaflet No. 10, *A Modern Family Farm,* p. 3.

[5] D. Gale Johnson, "Resource Allocation Under Share Contracts," *Journal of Political Economy,* **58** (April 1950).

[6] *Op. cit.,* p. 3.

This subcommittee is convinced that by the proportion the nation permits a lessening of the number of opportunities for venture into individual enterprises—for one to own his own farm or his own business—then by an even larger measure will the free enterprise system be weakened. Free enterprise is the spirit of the frontier. The frontier must be kept open for men to venture into and to achieve independence in individual and family enterprises. The self-interest of those who have a stake in the American system—and that is all Americans—requires this.

Thus, the strength and durability of the "family farm" as a policy goal in American agriculture can be explained by the belief that this method of economic organization of farms contributes substantially to the achievement of a number of important values held in our society.

In recent years, however, conditions have been changing and questions have been raised as to the future of the family farm as a goal for farm policy. Despite the continued assertions of agricultural economists regarding constant or decreasing returns to scale in farming, there has been an extraordinary growth in the number of farms in the highest economic class as determined by value of sales (Table 1, p. 27). This suggests that since the mid-1950's, there may have been a rise in the proportion of larger than family farms.[7]

Increasingly, the belief that farming in general and the family farm in particular makes a unique contribution to social and political stability becomes harder to sustain, especially in a predominantly urban society. Writers such as Griswold question whether it ever was a valid interpretation of history [8] and thus support for the family as a policy goal slowly shrinks.

If it should develop that agricultural economists have been

---

[7] Jackson V. McElveen, *Family Farms In a Changing Economy*, Agricultural Information Bulletin No. 171 (Washington: U.S.D.A., Mar. 1957); and, Radoge Nikolitch, *Family and Larger-than-Family Farms—Their Relative Position in American Agriculture*, Agricultural Economic Report No. 4 (Washington: U.S.D.A., Jan. 1962), both show that family farms' relative position in U. S. agriculture has remained about the same. However, both analyses end with data from the 1954 Census of Agriculture.

[8] A. Whitney Griswold, *Farming and Democracy* (New Haven: Yale University Press, 1952).

wrong in the past, or that technical and economic conditions have changed sufficiently so that the family farm is no longer the "most efficient" unit for producing farm products, then the family farm may lose further support as a policy goal. Instead of contributing to the simultaneous achievement of several values, it may turn out that family farms contribute to the achievement of some values and retard the achievement of others. If so, the family farm may lose its appeal as a universal goal of United States farm policy.

There is some evidence that the family farm as a policy goal is already losing some of its appeal for the major farm organizations. No mention is made of the family farm as a desirable goal in the recent resolutions of the American Farm Bureau Federation, and the place accorded it by the Grange in its 1960 resolutions was much less prominent than in the past. Neither the special message on agriculture nor the legislation introduced in 1961 included the family farm as a major policy goal. Thus, we may see a policy goal that has persisted since the founding of the republic steadily lose appeal and support.

Parity As a Policy Goal

As with the "family farm" the concept of parity has survived because it has been identified with the achievement of several values prized by our society.

The major support for parity as a policy goal exists because people believe parity will bring equality for farmers. Farmers tend to view parity as equality and it has been so defined by law in a relative sense.[9] Both *parity price* and *parity income* are seen as goals which, if achieved, would be consistent with the values relating to equal economic opportunity. Thus, the parity concept has become the operating goal for farm policy.

It is interesting to note that the "parity price" and the "parity

[9] Parity prices for agricultural products are defined as that price which will give a unit of an agricultural product the *same purchasing power* as that unit had in a base period. Parity income is generally defined as that income which bears the same relative ratio to nonfarm incomes (in terms of purchasing power) as did farm incomes to nonfarm incomes in a specified base period.

income" concepts probably relate to the different concepts of equal opportunity. Thus, the parity income concept relates to equal opportunity in a welfare sense, while the parity price concept relates to the value of "equal opportunity to develop to the limits of one's abilities." [10]

The adoption of parity as a goal must have rested upon certain beliefs which now increasingly appear doubtful. In order for constant purchasing power or constant relative incomes (regardless of how defined) to represent equality over time, it must be agreed that they represented equality in the base period. However, when it becomes apparent that parity prices or parity incomes as now defined (relative to a historical base) will produce per capita or per family incomes in agriculture well below the incomes of nonfarm people, it also becomes apparent that there were substantial income differences in the base period.

A second source of support for the parity goal in agricultural policy is related to the value placed upon general economic stability. This coupled with the belief, mentioned earlier, regarding the importance of high agricultural incomes to general economic stability has made the goal of achieving parity prices or parity income for agriculture a seeming contributor to general economic stability. However, as doubts arise regarding the proposition that general prosperity depends upon farm prosperity, this base of the parity goal appears weakened.

A third value to which the parity concept has been thought to contribute is that of growth. Economic growth is valued and, moreover, there is a widespread feeling that the benefits of such growth should be widely shared, especially by those that contributed. Since the parity concept, as defined, is a relative price and income, it has been assumed that it accurately measures attainment in this area. Thus, the Farm Bureau said: [11] "We reaffirm

[10] The position of the Grange and the Farm Bureau on these two as goals is consistent with the earlier assertion that the two organizations are expressing different values when they speak of equality of economic opportunity. The Grange calls for parity income, whereas the Farm Bureau approves the parity principle applied to prices and does not mention income.

[11] *Op. cit.*, p. 11. This was changed substantially in the 1962 resolutions and now says nothing about parity as a measure of balance. This would appear to represent a change in the beliefs regarding parity as such a measure.

our long-standing and continuous support of the parity principle
—which reflects agriculture's interest in there being a healthy balance between the various segments of our national economy."

For a variety of reasons the attractiveness of parity as a goal
for agricultural policy is rapidly diminishing. Largely it is because it has become apparent that parity, as defined legislatively,
will not contribute to the achievement of enough of the underlying values.

As yet there is no income or welfare goal that has arisen to
replace parity. There is one stirring, however—"reasonable return" or "fair return" on factors in agriculture, relative to what
these factors (labor, management, and capital) get in the nonfarm
economy. The Grange has made the transition by defining parity
income in this fashion: [12] "Parity income should provide farmers
a return for their labor, management, skill, risk and investment
in reasonable relation to that returned for these factors in other
segments of the economy."

The use of parity as a goal generally has been ridiculed by
economists as neither meaningful nor workable. The new definition (equal returns) should be dear to economists' hearts, because
it is one of the conditions defining the most efficient resource allocation in the market under competitive conditions.

Thus, perhaps parity income redefined as "equal returns" may
have a new lease on life, for economists will assert that when all
factors are employed so that marginal returns to factors in agriculture are equated both within the industry and between agriculture and the nonfarm economy, we will obtain the maximum
total output of goods and services. The goal of "equal returns,"
if attained, will contribute to the achievement of efficiency, to
equal economic opportunity for farmers, and to sharing in progress by farmers.

The appeal of parity based upon some historical period appears to be declining. But the name still has a favorable ring, and
in policy goals, as in merchandising, the name lives on even
though the product is a new one.

[12] *1960 Summary of Legislative Policies and Programs of the National Grange*,
p. 9.

Equal Bargaining Power and Supply Management

The newest farm policy goal is that of *supply management,* a new phrase which has arisen from the older goal of "equal bargaining power for farmers." Some variety of this goal is mentioned by each of the three major organizations, and it has become the major organizing rationale of a new organization, the National Farmers Organization. However, the methods by which it is to be achieved and exactly *what* is to be achieved differ substantially from group to group. But there is little doubt that the idea appeals strongly to farmers.

The idea that equal bargaining power and supply management are synonymous rests on the belief that the earnings of organized labor and of corporations are dependent upon their ability to control output.

It is believed that the wages of organized labor are heavily dependent upon the abilities of unions to withhold or control the supply of labor available to an industry, through closed shops, seniority, and if necessary, strikes. It is believed that many corporations can determine their product prices by controlling a major portion of the output of the industry and maintaining output at levels which will achieve the desired prices. Therefore, it is argued that if farmers had the ability collectively to control farm output, they would obtain the benefits that are believed to have accrued to labor and business. For labor and business it is asserted that this ability is derived from the granting of rights for private organizations of unions and corporations. In order to obtain the same benefits for farmers, many people believe the federal government would have to become the basis of the organization. However, the National Farmers Organization asserts it can be accomplished outside of government by contract and withholding action.

The support for this goal is based upon the beliefs of farmers that its achievement would further the simultaneous attainment of *several* of the values underlying farm policy. The most obvious value to be achieved is the desire for equal opportunity (in an income sense) for existing farmers. It is widely believed by many farmers (and claimed at least by some farm leaders) that low farm prices and incomes are the consequences of the buyers of farm products possessing greater bargaining power than the individual farmers whose products they buy. It is thus believed that "equalizing" bargaining power in the market would result in more favorable market prices to farmers.

The prospect of more favorable market prices to farmers via equal bargaining power also promises attainment of income distribution in accordance with one's contribution, another highly-prized value.

Also, the goal of equal bargaining power appears to offer attainment of the value that no person should have economic power over another. This stems from the belief that large non-farm concentrations of economic power enable the possessor to control the economic activities of the individual farmers who deal with it as sellers and buyers.

Thus, the stage is set for the goal of "equal bargaining power" and "supply management" to have a long and successful run on the policy scene, at least as long as the beliefs persist as to its potency as a method of simultaneously achieving several values. Two factors require examination to determine whether it will prove to be a useful goal. Does it do what is claimed for other groups, and even if it does, will it do the same for farmers?

Students of labor economics are divided as to whether unions have obtained higher wages for labor than would have existed in the absence of unions. Even if one grants success in this area, it appears that unions have not been able to maintain employment levels in industries where demand was not expanding. Thus, total union membership has declined and benefits have not been extended to all workers who might have desired them.

There are examples of large corporations which have been unable to maintain satisfactory earnings despite an alleged ability to maintain product prices. Therefore, it appears that the ability to influence output or product prices is perhaps a necessary, but not sufficient condition, to achieve what farmers hope to achieve via supply management. The sufficient conditions probably include continued increases in demand over a period of time and the ability of the firm to control technical change as well as output.

Allowing the possibility that some economic groups may have been able to improve their position via the use of market power to achieve supply management, it does not follow that this will produce the same results for farmers. First, even if supply management increased total incomes in agriculture, there are indications that these incomes will not be distributed among factors of production in a way to increase labor returns. Thus, income distribution in agriculture would be even more dependent upon asset ownership than at present. This may be inconsistent with equal income opportunity.

The necessity to use government to achieve supply management implies that while individuals may remove the alleged economic power of other organized groups, they may substitute some measure of control by government over the individual manager. This means that higher incomes may compete with freedom of individual management.

Supply management also may imply some loss of the value placed upon efficiency, depending upon the particular methods which are used. Certainly any form of it which uses land as a vehicle of output control is likely to reduce efficiency of resource allocation, as we shall discuss later.

Thus, much of the support for supply management or equal bargaining power rests upon beliefs which should be subjected to further examination. Such an examination may reduce the appeal of this concept as a goal for farm policy.

Sharing Our Abundance and "Food for Peace"

Sharing our abundance is repeatedly put forth as a policy goal. Historically, it has usually applied to the domestic scene. Recently, however, it has received new support with a new dimension and new title—*Food for Peace.*

Sharing our abundance domestically has lacked widespread support as a farm policy goal in the United States during the relatively prosperous postwar period. It has been argued that such a policy would improve farm income; and, therefore, we should share our abundance of farm products with the domestic needy via subsidized consumption programs. However, statistical evidence has shown that such domestic distribution programs would improve farm income little, if any, in a high-employment economy and, moreover, that there are relatively few persons in our economy who need special programs to share adequately in our agricultural abundance.[13] Also such programs will have little or no impact upon the demand for nonfood products. In the face of this evidence, there has been little support among farm people for domestic food distribution programs as a major policy goal in recent years, even in years of serious unemployment.

However, the *Food for Peace* program, a more recent claimant for admission to the select circle of major goals, has had much greater appeal. Basically, its goal is that we should not only make effective use of present government stocks, but that our farm policy deliberately should include production for distribution abroad outside the commercial market channels. This goal has particular significance because it receives widespread support from outside of agriculture as well as from within.

An important value that is hoped to be attained via such a policy goal is a stable, orderly world, subject to rule by law. That *Food for Peace* will contribute materially to its achievement rests upon two dubious assumptions regarding the outside world. First, it is generally assumed within the United States that "friendly" nations contribute to a stable, orderly world, whereas "unfriendly" nations do not. The strength of this belief apparently has been little shaken by our disastrous experience with friendly, unstable dictatorships in recent years and our extreme difficulties with friendly, unstable democracies, both old and new.

Second, we apparently still assume that the probability of a nation becoming "unfriendly" is inversely related to the caloric intake of its population, that friendship is a physiological rather than a psychological phenomenon. This view, commonly called "stomach communism," should have been dispelled since there

[13] John M. Wetmore, Martin E. Abel, Elmer Learn, and Willard W. Cochrane, *Expanding the Demand for Farm Food Products*. Technical Bulletin 231 (St. Paul: Minnesota Agricultural Experiment Station, April 1959).

are some nations that are obviously poor and non-Communist (friendly) and some nations which are quite well off and Communist (unfriendly).

A second value, the achievement of which is seen in the goal of *Food for Peace,* is that of equal (income) opportunity for farm people. In fact, this was one of the major underlying factors in the support of the farm organizations for the Marshall Plan, Public Law 480, and other special export programs for farm products. These special export programs for farm products are seen as a method of maintaining or increasing the earnings of resources in agriculture by having our government provide the "effective" portion of increased *effective* demands for United States farm products abroad.

It also apparently is believed that *Food for Peace* would contribute in a special way to the achievement of our desire to "share our abundance." We try to be practical people, so that while we want to share our abundance with the less fortunate the world over, we also want to do it with the most efficiency and least cost to us. Somehow it is assumed that foreign aid (sharing our abundance) in the form of farm products is as good, if not better, for the recipient countries as foreign aid in the form of other goods and services or dollars. Even if the price for the farm products in such transactions were not grossly inflated, as usually is the case, in terms of their real costs from other sources, it does not follow that the provision of United States foreign aid in the form of farm products is best or most efficient for the recipients. Certain goods and services desired abroad are available largely from the United States, and it is erroneous to assume that farm products, however cheap, are a substitute for dollars or these other items.

Another assumption underlying *Food for Peace* is that it represents the optimum or most efficient method of sharing our abundance because the program "costs" us less. To the extent that the farm products sent abroad come from existing government stocks for which alternative uses are limited, it is true that the opportunity costs of such products are low. It is quite incorrect, however, to assume that the opportunity costs are equally low if you deliberately encourage the production of certain farm products in excess of market demands for disposition via special export programs.

Another powerful source of support for *Food for Peace* as a policy goal comes from the belief that such a policy will contribute significantly to the achievement of greater economic development abroad. Our values in this area are much deeper than mere self-preservation, which would say that economic development abroad is necessary to prevent the advance of communism. True, this is involved, but the desire to speed development abroad also is based on the idea that all mankind has a *right* to better and more material things and that we have an obligation to help them realize this right.

At the same time, there is a widespread belief that ample supplies of farm products play a crucial role in economic development. The validity of this belief is apparent since some minimum level of food and clothing are essential for health and physical productivity, which are in turn essential to economic development.

What is less certain, however, is the validity of the assumption that farm products produced in the United States are as good or better than farm products produced in the developing country or elsewhere. Moreover, there is a parallel assumption that the farm products needed for development can be obtained in the United States at lower real cost than in the developing country or elsewhere in the world.

The latter assumption is the crucial one, and it again rests upon the failure to distinguish between the real opportunity cost of using present surplus stocks and the real opportunity cost of producing additional farm products in the United States for the express purpose of speeding development abroad. In the case of using stocks for development purposes abroad, the issue is clear —any real value they have in such uses probably is greater than any opportunity cost—therefore, there use is warranted unless other costs are too great. (Other costs may include unrest among farmers in the receiving nations if prices are adversely affected by the imports.)

The issue is complex and less clear as to whether the cause of international economic development is best served by our producing excess farm products for specific use in international development programs. Basically, the question is: Will a total development effort of a given size get more results if we use our resources to produce farm products while the recipient nations push the expansion of output in other industries, or will it be greater if we furnish other than farm products while they expand their output of farm products? This is an economic question of present and potential comparative advantage between the United States and other countries in the production of farm and nonfarm products. The answer to the question is uncertain, but it is important, for upon it hinges the answer to whether the *Food for Peace* program will maximize our contribution to international economic development.

Despite the doubtful validity of the assumptions upon which it rests, the *Food for Peace* program has achieved the role of a major policy goal in the United States agricultural policy. Its acceptance by both political parties and by powerful nonfarm groups attests to this new role. Its retention as a major policy goal will depend, however, upon the ability of such a policy to deliver its promised achievements—an ability which must at present remain in doubt.

Freedom As a Goal of Farm Policy

During the past decade there has been a movement on the part of the American Farm Bureau Federation and other groups allied with it, both farm and nonfarm, to make "freedom" a major goal of farm policy. Because of the effects that such an attempt has had upon the processes by which farm policy is made, it is desirable to examine the usefulness of this concept as an operating goal in farm policy.

First, discussions of the concept of freedom suffer from a semantic handicap, for different people mean different things when they use the word, and the same person often means different things at various times when the concept is used. Therefore, it is necessary to try to determine specifically what is meant by freedom when used as a goal for farm policy.

Apparently, the advocates of freedom as a goal for farm policy use the word in at least three different contexts. On one hand, there is the goal of freedom from government interference in the price-making mechanism, i.e., "free" markets. Second, there is the goal of freedom from government interference in the operation of individual farm or business enterprises. Third, there is freedom of individuals from political domination by central government. It is noteworthy that all of the concepts are expressed as freedom *from* government.

It is clear that at least two of the three concepts of freedom are related to some of the values discussed earlier as generally underlying our agricultural policy. The question, however, is whether any or all of these concepts of freedom, as an important policy goal, will be consistent with a sufficient number of values to attract support. There is a web of interlocking beliefs that suggest that freedom could be consistent with the major values, and an understanding of these beliefs is necessary to recognize the appeal of freedom as a policy goal.

There is a widespread belief that freedom from government interference in the market will contribute to the achievement of several aspirations of farmers. First, it is asserted that government intervention in the market reduces efficiency, or that "free" markets for farm products would result in a higher total output of goods and services. Second, it is asserted that government intervention will always result in the distribution of income without regard to individual contribution, whereas the free market will distribute incomes according to contribution. Third, and perhaps most important, it has been widely believed by many farmers that total net farm income and their *personal* net farm income would be higher in the absence of government intervention. Thus, the idea of free markets attracts powerful support as a policy goal if it can truly deliver the goods (values).

However, powerful doubts were cast over the likelihood of higher incomes for farmers in free markets, at least in the short run, by a series of technical studies in 1959 and 1960 which concluded that free markets would result in sharp and continuing lower incomes for commercial farmers.[14] Thus, the assertions that free markets would produce higher farm incomes in the immedi-

[14] See the *Report from the United States Department of Agriculture and a Statement from the Land-Grant Colleges, IRM-1 Advisory Committee on Farm Price and Income Projections 1960–65,* Senate Document No. 77, 86th Congress, 2nd Session (Jan. 20, 1960); and *Economic Policies for Agriculture in the 1960's, Implications of Four Selected Alternatives,* Materials prepared for the Joint Economic Committee, Congress of the U. S., Joint Committee Print, 86th Congress, 2nd Session (Washington: U. S. Govt. Printing Office, 1960).

ate future appear to rest on either unrealistic assumptions regarding resource mobility out of agriculture and the resulting supply curves of farm products, or upon inaccurate appraisals of the elasticity of demand for farm products.

Equally serious questions have been raised about the assumption that free markets will produce higher (or equal) farm incomes in the long run. Cochrane [15] and Johnson [16] use different analytical mechanisms to conclude that the structure of the agricultural industry is such that resource earnings in agriculture with free markets for farm products, will be continuously below those of the nonfarm economy.

This evidence has caused many farmers, farm organizations, economists, and policy makers to reject the assertion that farm incomes will be improved, all other things remaining equal, by a removal of government interference in the markets. Thus, one leg of the support for this concept of freedom as a policy goal is weak. What of the others?

The assertion that free markets result in the maximum output grows out of economic theory. Free markets as a policy goal, however, depend on whether the real world will produce the results predicted in theory. The assumptions of theory usually include perfect knowledge about both present and future events, perfect resource mobility, and no institutional barriers to instantaneous resource adjustment. As will be detailed in a later chapter, the real world of agriculture departs from these underlying assumptions of static competitive economic theory in several respects. These departures may result in major errors in resource allocation under free prices, so it is questionable whether free markets in agriculture will result in the maximum total national output of goods and services.

The assertion that free markets will allocate rewards (income) according to the individual's contribution to society also is based upon an interpretation of competitive economic theory. What the theory states is that if the underlying conditions or assump-

[15] Willard W. Cochrane, *Farm Prices, Myth and Reality* (Minneapolis: University of Minnesota Press, 1958).

[16] Glenn L. Johnson, *The Surplus Trap In American Agriculture,* a manuscript being prepared for publication (East Lansing, 1961).

tions exist, the market will allocate rewards in accordance with the *marginal* contribution of the factor to production. However, *income* distribution in the market is a function of the quantity and ownership of resources employed as well as a function of the *rate* of reward. Economic theory deals with *rates* of rewards, whereas many persons think it deals with *total volume* of rewards and, therefore, conclude that the free market will provide incomes in accordance with their values. Thus, the goal of a free market may not contribute to the achievement of values relating to income distribution.

There are several beliefs that support the idea that freedom from "government interference" in individual enterprises will further the attainment of several values. First, it is asserted that "government interference" always reduces the efficiency of the individual enterprise. Moreover, it is stated that "government interference" always operates to restrict equal opportunity to develop to the limits of one's capacities, and it also always operates to distribute income without regard to contribution. Finally, it is argued that "government interference" in individual enterprises always gives someone—the bureaucrat—economic power over the farmer. Therefore, the argument runs, a removal of "government interference" will increase efficiency, provide equal opportunity, improve income distribution, and remove unequal economic power!

The validity of these assertions has been subjected to less scrutiny by economists than has that regarding free markets. However, the assumptions imply that individual managers are always more intelligent and better informed than "government," that "government" has different values than do farmers regarding rewards and equal opportunity, and that even in a democracy "government" has power over individuals instead of the reverse. Also, if free markets mean farmers must face other concentrations of economic power in society, the domination of the farmer by others may persist even if government is absent.

The goal of freedom of individuals from political domination by government appears to promise solely the achievement of the value of equality of political power. This must rest upon the assumption that even in democratic government the distribution of political power is always adverse to farmers. The validity of this belief has clearly been challenged by the Grange in the statement cited earlier, and it is not widely accepted in our society. Widespread acceptance of the above assumption would seem to indicate, in fact, that as a society we do not believe representative government—"of the people and by the people"—will work.

Thus, in summary, it appears that the attempt to elevate "freedom" to the status of a major policy goal is unlikely to succeed, even though the concept of freedom is given multiple meanings, for it appears that it is unlikely that the goal of freedom, if attained, would produce the desired results in achieving other values.

Its probable failure will be due to the fact that its ability to achieve several values simultaneously is based upon invalid assumptions, incorrect interpretations of economic theory, and untenable conclusions regarding democracy as a form of government.

This is not to say that freedom does not exist as a major value and play an important role in farm policy. Farmers do prize the freedom to make production decisions on their farm. Farmers also prize the freedom to determine their own government programs, if any, for, in their view, this achieves the value of equal distribution of political power. However, freedom is a meaningless concept unless it is defined as freedom to do something specific, the doing of which will increase the attainment of values. Policies which include greater freedom to do or achieve a specific thing that will attain certain values will be preferable to policies which include less of this specific freedom. But freedom in the abstract appears of little use either as a goal or value in agricultural policy.

Future Goals of United States Farm Policy

The preceding analysis suggests that the traditional goals of farm policy, "parity" and the "family farm," are less appealing as operating goals than in the past, largely due to changes in beliefs about the ability of such goals to contribute to the attainment of several of the values underlying the demands for action via *public* policy. The new policy goals that are being put forth are based upon doubtful assumptions regarding their ability to attain the desired values. As a result, the nearly universal support, both inside and outside of agriculture, for certain longstanding goals of United States farm policy is declining, and the political support for most policy goals is substantially less than in earlier periods. This has been the situation in United States agricultural policy in the last decade, and it appears likely to continue for the next decade, if not indefinitely. Thus, a multiplicity of goals, each lacking the necessary widespread support, has contributed to a policy stalemate, which is not likely to be soon resolved.

The stalemate in farm policy is usually attributed to the breaking up of the "farm bloc." This implies diminution of the political power of agriculture, a matter which we shall examine later. Even without the changes in the political structure, it appears that the unanimity on farm policy would have decreased merely because of the change in the willingness of the various groups to universally support a few policy goals.

PART TWO

THE ECONOMICS

OF THE FARM

PROBLEMS

To MOST laymen the farm problem is *surpluses*—large stocks of farm products held by the government in shiny steel bins—periodically reported as mounting in size and maintenance costs. To the economist the farm problem is malallocation of resources—the use of too many resources producing farm products relative to other goods and services. To the farmers it is mainly their low and unstable income—despite hard work, careful management, and often large capital investments. To the Congress and the Executive the farm problem is a multibillion dollar drain on the federal budget, which, if reduced, would allow more public funds for other pressing needs. To many politicians the farm problem is a hopeless trap that increasingly promises to end their political futures as they are caught between unhappy farmers and irate taxpayers, with little hope of pleasing either, let alone both.

The farm problem has become all of these and more. There are actually several interrelated farm problems that often occur simultaneously for certain groups in agriculture. These problems have their roots in the basic structure of agriculture and in the economic forces in our economy. Unless these are understood, it is impossible to determine what the problems really are and, moreover, it is impossible to assess the effects that alternative policy solutions may have.

Chapter 4

Low Returns in Agriculture: Why Farmers Are Underpaid but Not Always Poor

The economic problems of United States agriculture have many facets and, as we shall see, actually must be considered as a bundle of interrelated problems. A major problem is that the reward for human effort in agriculture generally is below that for comparable human effort elsewhere in the economy. This represents a major resource allocation problem in the economy, in that total national output presumably would be increased by shifting resources from agriculture to the production of other goods and services.

The data reported in Chapter 2 show that under recent policies and programs, low returns for human effort in agriculture do not mean that all farm families have low incomes. In fact, farm operators' families on those farms producing more than $5,000 of products annually in 1959 had average incomes which were about the same as average incomes in the nonfarm economy.

The average income level of farm operators' families in 1959 does not alter the existence of low returns to human effort on such farms. First, the incomes from commercial farms represent returns upon much higher capital investments than do average incomes in the nonfarm economy, and this investment should produce some income regardless of the rate of return to human effort. Second, these incomes were partially due to government price and income policy for agriculture. In the absence of such programs, the net income from farming of these commercial farms probably would have been one-fourth to one-third lower than existed, and the returns to all productive factors consequently would have been lower. Therefore, it seems appropriate to typify the problem of low returns to human effort in agriculture as a situation where farmers are underpaid but not always poor.

It now appears that this problem is not new to United States agriculture but may have existed for several decades, at times disguised by other overriding economic forces. The roots of the problem lie in several characteristics of the agricultural industry which individually are insufficient to produce the chronic problem we now observe, but which together result in economic problems for the industry of major magnitude. These characteristics can be seen by examining: (1) the nature of the demand for farm products in the United States; (2) the nature of forces changing total farm output in the United States; (3) the difficulty of resource mobility out of agriculture; and (4) the outside economic forces that affect farmers.

The Nature of the Demand for Farm Products

Two concepts relating to the demand for farm products are important. One is the price elasticity of demand, which relates to the slope of the demand curve at a given point in time, and the other is the income elasticity of demand, which relates the position of the demand curve to changes in the real income of consumers.

A number of statistical studies are available which provide estimates of both the price and income elasticity for farm products.[1] They can be summarized by saying that the demand for farm products *at the farm level* is inelastic, so that a given percentage increase in quantity will only clear the market with a relatively greater decrease in price. Total revenue is, therefore, lower from a larger quantity than from a smaller quantity of farm products.

Different statistical studies show slightly different results, depending upon the particular time period and method used, but it appears price elasticity for farm products in the aggregate at the farm level is about .15 to .25. This means that the marginal utility of additional farm products is quite low to United States consumers. Moreover, there is some evidence that this value has been drifting slowly downward over a period of time. The price elasticity of different farm products varies substantially, but there are no major groups of products having an elasticity of 1.0 or greater and thus able to provide an outlet for large increases in output without a decline in total revenue.

Statistical studies show that the income elasticity of demand for farm products also is low in the United States.[2] This means that increases in consumer income move the demand curve for farm products to the right, little, if at all. It now appears that the income elasticity for farm products in the aggregate is somewhere between .15 and .20, so that a ten per cent increase in consumer income will increase the demand for farm products by two per cent at most. This leaves the growth in demand for farm products largely dependent upon the rate of growth in population.

The conditions relating to the demand for farm products in

[1] A summary of a number of such estimates can be found in T. W. Schultz, *Economic Organization of Agriculture* (New York: McGraw-Hill, 1953), Table 11-1, p. 188. W. W. Cochrane, *Farm Prices, Myth and Reality, op. cit.,* p. 41 concludes that the price elasticity of demand for food at the farm level is .08. This is lower than most other estimates at the farm level.

[2] Estimates of income elasticity for farm products at the farm level may be found in Rex F. Daly, "The Long-Run Demand for Farm Products," *Agricultural Economics Research,* 8(3) (July 1956), and in L. M. Goreux, "Income and Food Consumption," *Monthly Bulletin of Agricultural Economics and Statistics,* 9(10) (Oct. 1960), Rome: Food and Agricultural Organization of the United Nations. Goreux estimates that the income elasticity of farm products in the United States at the farm level is .16.

the United States are as follows: In a wealthy country, with a high-level consumption of farm products, the marginal utility of more farm products is low relative to that of other goods. Also, in such an economy, increases in income will increase the demand for farm products only slightly, if at all. Taken together, these characteristics of demand mean that increases in output at a pace much in excess of population growth will bring falling prices and revenue to the producers of farm products.

Care has been taken to differentiate between the farm product component of consumers' goods and the nonfarm-produced components of these goods. Food and clothing, as they are actually purchased by consumers, consist of raw farm products combined with some nonfarm-produced marketing services (processing, packaging, preparation, etc.). Evidence suggests that the income elasticity is high for the services usually associated with farm products. Therefore, measurement of price and income elasticities for farm products at the retail level always shows much higher values than at the farm level.[3] It is the low value at the farm level that is of concern here, however, for it is the resources producing farm products that are measured in our income statistics relating to agriculture.

Farm Output and the Demand for Farm Products

Most of the explanation of low prices and incomes in United States agriculture has been put upon the pervasive rise in aggregate farm output since 1940. And indeed, the record has been impressive, although there are several puzzles in it that need examination.

The index of net farm output of the United States Department of Agriculture shows a rise of one-fourth from 1940 to 1950 and another rise of one-fourth from 1950–1960. The usual explanation has been that this rapid rise in output has exceeded population growth; has pressed against a highly inelastic demand; has resulted in falling prices and incomes for farmers, government intervention, and the unhappy situation in which we now

[3] See L. M. Goreux, *op. cit.*, for comparative estimates of the income elasticity for farm products at the farm and retail level in different countries.

find ourselves. However, as we shall see, the situation is a good deal more complex than this.

The statistics on the relationship between output and population growth are enlightening, for they suggest that there may be other factors on the demand side not usually taken into account in our evaluation of the situation. Figure 1 shows the index of

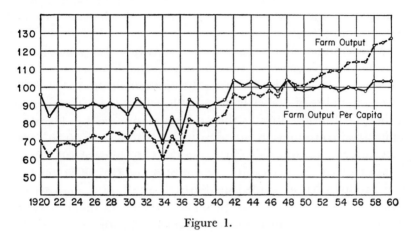

Figure 1.

Total and per capita farm output, 1920–60.

farm output per capita in the United States for the years 1920–60. Far from showing the expected sharp rise in output per capita since 1940, it shows a remarkable stability from 1942 through 1957. There was a marked upward shift in output per capita from the 1920's to the 1940's, and there appears to have been a slight upward shift in 1958. However, excluding the period 1934–1942, there is no pronounced upward trend in the index of farm output per capita!

There are several possible explanations of this apparent inconsistency between a relatively stable index of farm output per capita and falling farm prices. They are: (1) major declines in the exports of U. S. farm products have increased per capita supplies in the domestic market; (2) the domestic demand (per capita) for farm products has actually declined; or (3) the index of farm output has underestimated actual farm output.

The volume of agricultural exports has not declined, either in absolute or relative terms. Exports were equivalent to 10.7 per cent of farm output in 1947 and 14.7 per cent in 1960. However, export prices were lower in the latter period, so that even though volume has remained high due to special government programs, the higher exports may represent a movement along the demand curve rather than its movement to the right. Thus, the export demand curve for United States farm products probably has declined from the base period of 1947–49, which were years of extraordinary export demand.

An examination of the *relevant* statistics also suggests that there may have been an actual decline in the domestic per capita demand for farm products during the past two decades. The index of per capita use of domestic farm foods, which is a better measure of the use of farm resources than the commonly used index of per capita food consumption, stood at 96 in 1940 and at 99 in 1959.[4] This latter figure was a decline from the 1947 high of 107.[5] Thus, it appears that the per capita consumption of United States *farm* food products has expanded modestly, if at all, over the past two decades, despite rising real incomes. Higher incomes have increased the demand for the services associated with farm products, but the aggregate per capita demand for United States produced farm products has risen little.

It is generally assumed that there is no particular relationship between the demand for the farm-produced component of food and the demand for the associated marketing services. Reflection on the nature of marketing services suggests that there may be a relationship. It is likely that many of the marketing services have the effect of increasing the usable output of farm products. The various measures of consumption of farm products in the United States do not measure the quantity of farm products actually consumed. Instead, they measure the quantity of farm products entering the marketing system and, thus, available for consump-

---

[4] The index of per capita use of domestic farm foods is preferable, because it includes only the consumption of domestically produced products and has farm price weights. The index of per capita food consumption includes all foods and has retail price weights.

[5] Marguerite C. Burk, *Measures and Procedures for Analysis of U. S. Food Consumption*. Agriculture Handbook No. 206 (Washington: U. S. Govt. Printing Office, June 1961), p. 38.

tion. Our official indexes assume that the relationship between the volume of products entering the marketing system and the volume actually consumed has been unchanged over time. Even casual observation tells us this assumption does not hold.

Many of the innovations in food marketing have been to reduce waste, spoilage, and loss in the marketing system and by consumers. Better refrigeration (both in the marketing system and in homes), packaging, improved handling, and improved quality of products leaving the farm have increased the quantity of consumable final products available from a given quantity of farm products produced. Thus, the marketing services which bulk so large in consumer food prices are in part farm-product-saving in nature, so that actual food intake by consumers may have increased appreciably, even though the common measures of farm food consumption show only modest increases over the past two decades. The demand for marketing services which are product saving, therefore, constitutes a substitute for additional demand for farm resources.

In addition, the domestic nonfood demand for United States farm products has probably declined during the same period. The most striking example is for cotton, where per capita consumption declined one-fifth from 1940 to 1959. This, of course, was due to the substitution of man-made fiber for cotton during the period when total fiber consumption remained stable because better heating and more indoor employment offset the effect of higher income. Much the same story can be told for wool. The use of farm-produced oils as bases for paints has declined as nonfarm substitutes were developed, and detergents have largely displaced farm-produced fats in keeping us clean. Estimates are not available of the total effects of these and a multitude of similar changes upon the demand for farm-produced products, but taken together, they must represent a significant reduction in demand for farm products. Think, for instance, how easy the adjustment to higher yields per acre in cotton would have been if total domestic consumption of cotton had been one-third higher!

It is also possible that the official index of farm output underestimates the true farm output because of the way in which the index is constructed. Total crop output is probably measured

with reasonable accuracy. Estimates of total livestock output
probably have a wider margin of error. But the underestimation
of total output, if any, comes from the way the two are combined.
In order to avoid double counting of crops fed to livestock, it is
necessary to calculate feed fed to livestock. This is done, assuming
that there has been no change in the rate of conversion of feed to
livestock products, over the entire period for which the index is
computed.[6] To the extent that there has been increased feeding
efficiency, the index of net farm output underestimates total farm
output.

While the index of farm output in the United States has risen
steadily over the past three decades, the rise in output per capita
has not been sufficient to explain the downward pressures on farm
prices and incomes. It appears that the total domestic per capita
demand for farm products may actually have declined despite rising incomes, because of the substitution of nonfarm-produced
goods and services for farm products. This has meant that the
total demand for farm products has been dependent largely upon
population growth. The official index of farm output may understate actual output, so that actual output per capita may have
risen somewhat more than indicated in Figure 1, and this, together with the demand shifts cited above, would be consistent
with observed price and income trends in agriculture.

Farm Output and Income

Since over the past decade the total increase in farm output
has little more than kept pace with population growth, presumably this output should have cleared the market for farm products
at about stable relative prices. The situation that has developed,
however, has been somewhat different.

What has happened has been that the demand for farm products, including the government stocks under price-support pro-

[6] For a discussion of how this index is calculated, see *Major Statistical Series of
the U. S. Department of Agriculture—How They Are Constructed and Used*, Vol.
2, *Agricultural Production and Efficiency*, Agriculture Handbook No. 118 (Washington: U. S. Govt. Printing Office, Sept. 1957), beginning p. 27 and, especially pp. 34
and 35.

grams, has been such that the absolute level of farm prices has declined even though the general price level has been rising. Thus, there has been a sharp decline in the relative price of farm products, and the parity ratio (the ratio of prices received by farmers to prices paid by farmers) has declined from a level in excess of 100 (from 1942 through 1952) to an average of 80 for 1960. It would have been even lower in the absence of government intervention and stock accumulation.

The steady increase in farm output with lower farm prices has meant that the total cash receipts of farmers from marketings remained about the same from 1947 ($28.7 billion) to 1957 ($29.8 billion) while total farm output increased by over 20 per cent. From 1957 through 1960 cash receipts increased by about 10 per cent, largely because of an increase in total output of about 11 per cent, with price supports for many of the crops involved.

During this period in which gross revenue from sales of farm products has been relatively stable, the production expenses of farmers (in current dollars) have been rising steadily for two reasons. First, there has been an increase in the physical volume of purchased inputs used by farmers to produce the greater output. Second, there has been a persistent rise in the prices of these inputs. These two factors have increased total production expenses (including depreciation and rent to nonfarm landlords) from $16.8 billion in 1947 to $26.4 billion in 1960. The realized net income of farm operators from farming has decreased from 50 per cent of realized gross income in 1947 to 30 per cent of realized gross income in 1960. The total realized net income of farm operators from farming in 1947 was $17.3 billion, and in 1960 it was $11.7 billion. The total net income from agriculture (including net income of farm operators, farm wages, interest on farm mortgage debt, and rent to nonfarm landlords) reached an all-time high of $22.4 billion in 1948. By 1960, the total net income originating in agriculture was down to $16.6 billion.

Thus, the outline of the problem of low returns to resources producing farm products is visible. Agricultural output has continued to expand despite declining farm product prices, rising costs, and declining net income for the resources engaged in producing farm products. On the face of this evidence, it would appear that resources in agriculture had been earning more than elsewhere in the economy and that this was merely a normal movement to bring earnings in line. However, since this is inconsistent with all available evidence, the explanation must be sought elsewhere.

Changes Underlying Increased Farm Output

The continued expansion of farm output in the United States, in the face of falling product prices and falling incomes to factors of production, has become one of the great economic phenomena of the postwar period. Therefore, it is necessary to examine the facts that surround it and then see if these facts can be understood in light of economic theory as it applies to agriculture.

One of the illuminating ways of looking at the changes in farm output is to examine these changes in relation to the total quantity of inputs as they are usually considered, that is, land, labor, and capital. This has been done by Loomis and Barton, and they conclude that while farm output rose 51 per cent from 1940 to 1958, total conventional production inputs rose only about 4 per cent.[7] Thus, most of the increased farm output must be attributed to factors other than conventional inputs as measured in their study.

Even though the index of total inputs has remained relatively stable, there have been major changes in the input mix used to produce farm products. The index of farm labor input computed by Barton and Loomis declined by one-half from 1940–1958, while the index of mechanical power and machinery increased by 136 per cent and the index of fertilizer and lime used increased by 245 per cent. The index of farm real estate (land and buildings) increased by only some 8 per cent over the same period.

The authors' conclusion was that as time has passed an increasing fraction of additional farm output has been due to increased productivity in agriculture (Table 1). However, since the authors

---

[7] Ralph A. Loomis and Glen T. Barton, *Productivity of Agriculture, United States, 1870–1958*. U. S. Department of Agriculture, Technical Bulletin, No. 1238 (Washington: U. S. Govt. Printing Office, April 1961).

define change in productivity as a change in the ratio between measured input and measured output, this is equivalent to saying that an increasing proportion of output could not be explained by the inputs as measured in their analysis.

Table 1

**Sources and Annual Rates of Change in Output, Inputs, and Productivity,
United States Agriculture, Selected Periods ***

Period †	CHANGE IN OUTPUT ATTRIBUTABLE TO CHANGE IN—		AVERAGE ANNUAL RATE OF CHANGE IN—		
	Inputs	Productivity	Output	Inputs	Productivity
			Percentage		
1870–1911	72	28	2.45	1.77	.67
1911–1920	129	—29	.70	.89	—.19
1920–1939	16	84	1.08	.17	.91
1939–1945	34	66	3.05	1.04	1.99
1945–1950	49	51	.81	.40	.41
1950–1956	—9	109	1.89	—.17	2.06
1939–1956	22	78	1.98	.42	1.55
1911–1956	31	69	1.34	.41	.93
1870–1956	56	44	1.86	1.05	.80

* Based on indexes with 1947–49 = 100.
† The beginning and ending year of each period (except the year 1870) is the midyear of 3-year averages.

Source: Ralph A. Loomis and Glen T. Barton, *Productivity of Agriculture*. U. S. Dept. of Agriculture, Technical Bulletin, No. 1238 (Washington: U. S. Govt. Printing Office, April 1961), Table I, p. 9.

There are several possible explanations for the discrepancy between rates of change in measured inputs and output in United States agriculture. They are: (1) the measured inputs did not include all of the important inputs contributing to farm output; (2) the measures used did not accurately measure changes in inputs; (3) the increased specialization in agriculture; (4) the economies of scale in agriculture which have been realized in recent years, thus contributing to increased output from a given bundle of existing inputs.

T. W. Schultz has suggested that the failure to include improvements in the human factor in agriculture and investments in new knowledge is a major factor explaining the discrepancy.[8] These are no doubt important, as are other certain public expenditures which produce and disseminate information on production techniques to farmers.

Zvi Griliches [9] has turned his attention to the possibility that the methods used in measuring inputs substantially underestimate the actual inputs. He suggests that the underestimation of machinery stocks, the overestimation of machinery prices, the underestimation of fertilizer inputs, and the underestimation of labor inputs might account for as much as 30 per cent of the increase in "productivity" since 1940. Moreover, he suggests that the failure to catch all of the land improvements in recent years may be important and that the use of price weights which assume equilibrium prices, in an industry obviously in disequilibrium, could result in an overestimation of the decline in labor inputs.

Most of these criticisms of the Loomis and Barton measurements appear valid, but even so, if the critics are given all that they claim, it still appears that the increase in farm output has been achieved without proportional increase in the use of conventional inputs. Thus, contrary to early economic theory which suggested that agricultural output could only be increased by a resort to poorer resources with rising farm product prices as a result, we have for more than two decades in the United States achieved large increases in farm output from a bundle of only slightly larger resources and with falling product prices.

It is fashionable these days in economics to attribute increases in output which are not explained by increased land, capital, or labor, to higher productivity. Doing so tells us little about the sources of the increased output and, therefore, answers few questions of importance. What is needed is an explanation which gives us some idea of the cost of achieving increased output via differ-

[8] T. W. Schultz, "Reflections on Agricultural Production, Output and Supply," *Journal of Farm Economics*, **38** (Aug. 1956), pp. 748–62, and "The United States Farm Problem in Relation to the Growth and Development of the United States Economy," *Policy for Commercial Agriculture*, papers submitted by panelists appearing before the Subcommittee on Agricultural Policy of the Joint Economic Committee (Nov. 22, 1957), pp. 3–14.

[9] Zvi Griliches, "Measuring Inputs in Agriculture: A Critical Survey," *Journal of Farm Economics*, **42** (Dec. 1960), pp. 1411–27.

ent methods and, therefore, something of the underlying factors that actually have made possible the increased output.

One method of achieving increased output from a given set of resources—specialization—has been recognized since Adam Smith. There is no question that specialization has proceeded at a rapid pace in United States agriculture during the past two decades. There has been increased specialization between agriculture and the nonfarm economy as farmers have shifted to the purchasing of producers' goods instead of producing them on the farm and as farmers have increasingly shifted marketing activities to non-farm industries. There has also been increased specialization within production areas and increased specialization upon individual farms as the number of general farms declined or became specialized dairy, poultry, crop, or livestock farms. G. L. Johnson has suggested that the increased specialization at all levels of the agricultural industry has been a major source of the increased farm output.[10]

Another explanation of the increased output from a given set of resources might be that economies of scale exist in farming. Agricultural economists generally have concluded that there are no economies of scale beyond the commercial family-operated size unit. Even so, if there were scale economies up to the commercial family farm, the extensive consolidation of smaller units into these commercial farms might bring about increased output without a commensurate increase in conventional inputs. Johnson also has stressed this possibility.

By far the most popular explanation of the increased output is "new technology." Unfortunately, this explanation often becomes somewhat circular, since its users often define new technology to mean anything that increases output. There is no doubt that new technology, so defined, has been the source of increased farm output.

Probably the strongest advocate of new technology as the major source of increased farm output is W. W. Cochrane,[11]

[10] Glenn L. Johnson, "Sources of Expanded Agricultural Production," *Policy for Commercial Agriculture, op. cit.,* pp. 127–44.

[11] W. W. Cochrane, *Farm Prices, Myth and Reality* (Minneapolis: University of Minnesota Press, 1958).

although he is joined by many others.[12] He defines technology as: "An increase in output per unit of input resulting from a new organization, or configuration, of inputs where a new and more productive production function is involved."[13] Thus, he would include any changes in organization such as specialization or scale, as well as changes in the physical production functions, as technology.

Even if one defines changes in technology as a change in the physical production function which results in increased output from a given set of inputs, it is obvious that there have been many such changes in United States agriculture in the past two decades. Hybrid seeds and animals, new fertilizers, weed killers, insecticides, new engineering developments, and countless others could be listed.

Certain aspects of technology need to be kept in mind. First, it is virtually impossible to separate new technology from capital inputs or current inputs because new technology usually is embodied in some product purchased by the farmer. Second, new technology to an individual farm should not be confused with new technology to the agricultural industry, for, as we shall discuss later, the rate of adoption and extent of usage of a given technology may turn out to be very much determined by economic factors, and not an automatic event related to the passage of time.

Another useful view of the increases in farm output can be obtained by examining the components of the index of farm output as computed by the Department of Agriculture. The index of farm output measures the output of farm products that are available for eventual human consumption. In the United States economy, human consumption constitutes the bulk of the demand for farm products at the present time, except for those products that go to feed nonfarm animals—riding horses, domestic pets, etc.

The computation of the index of farm output makes it possible to identify the broad sources of increased farm output for human consumption. The Department of Agriculture has pro-

---

[12] See the material published by the Center for Agricultural and Economic Adjustment, Iowa State University, Ames, Iowa, for a number of papers suggesting that new technology has been the basic source of increased output in farm products.

[13] *Op. cit.*, p. 46.

vided such a breakdown for the period 1919–55.[14] A summary of the sources of change in the index for various periods is shown in Table 2.

It shows that up to the present time a major source of increased farm output for human consumption has been the reduction in the number of horses and mules on farms. In the period 1919–1940, this accounted for 51 per cent of the increase in net farm output, and for the period 1940–55, it still accounted for 23 per cent of the annual increase! In 1920, about 90 million acres of cropland were used to produce feed for horses and mules used on farms. As these animals were replaced by machines—tractors and autos—the acreage formerly used to feed them was available to produce feed for poultry, meat animals, and dairy cows, thereby increasing the output available for human consumption. What the report does not say is that from 1919–40 there was a concurrent decline in nonfarm animals, as trucks and autos replaced horses used in cities and towns. This latter change also increased the farm products available for *human* consumption, although it did not affect the index of net farm output.

Prior to 1940, the second most important source of increased farm output was increases in crop production per acre. Since 1940, this has become most important, accounting for 43 per cent of the total annual increase in output in the latter period. The absolute level of contribution of this source in the period 1940–55 was triple that of the period 1919–40.

In recent years, change in product added by livestock has contributed increasingly in both an absolute and relative sense. This is due to high production per breeding unit and expansion of feed base since the computations *do not allow* for improved feeding efficiency.

The effects on farm output of increased pasture consumed by livestock and increased cropland have been negligible over time; in fact, they were negative in some periods.

---

14 For a discussion of how this index is calculated, see *Major Statistical Series of the U. S. Department of Agriculture—How They Are Constructed and Used*, Vol. 2, *Agricultural Production and Efficiency*. U. S. Department of Agriculture, Agriculture Handbook, No. 118 (Washington: U. S. Govt. Printing Office, Sept. 1957), beginning p. 27 and, especially pp. 34–5.

Table 2

Annual Changes in Index Points of Farm Output, by Source of Change, United States, Specified Periods, 1919–55 *

Source of Change	Change, 1919–21 to 1938–40		Change, 1940–41 to 1951–52		Change, 1951–52 to 1955		Change, 1940–41 to 1955	
	Index Point	Percentage of Total	Index Point	Percentage of Total	Index Point	Percentage of Total	Index Point	Percentage of Total
		(Per cent)		(Per cent)		(Per cent)		(Per cent)
Reduction in farm-produced power	.39	51	.45	24	.38	19	.44	23
Change in product added by all livestock	.12	15	.41	22	.62	31	.47	25
Change in pasture consumed by all livestock	.03	4	0	0	.16	8	.04	2
Change in cropland used	—.03	—4	.20	11	—.08	—4	.13	7
Change in crop production per acre	.26	34	.80	43	.92	46	.82	43
Total change in farm output	.77	100	1.86	100	2.00	100	1.90	100

* Changes are measured in farm output index points, with the average of the years 1947–49 taken as a base of 100 points. This provides a measure of absolute change and makes possible comparisons of the relative importance of sources of change within a period as well as between periods. For example, during the interwar period, the annual increase in farm output averaged 0.77 per cent of the average 1947–49 volume of farm output in the United States; from 1940–41 to 1955, it averaged 1.90 per cent annually.

Source: Donald D. Durost and Glen T. Barton, *Changing Sources of Farm Output*. Production Research Report, No. 36, U. S. Department of Agriculture, Agricultural Research Service (Washington: U. S. Govt. Printing Office, Feb. 1960), Table 8, p. 17.

These figures help give the past increases in United States farm output a perspective sometimes lacking in recent discussions. In 1920, approximately 90 million acres of cropland were used to feed horses and mules on farms, and some unknown additional acreage produced feed for similar animals off farms. By 1960, less than 10 million acres were used for this purpose. Thus, the output of one-fourth or more of all the cropland in the United States was shifted, *once and for all,* to the production of farm products for human consumption at a time when other developments were bringing rapid increases in output per acre of cropland.

But, having once released this cropland, this source of increased farm output is exhausted. It will require a 50 per cent further rise in the rate of increase in crop production per acre or a similar change in product added by livestock above recent years to maintain the same rate of increase in total farm output in the years ahead. Such changes are not impossible, but they seem unlikely with a rational agricultural policy.

At this point, the economic nature of one of the major farm problems—that of persistently low returns for resources in commercial agriculture, especially for labor—can be summarized. The demand for farm products in the United States is inelastic and has been increasing slowly, if at all, as the increased demand arising from higher incomes has been partially or completely offset by increased efficiency in the marketing system and new and improved substitutes for farm products. Thus, even though the per capita output of farm products has remained relatively stable since World War II, there has been a marked downward trend in farm prices and income which has been partially forestalled by expensive governmental intervention.

During this period the output of farm products has continued to keep pace with population growth with some evidence of outstripping it. The higher output has been the result of both greater total productive resources in agriculture and increased output from these resources. Apparently, at a time when resource earnings, at least for labor, were below those of the nonfarm economy, farmers kept adding certain kinds of resources (mostly capital in the form of power and machinery and variable inputs like fertilizer, lime, and insecticides) at a sufficient rate to maintain (or increase if measured properly) the total resources producing farm products. For some time a situation has existed whereby if the resources in agriculture produced farm products for an unsupported market, the market-clearing prices would be well below the recent level of farm prices, and the earnings of resources would be well below the present levels.

An equilibrium level of resource returns in agriculture would be where the resources producing agricultural products were earning rates of return comparable to resources employed elsewhere in the economy. Comparable returns do not imply that all resources will have the same return, for different individuals have different occupational preferences. However, occupational preferences are an insufficient explanation of the low returns for human effort in farming; and since capital is presumably neutral as to its use, and its owners close to neutral, one cannot explain low returns to capital in agriculture on this basis. Conceptually, the equilibrium level of prices for farm products would be a level of prices that would enable resources in agriculture to receive returns equal to their opportunity costs at the time they entered production.

The competitive equilibrium of economic theory is never reached in a dynamic growing economy, for it is the opportunity to improve earnings that encourages resources to move from producing one product or service to another. Indications are that most of the economy market prices produce results approximately in line with theory, in that earnings are approximately comparable for comparable resources. In agriculture, however, there appears to be a persistent tendency in normal times for market prices to produce earnings which are well below those of comparable resources elsewhere. Thus, the market appears to produce results substantially different from the theoretical competitive equilibrium, and the difference appears to continue. Why does agriculture tend to have this difficulty that is not experienced by other industries, so that the disequilibrium appears to be larger and virtually permanent? The answer to this question carries with it many policy implications, for most of our farm price and income policy has the achievement of equilibrium prices and incomes for farm people as its implicit goal.

Resource Adjustment in Agriculture

It is not new to find economists pondering the disequilibrium in agriculture that has resulted in low farm prices and incomes. There have been periods in the past, usually during nonfarm business declines, in which farm prices have fallen but farmers have not appreciably reduced output. In fact, in some years of declining prices, farm output has increased, leading some persons to argue that falling prices cause farmers to increase output. Other evidence suggests, however, that most of the increases in farm output in the face of falling prices were unplanned, resulting primarily from changes in weather.[15]

Prior to the decade of the 1950's, every major decline in farm prices was associated with a business contraction in the nonfarm economy; while, conversely, there was no period of nonfarm business expansion in which the index of prices received by farmers failed to rise. Therefore, economists' attention was concentrated upon the failure of farmers to contract output significantly over a relatively short period of time. Even here there is evidence that some contractions were planned, because variable inputs were sharply reduced during periods of falling prices and incomes, and there is evidence that the index of crop production per acre moved positively with farm prices.

The explanations of the failure of farmers to reduce inputs and outputs appreciably in periods of falling prices have grown over the years, and as events have proven inconsistent with the prevailing theories, the latter have been complicated and embellished.[16] It is useful to review these explanations because our present theories build on earlier ones.

One of the earliest explanations of the maintenance of farm output during periods of falling prices was that farmers generally

[15] D. E. Hathaway, "Agriculture in an Unstable Economy Revisited," *Journal of Farm Economics,* **41** (May 1959).

[16] For a review of a number of the then existing explanations of the maintenance of agricultural production during depression years, see J. K. Galbraith and John D. Black, "The Maintenance of Agricultural Production During Depression: The Explanations Reviewed," *Journal of Political Economy,* **46** (June 1938), pp. 305–23.

have some fixed debt commitments and, consequently, some target goal of cash income necessary to meet these commitments and maintain family levels of living. When farm prices fall, farmers attempt to increase output sufficiently to maintain their income, hoping to offset lower prices per unit of output by increasing the number of units produced.

While nearly everyone cites a farmer in just the position described, this explanation cannot suffice to explain the output behavior of the total industry and its continued disequilibrium. Presumably, if the farm firm were using the various factors of production at the most profitable level (where their marginal value product just equaled their cost), a reduction in product price would lower the marginal value product of the inputs, and their use should decline. If, however, one assumed that as income fell the marginal utility of leisure fell relative to the marginal utility of income, then farmers might reduce other inputs and substitute increased family labor. This does not appear consistent with the facts of the postwar period since the use of unpaid labor has declined by one-half while the use of purchased inputs has increased substantially. Therefore, the increases in output have increased farmers' expenses and reduced net income, which is inconsistent with the position described above.

Long-Run Production Processes

Another explanation offered for the behavior of agricultural output over the business cycle has been the length of the production cycle in agriculture. It is argued that the production process in agriculture is long, especially for some livestock products. Therefore, farmers cannot rapidly adjust output downward, but must wait until a new production phase begins in order to make adjustments.

Within certain limits this explanation has some validity. Aggregate crop output is more sensitive to changes in output prices than is livestock output, presumably because farmers can make short-run adjustments in crops more easily. However, if farm prices fell so low that the marginal cost of completing the production process exceeded the price of the product, rational economic behavior would abandon the production at that point.

Such action is not uncommon for fruit and vegetable crops where harvest costs are high, but it is relatively rare in other parts of agriculture. Therefore, explanation for the relative stability of most agricultural output must be found elsewhere.

Even if the long production process explained the failure to reduce agricultural output during short-run cyclical fluctuations in farm prices, it would not explain the postwar phenomena which has continued over a period long enough to allow producers to adjust products with the longest production cycle. Since the recent experience in United States agriculture has spanned more than a decade, this explanation cannot suffice.

The Competitive Structure of the Industry

Another common explanation of the maintenance of aggregate farm output is the competitive nature of the industry. It is argued that in agriculture, producing under conditions that approximate pure competition, the individual producer cannot affect total output or price by reducing individual output, whereas, noncompetitive industries can maintain prices by reducing individual output. This may be relevant as an explanation of structure, but it does not appear to explain output behavior.

If product prices fall, why should farmers continue to use the same quantity of inputs? Rationally, the input use should be determined by the point at which the value of the additional output obtained from adding another unit of input (marginal value product) equals the price of the input. Therefore, unless input prices fall, the quantity of inputs should decline regardless of whether the firm in question produces for a competitive or imperfect market. Structure, in and of itself, cannot explain the maintenance of output. Even so, as we shall see, the competitive structure of the industry plays an important role in later, more complex, explanations.

Fixed Costs

Probably one of the most widely-accepted explanations of farm output behavior in periods of falling prices is the high ratio of fixed costs in agriculture. It is reasoned that much of the labor in agriculture is family labor, and the land is owned by the firm. Therefore, since these items make up a large portion of total inputs, it is stated that farmers will continue to use them to produce farm products, thus maintaining production. D. Gale Johnson, in an examination of these explanations of the maintenance of farm output during a depression,[17] rejected this explanation as inconsistent with the behavior of farmers regarding the use of hired labor and rented land during a depression, and he pointed out that it is inconsistent with the maintenance of livestock production, where feed is an important factor in total cost. Even so, as we shall see, a modified version of this approach has been developed with much greater explanatory powers than the old theory.

Opportunity Costs and Farm Output

D. Gale Johnson examined the previous explanations of the maintenance of farm output during depressions, rejected them all, and put forth his own theoretical explanation.[18] He suggested that resources were maintained in farm production because in periods of falling prices the major resources used in agricultural production have a supply price elasticity close to zero. The explanation for the low supply elasticity for factors is that land and farm machinery have low opportunity cost due to the few alternative uses outside of agriculture, and that the supply price for farm labor is also highly inelastic during depressions because of unemployment outside of agriculture. Thus, in a depression, land prices, rents, and farm wages would fall, but the employment of land, labor, and machinery would not change appreciably. On the other hand, declines are to be expected in the usage of fertilizer, lime, and other inputs, where prices do not decline.

Mr. Johnson was satisfied with his explanation of the reasons for farm output failing to contract during depressions. He then extended his explanation to cover the probable response of agri-

[17] D. Gale Johnson, "The Nature of the Supply Function for Agricultural Products," *American Economic Review*, **40** (Sept. 1950), pp. 539–64.
[18] *Ibid.*

culture to a decline in farm prices during a period of full employment—although he pointed out that no period of full employment and falling farm prices was available in the United States
experience since 1900! He also suggested that such a period might
be emerging, starting in 1949, and suggested what could be expected under such conditions.

Under full-employment conditions, Johnson stated: [19]

A decline in the price of real output will lower the marginal products of the factors. At previous prices of the factors, farmers will demand smaller quantities of the factors. For downward movements in
factor prices, the supply function for land is almost perfectly inelastic
in the short run. Land is an asset with no alternative use outside of
agriculture and its quantity will be affected only as depreciation and
depletion exceed maintenance expenditure. A protracted decline in
prices would lead to the former exceeding the latter and thus to a decline in the quantity of land supplied.[20] Capital equipment of a durable nature also has an inelastic supply function for downward price
movements in the short run. A given quantity of such equipment exists and its quantity can be reduced only by depreciation since it has
no alternative use outside of agriculture. The value of the existing
assets would decline and new purchases from the nonfarm sector would
be reduced. The marginal product of labor would decline and the
demand for labor would decrease. Given flexible wage rates in agriculture, labor employment would decrease as a result of migration
though unemployment would not emerge.

Under the conditions postulated by Johnson, a decline in farm
prices during a period of full employment could be expected to
lead to a decline in land prices, a decline in the value of durable
assets owned by farmers, a reduction in the purchases of new machinery and equipment, a decline in the demand for labor and
the rapid outmovement of labor from agriculture, and a decline
or leveling off of output.

However, the history of the last decade in agriculture has not

[19] *Ibid.*, pp. 555–56.
[20] Unless the government subsidizes maintenance through payments for "soil
conservation" or increases the available supply of land through irrigation and
reclamation projects.

followed this path. Despite the decline in farm prices and income, land prices nearly doubled from 1947 to 1960, and they rose in every year but one—1953. There was no appreciable depreciation of durable assets in the form of machinery over the period. Farmers had a book capital gain on the machinery they owned in seven of the ten years, which was more than enough to offset the three years of book capital loss (1950, 1952, 1954). However, farmers experienced a capital loss on the livestock they owned in five of the ten years 1950–59, but the gains in the other five years exceeded the losses by nearly $2 billion. The purchases of machinery slackened but did not cease. The number of tractors on farms rose 41 per cent from 1950–60; corn pickers and picker-shellers increased 71 per cent in that period; pickup balers more than tripled, and the number of field forage harvesters nearly tripled. Neither did the use of other nonlabor inputs decline. Fertilizer use continued to climb, with the use of nitrogen nearly tripling from 1950–60.

There was, however, one item which moved as expected. The outmovement of labor from agriculture continued, with the labor input declining by nearly one-third over the decade according to the United States Department of Agriculture index.

Farm output neither leveled off nor declined. Instead, it continued to rise, with eight of the ten years (1951–60) higher than the previous year and two years in which output was the same as the year before.

However, Johnson suggested that falling farm prices might not produce a decline in aggregate farm output, if there was an autonomous shift in the production function due to technological change. This was because the shift in the production function might increase the marginal physical productivity of the resources enough to offset the decline in resource use. This, he suggested, would be consistent with long-run equilibrium in the factor markets. However, we appear to have experienced a rise in farm output despite continued disequilibrium in the factor markets.

It is apparent that the explanation by D. Gale Johnson of the failure of agricultural output to contract in a depression needs substantial modification to explain the events that have occurred in United States agriculture in the past decade. However, further explanations and modifications have not been lacking.

The Agricultural Treadmill

W. W. Cochrane began to write on the phenomena of aggregate agricultural output in the early postwar period, but his position on the subject did not develop fully until the publication of *Farm Prices, Myth and Reality*.[21] In it he develops his thesis of ever-expanding agricultural output and chronic disequilibrium which he calls *the agricultural treadmill*.

Cochrane's explanation goes back and neatly picks up the earlier argument about the competitive nature of the industry and combines it with the concept of technology as a shifter of the supply curve, to explain the ever-increasing farm output.

He asserts that the supply function for agricultural products is completely inelastic, i.e., that increases in output come not from additional resources but from new technology which increases output from a given set of resources. He then uses the competitive structure of the industry to explain the continued adoption of the output-increasing technology.

According to Cochrane, in the competitive market structure in which farmers operate, the individual farmer recognizes that he cannot influence the price received for his product. Therefore, his method of achieving the increased income is by adopting cost-reducing technology. For the early adopters this practice is successful, for their costs are lowered by the new technology which lowers cost per unit of output, *although total cost is not lowered*. Unfortunately, the technology is always output increasing, so that with the inelastic demand for farm products, farm prices fall. The falling farm prices put a cost-price or income squeeze upon farmers who are not using the new technology, thus forcing them to adopt it to reduce their costs, and consequently increasing output and forcing farm prices and incomes even lower. By the time this process is completed, "Mr. Average Farmer is right back where he started, as far as his income position is concerned." [22] Therefore, "The average farmer is on a treadmill with respect to technological advance." [23]

21 (St. Paul: University of Minnesota Press, 1958.)
22 Cochrane, *op. cit.*, p. 96.
23 *Ibid.*

In Cochrane's view, there is no stopping or slowing down of this process as long as the new technology is available and as long as farmers' asset positions are such that they can continue to finance the new technology. Since the discovery and dissemination of new technology is asserted to be largely on the public account, through the agricultural experiment stations and cooperative extension service, it is produced and made available without regard for its impact upon farm income. Only a financial crisis in agriculture that renders farmers incapable of purchasing the new technology will bring the advance of farm output to a halt.

This analysis is appealing in its simplicity, and it has won widespread acceptance among farm leaders and farm economists. However, it appears to explain too much with too little, is not completely internally consistent, and is not always consistent with the observed facts.

First, not all of the increased output since 1920 is the result of improved technology without an increase in resources used in agriculture. The United States Department of Agriculture calculations show a rise of some 10 per cent in total inputs over the period. Griliches suggests that a more accurate measurement would show a rise in total inputs used of 15 per cent from 1940 to 1958, compared to the United States Department of Agriculture figure of 3 per cent. What is more important is that even the United States Department of Agriculture index, which probably understates the rise in purchased inputs, *shows an increase in purchased inputs of 38 per cent from 1940 to 1958* and a decline in unpaid inputs (mostly family labor) of 28 per cent which largely offsets it. Thus, capital inputs made up about 30 per cent of total inputs in 1940 and 54 per cent in 1957.[24] These figures suggest the increases in farm output have been closely related to farmers' purchases of new inputs, and have not been the result of changes in productivity of existing inputs.

In one place, Cochrane argues that with either rising or falling prices farmers will continue this process to the verge of individual and collective bankruptcy.[25] However, elsewhere he

24 Loomis and Barton, *op. cit.,* Table 2, p. 11.
25 *Op. cit.,* p. 96.

says: [26] "Thus, farmers adopt those production practices in prosperous times that they know they should, because financially they can; but they fail to make those technological advances in hard times that they know they should, because sources of financing have dried up."

The facts appear to be more consistent with the statement that the rate of adoption of new practices is related to price and income levels in agriculture. I have shown elsewhere that purchases of nonfarm-produced inputs vary significantly with the business cycle and that changes in weather have been such to account for many increases in output during periods of falling prices. Loomis and Barton show that there is a high positive correlation between farm income and capital purchases; fertilizer and lime used; feed, seed and livestock purchases; and all farm labor inputs. They also show that from 1910–56 total farm output changes, total inputs, and productivity changes in agriculture were, on the average, positive during periods of general economic expansion and negative during periods of general economic contraction.

Cochrane suggests that the agricultural treadmill does not necessarily mean that the labor income to operators and hired labor must fall, even when the farm price level is falling.[27] If mechanization replaces labor at a rate such that gross returns are unchanged, then the labor income of the remaining workers must rise. If output expands rapidly enough to decrease total revenue, then the average labor income of those remaining in agriculture "develops into a three-cornered race between declining total revenue, declining total costs, and declining number of workers." [28]

The agricultural treadmill explanation is useful, but it does not adequately explain the changes in United States agriculture in the 1950–60 decade. If farmers are rational and profit maximizing, why do they continue to purchase additional machinery, fertilizer, chemicals, irrigation, and other output-increasing products unless the expected additional revenue exceeds the cost of the item? What is it about the nature of the industry that causes it to adjust in this fashion?

[26] *Op. cit.,* p. 52.
[27] *Op. cit.,* p. 97.
[28] *Ibid.*

Merely saying that the industry is competitive is not an adequate answer to these questions, for static economic theory does not imply that the operators of competitive firms automatically will operate in a fashion that will drive the returns to labor in the industry substantially below the returns to human resources elsewhere. Moreover, Cochrane's book leaves it unclear as to what will happen to labor returns in agriculture, or when farmers will finally find it unprofitable to cease adopting new output-increasing technology. Certainly at some point this will happen, but for our purposes it becomes highly important to know what this point is, and the agricultural treadmill theory offers no insight.

Fixed Assets and Agricultural Adjustment

The most recent addition to explanations of the supply function and output behavior of United States agriculture has been developed by Glenn L. Johnson.[29] Johnson starts with a general dissatisfaction with the way in which neoclassical economic theory defines a fixed asset or a fixed cost, basing it largely upon the length of expected useful life of the asset. Both observation and common sense show that regardless of the potential useful life of an asset there are times when it pays to change the quantity of the asset used. Witness the frequent demolition of perfectly good buildings in every large city.

Johnson defines a fixed asset as one for which the marginal value productivity in its present use neither justifies acquisition of more of it, nor its disposition.[30] This definition is used to define: (1) an asset fixed in a single farm enterprise; (2) an asset fixed for a given farm but variable between farm enterprises; (3)

[29] The first published material on fixed asset theory is found in Glenn L. Johnson and Lowell S. Hardin, *Economics of Forage Evaluation*, Station Bulletin **623** (Lafayette: Purdue University Agricultural Experiment Station, April 1955). Further developments and proofs are found in Clark Edwards, "Resource Fixity and Farm Organization," *Journal of Farm Economics*, 41 (Nov. 1959); Glenn L. Johnson, "Some Basic Problems for Economists and Statisticians Arising from U. S. Agricultural Policies," *Manchester Statistical Society* (Nov. 1959), and Glenn L. Johnson, *The Overproduction Trap in U. S. Agriculture*, Manuscript (1962).

[30] G. L. Johnson, "Supply Function—Some Facts and Notions," *Agricultural Adjustment Problems in a Growing Economy* (Ames: Iowa State College Press, 1958), p. 78 ff.

an asset fixed for an industry in the production of a product or type of product; and (4) an asset fixed for the agricultural sector as a whole. These various types of fixities will be dealt with after discussing the theory.

An important element of asset fixity in agriculture hinges upon the concepts of *acquisition cost* and *salvage value*. Acquisition cost is what a farm operator (or the industry) has paid for a productive asset or would have to pay in order to acquire more of a particular productive asset (input). Salvage value is what the farm operator (or the industry) could get for the asset (input) if it were sold rather than used in farm production.

Neoclassical economic theory assumes that markets are such that an entrepreneur can purchase more of an asset if it is profitable and that he can dispose of unwanted (unprofitable) quantities at the same price. Such a situation is shown in Figure 2 for one variable, where line AP equals the price of the input. If the

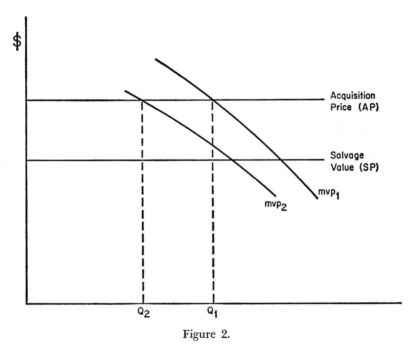

Figure 2.

Quantity of an input used when acquisition and salvage prices
for it are equal and unequal.

output price declined so that the marginal returns declined from mvp_1 to mvp_2, then the farmer would use Q_2 of the input and reduce output.

However, suppose that the salvage value (SP) of the asset is well below the acquisition price (AP). A farmer might have to pay $1.10 to have additional corn delivered to his farm to feed hogs, but if he decided to sell the same quality corn from stocks on hand to the same elevator, he could expect to realize about 90 cents per bushel. In this situation even though the product price fell enough to move mvp_1 to mvp_2, it would be more profitable to use all of the corn on hand because its value in use still would exceed its salvage value. Thus, the amount of corn fed would not vary despite substantial variations in product prices.

The fuller implications of these modifications can be seen when two or more inputs are combined. In Figure 3, we have the conventional iso-value-product lines showing the value of the prod-

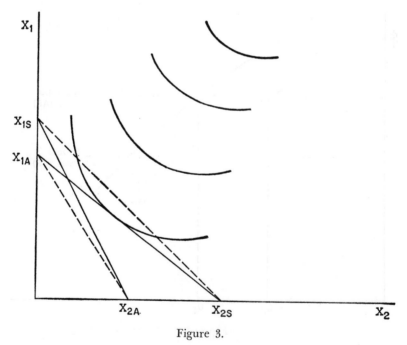

Figure 3.

Input costs and iso-value-product curves for two inputs where their acquisition costs exceed their salvage values.

uct which can be produced from two inputs, X_1 and X_2. In this case, however, for each input it is assumed that the acquisition cost of the inputs (X_{1A}, X_{2A}) exceeds the salvage value of the input (X_{1S}, X_{2S}). Thus, the point at which the price ratio lines are tangent to the iso-value-product curves depends upon which price is used for each input.

With this modification we get four expansion paths instead of the normal one, and we get four high profit or "least loss" points as shown in Figure 4.[31] Expansion path b is the one where both

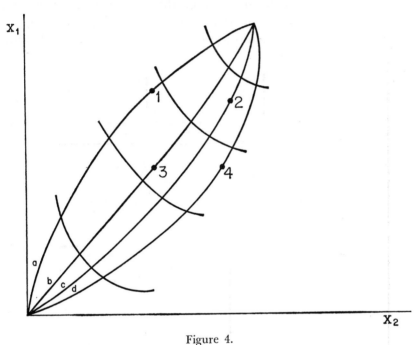

Figure 4.

"Expansion" paths for two inputs when their acquisition
costs exceed their salvage values.

inputs are priced at their acquisition cost and c is where both are priced at salvage value. Therefore, the high profit point on

[31] Actually, *expansion path* and *high profit points* are slight misnomers. Production might expand along the line representing both inputs priced at acquisition cost, but will never contract on it. The reverse is true for the line representing both inputs priced at salvage value.

c (point 2) will always be at the higher output level than on b (point 3) as long as acquisition costs are above salvage values. By the same token, it follows that the high profit points on lines a and d, where one input is priced at acquisition cost and the other at salvage value, will be at higher levels of output than on line b (both priced at acquisition cost) and lower than on line c (both priced at salvage value).

The first three diagrams deal with how much of each of the inputs X_1 and X_2 should be purchased or acquired under different conditions. Now let us combine this with a diagram dealing with profitable levels of utilization of these two inputs. In Figure 5, line e represents a locus of points at which the marginal value

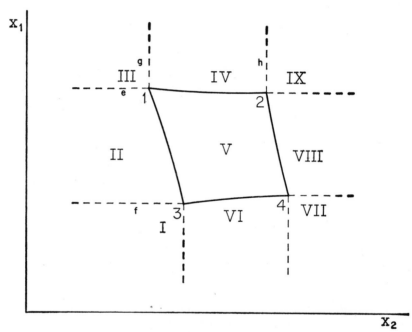

Figure 5.

The most profitable level of input use when their acquisition costs exceed their salvage values.

product of X_1 equals the salvage value of X_1 for different levels of X_2. Line f represents the same series of points except they are where the marginal value product of X_1 equals the acquisition cost of X_1. The meaning of these lines is as follows: If a firm has a quantity of input X_1 greater than represented by line e, it would be more profitable to dispose of the quantity in excess of that represented by line e than to use it in production. If a firm had a quantity of input X_1 less than the quantity represented by line f, it would pay the firm to acquire more of input X_1, because the marginal value product of X_1 to the firm exceeds its acquisition cost. If the quantity of X_1 on hand was between lines e and f, it would not pay to vary the quantity of X_1 used because it is worth more in production than could be obtained by selling it, but it is not worth enough in production to pay to acquire more of it.

It will be noted that the points labelled 1, 2, 3, and 4 in Figure 5 correspond to the same points in Figure 4. Point 3 in both diagrams has a special significance for, at this point, each of the inputs would be earning a marginal value product in production equal to its acquisition cost. Assuming that similar conditions were met elsewhere in the economy, *resources engaged in agricultural production would be earning the same as similar resources elsewhere and the optimum resource allocation of competitive theory would exist.* Point 3 would represent the only point where all resources in agriculture would be receiving returns comparable to earnings elsewhere in the economy. Let us examine, however, different situations for individual farms to see why they may not be able to reach point 3 in our diagram.

The various sectors of Figure 5 are numbered I through IX depending upon their relationship to lines e, f, g, and h. In each of these sectors, a farm has been organized which owns or controls some combination of inputs X_1 and X_2. What is the most profitable change, if any, the operator may make regarding the use of these two inputs?

A farm organized in sector I would find it profitable to expand its use of both X_1 and X_2, because for both inputs their mvp's exceed their acquisition cost. Such a farm would move to point 3 on the diagram, output would expand, and the inputs X_1 and X_2 on the farm would be earning as much as comparable inputs elsewhere, assuming that in the nonfarm economy the mvp of resources does equal their acquisition cost.

If a farm were in situation II, things would be quite different.

It would pay to increase the use of X_2 to the level represented by line g, but it would not pay to vary the use of X_1. Thus, total output would increase; input X_2 would be earning its acquisition cost, but input X_1 would have earnings below those for comparable factors elsewhere. Even so, it would not be profitable to reduce the total quantity of X_1 used.

In sector III, it would be profitable to dispose of some quantity of input X_1 to a quantity on line e, but the use of X_2 would be expanded until point 1 was reached. At this point X_2 would be earning its acquisition cost, but X_1 would be earning less than its acquisition cost, and output would probably increase and be greater than the output at point 3.

In sectors IV and VI, the quantity of X_2 used would not change because it would not pay to vary it but, in the first case, some X_1 would be disposed of and, in the latter situation, more would be acquired. In sector IV, both inputs would be earning less than acquisition cost, whereas in sector VI, X_1 would be earning acquisition cost but X_2 would not be. A move to the most profitable point would bring a decline in output in sector IV and an increase in sector VI.

In sector V, the quantity used of both inputs would remain unchanged even though both were earning less than their acquisition costs. Thus, no change in resource use or production would occur despite earnings of resources in agriculture below those expected and received elsewhere.

In sector VII, it would pay to dispose of some of X_2 and acquire more X_1 to reach point 4. At this point, however, output would be well above the level of point 3 and input X_2 would have lower earnings than at point 3.

In sector VIII, some X_2 would be disposed of, but the quantity of X_1 used would remain unchanged. Both inputs would be earning less than acquisition cost, and output would be higher than at point 3.

In sector IX, enough of both inputs would be sold to reach point 2, however, at this point, both inputs would be earning well below acquisition cost, output would be well above the level where all resources earn their acquisition cost, and the inputs would still be more profitable continued in production than if sold.

It should be noted that under the conditions postulated, where acquisition cost for one or more productive assets exceeds salvage value, there are numerous situations in which there would be no incentive to change the inputs used or output. However, there is only one situation, where returns to factors equal acquisition costs, that satisfies all of the values relating to agriculture. There are a number of situations where no gain in efficiency will be realized in the economy by moving resources from agricultural production to other uses—once the asset is fixed in agricultural production, but there is only one condition where both the value relating to efficiency and that relating to equal returns are met, that being the condition where earnings equal acquisition costs.

Therefore, this situation (where earnings equal acquisition costs) is the only situation that can be defined as representing *equilibrium* in agriculture. Other situations where earnings are less than acquisition costs, even though they represent points where no changes may occur, are defined as *disequilibrium*.

Several general implications of this modification of economic theory can be seen. First, in cases I, II, and VI, the adjustment that will maximize profit will always involve an increase in the use of one or more inputs and an increase in output, even though, with the exception of case I, one of the inputs is earning less than its acquisition costs. In cases III and VII, the optimum adjustment will always increase the use of one input, and the most profitable output level will exceed the equilibrium level, although whether output expands or contracts depends upon the production functions involved and the particular starting point in the sector. In cases IV, VIII, and IX, output will remain above the equilibrium level, and the earnings of one or both inputs will be low, even though the situation will call for the disposal of some of one or both inputs. In case V, no changes will be profitable, even though both inputs are earning less than acquisition costs.

Thus, in several situations the most profitable adjustment will increase output, even though the firm or industry is already producing at above equilibrium level. Moreover, under the conditions postulated, there is no adjustment that can be made in any situation other than case I which will enable the farm to be organized so that both inputs are earning their acquisition costs. This could explain why an industry already in disequilibrium will expand output and why a substantial disequilibrium might persist.

If the concept of a substantial difference between acquisition cost and salvage value for important productive assets in agriculture can be verified, this explanation of the behavior of agriculture becomes very useful. Therefore, let us return to the concept and its relevance. Three points need to be examined. They are: (1) the concept of a divergence between acquisition and salvage value; (2) how these are related, if at all, to previous economic theory; and (3) what changes or events cause individual farms or the industry to be in the various situations described above in I through IX?

ACQUISITION COST AND SALVAGE VALUE

Let us start with an examination of the possibility of a significant divergence between acquisition cost and salvage value for an input at a given point in time. Can acquisition cost and salvage value vary for an individual enterprise on a farm, on a given farm, or for the industry as a whole?

First, consider durable assets with a life of more than a single production period. For certain items, such as fruit trees, fencing, barns, drainage tile, and other assets, the acquisition cost will be determined by the cost of purchasing the items from the nonfarm economy and/or the opportunity cost of the farm operator's labor and supplies if he produces them. The salvage value of such assets off the farm is zero or, in some cases, negative (removing fruit trees); and for many such durable inputs the asset is not only fixed for the industry and the farm but for the individual farm enterprise (fruit trees, milking parlors, etc.). Durables such as tiling, fences, irrigation wells, and storage buildings are fixed over wide ranges of prices for the industry and the individual farm, but not for individual farm enterprises.

A second group of durable inputs exists for which the situation differs somewhat. These are specialized durable inputs which are produced off the farm, such as corn pickers, grain combines, hay balers, forage choppers, etc. For the *agricultural industry* the acquisition cost is the cost of buying such durables from the nonfarm producers, and the salvage value is probably very low since such machines have little use outside of agriculture.

For such durables the situation that faces an *individual farm* varies depending upon outside conditions. During certain periods when output is expanding, the acquisition cost to the farm will be the price of new machines, and the salvage value will be the price that the machinery will bring on the used market, usually from a dealer. The difference between the acquisition cost and salvage value may vary from 10 to 50 per cent depending upon the competition among dealers, the transportation and transfer costs involved, etc. Thus, at a given point in time, a difference between acquisition cost and salvage price may exist for an individual farm for such durables. In periods of falling product prices, the acquisition cost of machinery to a farm may be the cost of used machinery sold by other farmers or the cost of a new machine. Even in the former case, there may be a significant variance between acquisition cost and salvage value because of dealers margins, transfer costs, etc.

Within individual farms the salvage value of such specialized durables is their opportunity costs for use in other enterprises, which is low or zero. Once in the agricultural industry, such durables will be used to produce specialized products until they are used up, almost without regard to product prices, although there may be interfarm transfers of these durables during the period of their life.

There is still another group of durable inputs for which the situation is different. These are farm-produced durables such as dairy cows, beef breeding herds, poultry flocks, etc. To the industry the acquisition cost is primarily the cost of producing these animals. However, their salvage value to the industry is determined largely by their slaughter value, and this may be well below their acquisition cost in some periods, either because of the demand for their products or because of the supply of substitute products. To the industry there may be a wide divergence between acquisition cost and salvage value at a given point in time.

For the individual farm the cost of acquiring such inputs may be either the opportunity cost of producing them or the cost of buying them. In the latter case, there may be a difference between acquisition cost and salvage value at a given time because of marketing costs (the cost of finding suitable animals), transportation costs, and other transfer costs.

In the individual farm enterprise the opportunity cost of using such animals is usually low, so that once they are acquired they are generally used to produce their specialized products (milk, eggs) or are disposed of off the farm. Thus, once they are produced or acquired by the industry or a farm, such animals are maintained in production of their specialized product until they are sold.

The most important single input in agricultural production is human effort. Some care is needed in defining the acquisition cost and salvage value for labor in agriculture, both to the industry and to individual farms. The problem lies largely with the definition of a relevant acquisition cost.

For an individual engaged in farming the acquisition cost is the opportunity cost of the income foregone by not entering another occupation *at the time he entered farming*. Thus, for a forty-year-old farmer it is the earnings of forty-year-olds in other occupations requiring comparable abilities. For new entrants into agriculture at a specific point in time, the relevant acquisition cost is the opportunity cost of other potential income which is foregone. Thus, allowing for skills, preferences, etc., it is the wage which would induce an individual to work in agriculture rather than elsewhere, assuming he has other alternatives open to him. This should be the "comparable" earnings which would indicate optimum resource allocation.

The salvage value of labor from the agricultural industry is essentially the earnings that are available to farm people in other industries. Because the specialized skills in agriculture have little or no value in other industries, farmers who want to leave agriculture can rarely command the wages of experienced nonfarm workers. Because the nonfarm labor market favors younger workers, young persons desiring to leave agriculture probably have a higher salvage value than older farm people. However, most farm people live on farms, so that to accept nonfarm employment they will have either to commute or migrate to find employment, thereby reducing the salvage value of their labor by the cost of their commuting or migrating. Since the cost of migration is lower and their expected production life is longer, the gains from migration are highest for younger persons. Given these two factors, it is not surprising to see that most migration from agriculture is concentrated in the age groups 19–29 and that very low returns in agriculture are necessary to induce outmigration of established older farmers.

Thus, for the agricultural industry the divergence between acquisition and salvage value for labor is relatively low for new entrants to agriculture, depending largely upon the cost of commuting or migrating from a rural area to an area where nonfarm employment is available. The divergence increases over time, however, as seniority and experience improve the earnings of nonfarm workers, until the gap for older workers becomes very large.

This situation exists apart from the effect of cyclical fluctuations in employment upon the salvage value of labor outside of agriculture. The situation is accentuated by periods of nonfarm unemployment when the salvage value of labor outside of agriculture falls rapidly and probably approaches zero.

To the individual farm the relevant acquisition cost of labor is much the same as for the industry, with some modifications. For farm operators it is the opportunity cost, appropriately adjusted, for comparable persons. For farm workers or laborers it is the opportunity costs both outside agriculture and on other farms. At a given time, the salvage value of the farmer's labor will depend upon his location, age, skills, and the general employment situation. For some it may be very low even in periods of full employment, and it is very low for nearly all farmers during periods of substantial nonfarm unemployment. Thus, there is likely to be a divergence between acquisition cost and salvage value for operator's labor on individual farms located some distance from nonfarm employment, even during periods of full employment, and there is likely to be an even greater difference during periods of unemployment. However, on individual farms the salvage value of labor on another farm may exceed present earnings, so we would expect to find more labor mobility between farms than between agriculture and nonfarm employment.

Within farm firms neither operator, family, nor hired labor is usually specialized, so that the salvage value of the labor in a given enterprise is generally the opportunity cost of using it in another enterprise. Thus, labor is less likely to be fixed to individual enterprises within the farm even though it is fixed to the farm or to the industry, except on specialized farms where the opportunity cost of an alternative enterprise is very low.

Another important input in agriculture is land. For the industry the acquisition cost of farm land is the cost of developing new land or, in certain areas, the opportunity cost of using land suitable for nonfarm real estate development. Except for certain limited areas, the salvage value of farm land outside agriculture is virtually zero. Thus, except for a small fraction of the farm land located adjacent to large centers of population, the acquisition cost and salvage value of land to the industry diverge substantially at a given point in time.

To the individual farm the acquisition cost of land depends upon finding some suitably located land which someone is willing to rent or sell. In the case of rentals, if the land is some distance away, the acquisition cost will include the cost of going back and forth to work it, in addition to the rent. The same is true for purchased land that is located other than adjacent to the farm trying to acquire land. Moreover, to buy or sell land there are legal fees, transfer taxes, and other costs including real estate agent's fees. Thus, there is bound to be some difference between acquisition cost and salvage value of purchased land, even if the farm is next door, and the difference will be greater as distance increases. Except in the case of rentals of adjoining farms, the physical fixity of land means that the individual farm faces a difference of some significance between acquisition cost and salvage value for land.

Another category of inputs which needs to be considered are farm-produced nondurable inputs, such as feed, hay, forage, and pasture. For such inputs there is one relevant acquisition cost to the industry, that being the opportunity cost of producing these products. Since this has some positive value and their salvage value outside agriculture is generally low, there may be a wide divergence between acquisition cost and salvage value at a given point in time.

On the individual farm there may be two relevant acquisition costs for such farm-produced expendable inputs: the first is the opportunity cost of producing them on the farm, and the second is the cost of buying them from another farm. The salvage value of these inputs is determined by what they are worth if they are sold off the farm. Since many of these items are bulky or not easily transportable, it is easy to see that a substantial divergence might occur between acquisition cost and salvage value at a given point in time, thus fixing them as inputs until they are exhausted, despite wide changes in product prices.

Within the farm firm the acquisition cost of such inputs to an individual enterprise is again their purchase cost outside or their opportunity cost if produced. Their salvage value to a particular enterprise, however, could be either their value in another enterprise or their off-farm salvage value. Since the former is often above the latter, we might expect to see such inputs diverted quickly from one enterprise to another within farms but with less farm to farm sales, and virtually no intersector sales.

A final class of inputs are nonfarm-produced flow inputs, such as fertilizer, insecticides, and sprays. Since they are flow inputs purchased largely as needed, it is to be expected that their use will be dependent upon their marginal value product exceeding their current acquisition cost. Therefore, their use should and does vary with product prices.

At this point, it should be possible to generalize regarding the probable occurrence and magnitude of a divergence between acquisition costs and salvage values for the agricultural industry, for individual farms, and for individual enterprises within farms.

For the agricultural industry it appears that, for a given point in time, there may well be a wide divergence between the acquisition cost and salvage value of agricultural land, nonfarm-produced durables, and certain specialized farm-produced durables (fruit trees, fences). Thus, such inputs, once committed to the production of farm products, are likely to remain in production despite substantial decline in farm prices because their value in use would exceed their salvage value outside the industry. For certain other major inputs, namely human labor and farm-produced durables such as breeding livestock, there also may be a substantial divergence between the relevant acquisition cost and the salvage value. However, variations in outside economic conditions tend to alter the acquisition and salvage values of these inputs substantially, and these resources leave agriculture if product prices fall or salvage values rise to levels where salvage values exceed value in use.

For both farm-produced and nonfarm-produced expendables, the acquisition cost and salvage value to the industry may vary substantially at a given point in time. Therefore, one would expect the supply on hand to be used in production, unless a high salvage value (like a government loan program for feed grains) makes them more valuable elsewhere than in current use.

For the individual farm there may be an appreciable difference between the acquisition cost and salvage value of the operator's labor and, to a lesser extent, land and purchased durable inputs, depending upon his location. A substantial difference might also exist for farm-produced durable capital and for farm-produced expendable inputs.

Within farm firms the acquisition costs of most labor, of land, of farm-produced expendables, and of nonspecialized inputs are the opportunity cost of using them in alternative enterprises, and the salvage value is either the earnings from using them in an alternative enterprise or selling them off the farm. Thus, when the off-farm salvage value of such inputs is low, you might expect them to flow quickly from one enterprise to another. This explains much of the difficulty of trying to control total agricultural output by controlling one input or the output of one crop. On the other hand, specialized inputs on an individual farm could be expected to remain in the production of the specialized product despite wide changes in product prices. Thus, it ought to be easier to control the output of fruit than of grain, since most of the assets used in fruit production have low salvage value in other crop production.

These conditions are consistent with those observed for United States agriculture. Over a wide range of economic conditions asset fixity is important for the industry, in that resources once committed to farming tend to remain in the industry. Thus, over a wide range of product prices the aggregate supply function for farm products appears to be completely inelastic or, in extreme cases, backward bending. There are conditions, however, such as in wartime, when the aggregate supply function appears relatively more elastic.

Within agriculture we find that resources fixed in the industry tend to be less fixed on individual farms and much less so in the production of individual commodities. Thus, we find the apparent supply elasticity of individual farm products much higher than for the aggregate, with noticeable responses to relative product prices. These latter responses often have been erroneously extrapolated to aggregate farm output, which leads to the assumption that modest declines in product prices will result in appreciable changes in aggregate output.

FIXED ASSETS AND ECONOMIC THEORY

The neoclassical marginal analysis, upon which most supply analysis depends, uses the law of diminishing returns. When certain variable inputs are combined with certain fixed inputs, the law of diminishing returns operates, determining the marginal cost curves of the firm and the supply curve of the firm and industry.

However, the usual marginal analysis lacks an explanation as to when and why an asset is fixed for an individual firm or the industry. For multiple-use assets the principle of opportunity cost was developed for pricing fixed assets within multiple-product firms. It implicitly assumes that the factor markets are perfect, in that firms or the industry can buy and sell inputs at a single price.

Johnson's modification consists of relaxing the assumption that firms and the industry can buy and sell inputs with a useful life of more than one production period for the same price. The result is an explanation, using conventional marginal analysis, of why such assets may continue in production in individual firms or in the industry despite large changes in factor earnings. Thus, in large part, Johnson's contribution consists of recognition that factor markets are imperfect for agriculture and for individual firms within the industry.

Agricultural Adjustment and Continuous Disequilibrium

Fixed assets alone will not suffice to explain the large and persistent disequilibrium in output and earnings which is almost unique to agriculture. It would appear that the same phenomena might be found in many nonfarm industries employing durable inputs having a life of more than one production period. However, the problem of fixity of labor and land and their importance to agricultural production probably is greater in agriculture than elsewhere.

Several characteristics of the agricultural industry now have been discussed. They are: (1) a highly inelastic demand for products; (2) a low income elasticity for products; (3) rapid rates of technological change which increase the physical productivity of certain inputs; (4) a competitive structure; and (5) a high degree of asset fixity which reduces resource mobility from the industry. No one of these characteristics is unique to agriculture, nor would any one of them alone suffice to explain the large and extended disequilibrium in agriculture. The combination of characteristics does appear to be unique to agriculture, and the combination will explain a large and persistent disequilibrium, especially one which results in chronically low returns for some resources in the industry.

Some industries may have "fixed" assets and technological change, but if the demand for their product is relatively elastic or growing rapidly, the new technology will not reduce the earnings of the fixed assets much below equilibrium levels. Moreover, if labor is not fixed in the industry, labor returns may not be low.

If the industry is in an imperfect product market, it may be able to influence product prices and, thereby, maintain factor earnings at approximately equilibrium levels; and if it is in an imperfect factor market, it may influence the rate of adoption of new output-increasing technology enough to prevent a large disequilibrium. Agriculture can do neither.

Given the five structural characteristics of the agricultural industry, let us examine how they interact to produce the large and persistent disequilibrium which is observed. The observed changes in United States agriculture in the post-World War II period appear to be consistent with the interaction that would be expected.

During and immediately following World War II and again during the Korean War, farm prices rose substantially. This increased the marginal value product of resources producing farm products. In Figure 5, this raised line f in relation to the vertical axis, and moved line g to the right in relationship to the horizontal axis. Greater quantities of these factors were then profitable in agriculture. However, when the extraordinary wartime demands were ended, farm prices fell. As a result, some resources became fixed assets and were "trapped" in agriculture because they had been moved to area V where they were not earning enough to pay to add more of them, and they were earning more in agriculture than could be expected outside the industry.

Before long, new resources became available with productivity high enough that they were profitable even at lower product prices. These new resources were added to the industry, and the result was an increase in output, lower product prices, and even lower earnings for "trapped" resources. At some point in this process, the salvage value of some of the existing resources in agriculture exceeded their value in use in agricultural production and they left agriculture. However, as long as the salvage value is substantially below the acquisition cost for most resources, the outmovement of resources will never be sufficient to produce equilibrium earnings in agriculture for all the resources in the industry.

This illustration suggests that economic events outside of agriculture have a great influence upon the extent and duration of resource fixity in agriculture and upon the capital loss experienced by the owners of the resources if they are sold. Substantial increases in real wages in the nonfarm economy have the effect of increasing the acquisition cost of labor to the agricultural industry. Cyclical and structural unemployment have the effect of substantially lowering the salvage value of labor in agriculture, thereby increasing the decline in farm prices necessary to induce outmigration.

While these factors were at work, other developments in the nonfarm economy were inducing additional use of certain output-increasing inputs in agriculture. One development was the relative decline in the real price of fertilizer, which meant that more fertilizer use has been profitable, even with the lower product prices. The same has been true of other new developments, including machinery, even though its real price did not fall. Most of these developments are output increasing, and as a result, they have lowered even further the marginal value product of "fixed assets" in agriculture. New technologies, forms of organization, and inputs do not have to be cost-reducing in order for them to be adopted. The only condition that needs to exist is that the expected marginal value product of the particular input exceeds its current acquisition cost, and it will be adopted regardless of whether it is cost increasing or cost decreasing. As long as certain major productive assets are fixed, total output will not contract and may even expand, despite falling product prices and low earnings on fixed assets.

For the industry as a whole it appears that human labor, land, and durable capital are most likely to have substantial divergences between acquisition costs and salvage values. Therefore, one would expect these items to be fixed and most frequently subject to low earnings and/or capital losses. However, durable capital eventually is depreciated and will not be replaced unless its marginal value product exceeds its acquisition cost; so low returns on durable capital inputs should not persist, unless conditions in agriculture are changing so rapidly to make future earnings completely unforeseeable. This is consistent with available facts which, for agriculture as an industry, show low returns to labor, relatively low returns on investments in real estate, and returns to machinery and working capital about in line with returns to capital elsewhere in the economy.

On individual farms the situation is somewhat different and

one would expect different results. Since the majority of United States farms are still owner-operated, the labor input to an individual farm is not a continuous function as it is to the industry, in that it often is not possible to sell part of the operator's labor elsewhere. Many off-farm jobs are full-time jobs, with any farming done in addition to the full-time job.

On an individual owner-operated farm, labor is often a fixed asset. However, mechanization will increase labor productivity and often makes the marginal value product of additional land exceed its acquisition cost. In recent years, farm enlargement has become an increasing factor in the sale of farm land, as farmers who find their labor is a fixed asset bid land prices up in an attempt to expand individual operations.

On individual farms the operator's labor is most likely to be fixed because of a difference between its acquisition cost and salvage value. Land may be subject to fixity on many farms, but should be much less so, and the same should be true of machinery. Thus, functional or budget analyses of individual farms might be expected usually to show low returns for the operator's labor and modest to high returns for durable capital and land. This is what is generally reported by such studies.

Summary and Implications

Whereas most of the previous explanations of the failure of agriculture to adjust to an equilibrium position were either incomplete, had poor predictive power, or were inconsistent with observed facts, the addition of "fixed asset" theory developed by Glenn L. Johnson appears to overcome some of these problems. It, together with the other structural characteristics of the industry, provides an explanation of the observed persistent disequilibrium in agriculture which is most evident in the low returns to human effort, even in commercial agriculture.

Several things need to be done in relation to the idea. There should be empirical investigation of the existence and magnitude of differences between acquisition costs and salvage values, both for the industry and for individual firms. More information is needed about resource flows within agriculture and between agriculture and the nonfarm economy. Some of the evidence on these subjects is touched elsewhere in this volume, but much remains undone.

The policy implications of this persistent disequilibrium in agriculture are great. It suggests that much of the difficulty within agriculture arises from outside the industry, in that outside changes markedly influence the resource movements into and out of the industry. It also suggests that once resources are committed to producing farm products, if these resources have characteristics fixing them in the industry, the owners of these resources will experience low earnings or capital losses from increases in farm output. Thus, while improvements in production methods that increase productivity and output in agriculture contribute to economic growth in the economy at large, in so doing they also create low earnings and/or capital losses for the people engaged in farming.

The ability of our economy to produce new inputs or to develop new combinations of inputs has been a major source of our growth in real income and in national output. Certainly our ability to provide increased quantities of farm products without a substantial increase in the real resources used has been a major factor in this growth. However, the reoccurring fixity of assets in agriculture has meant that people in agriculture have borne part of the burden of this growth in the form of low earnings. The disequilibrium in agriculture also means the economy has been unable to realize the full potential of its productivity because of the inability to shift "trapped" resources from agriculture to more productive uses. Much of the controversy over the appropriate economic policy for agriculture revolves around the question of which of the characteristics of the industry should be modified by public policy so as to reduce or remove the disequilibrium in the industry.

Chapter 5

The Changing
Nature of the
Stability Problem

Attempts to explain disequilibrium prices and income in agriculture have, until the last decade, concentrated upon explanations of the failure to achieve resource adjustment during short-run periods of falling farm product prices. The almost exclusive concentration on these problems suggests that price and income instability has been considered the major problem facing farmers. Until the last few years it was generally believed that the disequilibrium problems in agriculture were the result of short-run instability, and most of our price and income policies have been directed toward a reduction of this instability. However, it now appears that the nature and magnitude of the instability problem facing agriculture have changed significantly during the postwar period and that little attention has been given to the significance of these changes.

The characteristics of the demand for agricultural products were discussed earlier, and these characteristics also are important in the problems of stability in the agricultural industry. The price elasticity of demand for agricultural products at the retail level is low, and at the farm level it is even lower, thus, changes in output bring proportionately greater changes in prices, and gross

131

revenue from a large output is less than from a smaller output. This holds not only for farm products in the aggregate, but for virtually all individual products.

Moreover, as was developed in the preceding chapter, the aggregate supply curve for farm products also appears to be highly inelastic, although less so for farm product price increases than for product price decreases. This means that shifts in the aggregate demand curve for farm products result in proportionately large inverse changes in farm prices and gross revenue. Keeping these characteristics in mind, let us examine the sources, magnitude, and frequency of short-run shifts in the demand and supply of farm products and the way in which forces underlying these shifts have changed in recent years.

Shifts in the Aggregate Demand

There are several potential sources of shifts in the aggregate demand for farm products. They are: (1) changes in population; (2) changes in tastes and preferences; (3) the development of new uses and/or substitutes for farm products; (4) shifts in export demand; and (5) changes in the level of income and employment.

Over long periods of time one of the major factors influencing the demand for farm products is population growth. Even though there is some evidence of cyclical fluctuations in birth rates, these are neither large enough nor changing rapidly enough to induce sharp short-run shifts in the aggregate demand for farm products. While population growth may be an important determinant of the ease or difficulty of the adjustment of the agricultural industry to the changes discussed in Chapter 4, natural population growth has not and is not likely to become a source of significant short-run shifts in the demand for farm products.

Much the same can be said for changes in tastes and preferences. Except for rare instances, like the great cranberry scare of 1960, sharp short-run changes in tastes and preferences for individual farm products are unusual, and for farm products in the aggregate, they are unknown in the United States. Instead, changes in tastes and preferences proceed slowly over a period of time as broader social changes occur; and their impact in a given year is not likely to be a source of a major shift in the demand for either an individual farm product or farm products in the aggregate.[1]

The development of new uses for farm products and new substitutes for farm products also are likely to proceed relatively slowly. As pointed out earlier, over a period of years these may have an appreciable impact upon the total demand for farm products, but in any given year, this is not likely to provide a major source of instability for either individual products or for farm products in total.

EXPORT DEMAND

Historically, changes in the export demand for United States farm products have been significant from year to year and have been an important source of demand instability. These changes in demand for United States farm product exports arise from two sources: first, sharp changes in the available supplies of farm products in other countries; and second, changes in the demand for United States farm products in major importing countries.

Changes in foreign supplies of farm products may arise as a result of adverse growing conditions for major crops, or they may arise from the interruption of foreign agricultural production as a result of wars and their aftermath. The first is likely to be less general, while the latter is likely to affect larger areas and generally occurs at a time when the domestic demand for farm products also is high.

Shifts in the export demand for farm products may also arise because of sharp shifts in the levels of employment and income in major importing countries. Historically, large shifts in employment and income in major importing countries have tended to coincide with similar internal changes. Some idea of the frequency and magnitude of the changes in export demand for United States farm products can be obtained from Table 1. Of course, not all of the changes in quantities represent shifts in the demand curve, but a comparison of the quantity index and the

---

[1] This is not to say that there are not sharp short-run changes in the quantity of individual farm products consumed. But these are generally changes along a stable demand curve rather than shifts in the demand curve.

Table 1

United States Agricultural Exports: Value at Actual and Constant Prices 1925–61

Year Ending June 30th	VALUE AT	
	Actual Price Bil. $	Constant Prices * Bil. $
1925	2.3	3.5
1926	1.9	3.0
1927	1.9	3.9
1928	1.8	3.2
1929	1.8	3.3
1930	1.5	2.8
1931	1.0	2.6
1932	.8	2.8
1933	.6	2.5
1934	.8	2.5
1935	.7	1.6
1936	.8	1.9
1937	.7	1.7
1938	.9	2.3
1939	.7	1.9
1940	.7	2.1
1941	.4	.8
1942	1.0	1.6
1943	1.5	1.8
1944	2.3	2.2
1945	2.2	2.1
1946	2.9	3.2
1947	3.6	3.3
1948	3.5	3.0
1949	3.8	3.7
1950	3.0	3.4
1951	3.4	3.4
1952	4.1	3.9
1953	2.8	2.8
1954	2.9	3.0
1955	3.1	3.4
1956	3.5	3.9
1957	4.7	5.4
1958	4.0	4.6
1959	3.7	4.4
1960	4.5	5.7
1961	4.9	6.1

* Expressed in 1952–54 prices.

Source: 1962 Agricultural Outlook Chartbook, U.S.D.A., p. 61.

value of exports suggests there have been large and frequent changes in the export demand for farm products.

Short-run changes in the export demand for United States farm products can be summarized historically: During and immediately after wars, the export demand for many United States farm products rises sharply, and with the restoration of normal production patterns, this demand usually subsides. The aggregate export demand for United States farm products has also fluctuated sharply with general economic conditions in major importing countries, because even in Western Europe the income elasticity for farm products is well above that for the United States, so that changes in consumer income tend to shift the demand for farm products significantly in the short run.[2] In addition, adverse or ideal local growing conditions in importing nations or other supplying nations may shift the export demand for individual United States farm products substantially from one year to the next. Thus, historically, shifts in export demand have been an important source of instability of demand for several United States farm commodities.

In recent years the impact of this source of instability has been substantially reduced by the operation of the federal price-support program for most of the major export crops. Since about 1950 any shifts in export demand for supported crops have resulted primarily in changes in the rate of government stock accumulation rather than changes in commodity prices. This has been especially true for products where stocks were large so that increases in demand could be met from stocks.

As a result of the price-support programs, export subsidies, and special export programs, all of which will be discussed in greater detail later, the producers of cotton, wheat, tobacco, and feed grains have been largely isolated from short-run changes in export demand. Producers of oil-seeds have been isolated less, because the government has not accumulated stocks of these products to as great an extent. The producers of animal products and of fruits and vegetables, which lack direct price supports, are still subject to short-run changes in export demand, although some

[2] See the article by L. M. Goreux, *op. cit.*, for estimates of the income elasticity in several other countries.

of the impacts for fruit have been reduced by export subsidies and domestic demand expansion programs. Since the price supported crops make up three-fourths or more of our total agricultural exports, it appears that the impacts of shifts in export demand have been substantially reduced and are unlikely to be major destablizing forces on United States farm prices and income, as long as present programs are continued.

DOMESTIC DEMAND

The bulk of United States farm products, about 90 per cent, is consumed domestically, so that shifts in domestic demand have been the most important source of change in the aggregate demand for United States farm products. The most important short-run shifts in the domestic demand arise from shifts in employment and income, commonly called *business cycles.*

It is useful at this point to review the connecting links between changes in employment and national output and the demand for farm products, for there is strong evidence that these links are being altered, with important implications for the future stability of demand for farm products.

Business cycles are a short term for fluctuations in real national output or gross national product (GNP). Therefore, let us trace the relationship between the gross national product through the national income accounts to the demand for farm products. Gross national product minus depreciation allowances, indirect business taxes, business transfer payments, surplus of government enterprises, plus subsidies, equals national income. National income minus corporate profits, contributions for social insurance, and excess of wage accruals over disbursements plus government transfer payments, net interest paid by the government, dividends, and business transfer payments equals personal income. Personal income minus personal tax liabilities equals disposable personal income. Changes in disposable personal income should be the element which influences the demand for farm products.

If the relationship between changes in national income and disposable personal income is positive, and the income elasticity of farm products is other than zero, fluctuations in national income should shift the demand curve for farm products. Assuming a positive income elasticity, the change in the demand for farm products should be in the same direction as the change in national income. The magnitude of the shift in demand should depend upon the magnitude of the shift in national income, and upon the relationship between changes in national income and changes in disposable personal income.

Table 2 shows the years since 1910 divided into periods of business expansion and contraction.[3] It shows that in every business expansion prior to World War II there was an increase in current and real prices received by farmers.[4] Since World War II this relationship appears to have changed drastically. During the period 1946–48 and 1949–53 money prices of farm products rose, but the purchasing power of farm products declined in both cases. During the period 1954–57 and 1958–60 both the money prices of farm products and the purchasing power of farm products fell. During each of these postwar expansions there was a significant increase in farm output, so that it is impossible from these data to determine whether there was a shift in the demand for farm products. However, it is obvious that any increase in demand, if any occurred, was not large enough to alter the terms of trade in favor of agriculture.

The historical impact of nonfarm business cycles on agriculture can be seen more vividly during periods of decline in national income and employment. Prior to World War II, every substantial decline in national income was marked by a decline in the current and real prices of farm products and by a decline in the current and real value of cash receipts from farm marketings.[5] However, since World War II this relationship has been broken. Despite a decline in real GNP from 1944 to 1946, both the current price and purchasing power of farm products rose. The same

[3] The necessity of using annual data complicates the problem and tends to blur the relationships for years in which the turning point in a business cycle was near midyear. Where this occurred, the final decision as to the classification depended upon whether real GNP rose or fell.

[4] Changes in current prices may be due either to a shift in the real demand for farm products, to a change in the general level of money prices due to inflation or deflation, or to a change in market supplies.

[5] The recessions of 1923–24 and 1926–27 were exceptions for cash receipts, but both were relatively mild, so that large shifts in demand are not to have been expected.

Table 2

Changes in Agriculture During Periods of Business Expansion and
Contraction—Prewar and Postwar

| | Per Cent Change from Beginning to Ending Year in: | | | | | |
| | Farm Prices | | Cash Receipts | | Per Capita Income of Farm Population from All Sources | |
Period of	Current $	Purchasing † Power	Current $	Purchasing † Power	Current $	Purchasing † Power
Expansion						
Prewar:						
1911–13	+ 8.5	+ 5.2	+ 11.7	+ 8.4	*	*
1914–19	+114.9	+12.2	+140.9	+25.9	*	*
1921–23	+ 14.5	+11.3	+ 18.5	+15.4	*	*
1924–26	+ 1.4	+ 2.3	+ 3.3	+ 3.3	*	*
1927–29	+ 5.7	+ 4.5	+ 5.4	+ 4.7	*	*
1932–37	+ 87.7	+60.3	+ 86.7	+59.8	+ 72.9 ‡	+ 64.8 ‡
1938–44	+103.1	+38.5	+165.9	+81.1	+186.6	+101.9
Postwar:						
1946–48	+ 21.6	− 2.7	+ 21.9	− 2.4	+ 21.9	− 1.7
1949–53	+ 2.0	− 8.0	+ 11.9	+ 1.4	+ 28.1	+ 15.8
1954–57	− 4.5	− 7.8	− 0.4	− 3.5	+ 6.7	+ 2.3
1958–60	− 4.8	− 5.9	+ 1.8	− 0.2	+ 4.8	+ 3.8
Contraction						
Prewar:						
1910–11	− 9.6	−10.3	− 3.4	− 4.4	*	*
1913–14	− 1.0	− 3.0	− 3.2	− 5.2	*	*
1920–21	− 41.2	−19.2	− 36.1	−11.7	*	*
1923–24	+ 0.7	0	+ 7.1	+ 6.5	*	*
1926–27	− 3.5	− 3.3	+ 1.7	+ 2.3	*	*
1929–32	− 56.1	−37.0	− 58.0	−40.0	*	*
1937–38	− 20.5	−16.1	− 12.9	− 8.0	− 19.2	− 15.4
Postwar:						
1944–46	+ 19.8	+ 4.6	+ 20.8	+ 5.7	+ 18.8	+ 2.1
1948–49	− 12.9	− 9.1	− 7.9	− 4.6	− 18.3	− 15.4
1953–54	− 3.5	− 3.3	− 3.8	− 3.8	− 0.9	− 0.8
1957–58	+ 6.4	+ 3.7	+ 12.0	+ 9.3	+ 12.3	+ 11.1

* Not available.
† Current dollar figures divided by the index of prices paid by farmers.
‡ For years 1934–37. The figure for 1932–37 would be much larger.

is true during the 1957–58 recession. During the other two post-war recessions (1948–49 and 1953–54) the movement of farm prices was consistent with earlier patterns. Thus, it appears that the previous strong relationship between nonfarm business cycles and price fluctuations in agriculture has been reduced if not reversed. Whereas, prior to World War II, farm price movements were highly correlated with nonfarm shifts in employment and income, it now appears that farm prices are subject to much less influence from these sources, with changes due more to changes in supply than to fluctuations in consumer demand arising from changes in nonfarm income and employment.

There are several reasons to account for these changes. First, during the postwar period price supports for major farm commodities have been in effect and total supply has been such that commodity prices have been resting at or slightly below support levels during recent years. Thus, changes in consumer demand for these products, if any, have been reflected by variations in the rate of stock accumulation rather than fluctuations in prices received.

Equally important has been the structural change in the non-farm economy which has changed the linkage between gross national product and disposable personal income. During the last two decades a number of "built-in stabilizers" have been incorporated into the economy. These include the graduated corporate and personal income tax, unemployment insurance and compensation, and the use of government transfer payments.[6] These work to mitigate the effects upon disposable income of a decline in national income.

The effects of these stabilizers is shown by the shifting relationship between changes in national income and changes in disposable personal income. For the period 1919–29, changes in national income accounted for 92 per cent of the variation in disposable income, and a 1 per cent change in national income resulted in, on the average, an .83 per cent change in disposable income.[7] For the period 1929–41, a 1 per cent change in na-

[6] Of course, the income tax is much older, but its countercyclical effects have increased sharply as a result of inflation and rate changes.

[7] Robert S. Firch, *The Increasing Insulation of Agriculture from Our Unstable Economy*, Unpublished Ph.D. Thesis (University of Chicago, 1962).

tional income only resulted in a .70 per cent change in disposable income ($R^2 = .94$), and for the postwar period 1947–59, a 1 per cent change in national income only resulted in a change of .51 per cent in disposable income ($R^2 = .89$). Thus, if the income elasticity for farm products were unchanged in the postwar period, the changes in the nonfarm economy have been such that a given change in employment and national income would only change the demand for farm products by about two-thirds as much as in earlier decades.

An additional element may mitigate the effects of nonfarm fluctuations in income even further. Friedman has suggested that income should be considered as consisting of a permanent component and a transitory component.[8] If, as he suggests, the demand for farm products is largely dependent upon permanent income, this further explains the stability in postwar demand, because permanent income has been more stable than total income in the postwar period, in fact, showing a rise in every year from 1948 to date.

All of this would explain the weakened relationship between nonfarm employment and farm prices *if the income elasticity for farm products were unchanged.* But, it also appears that the income elasticity for farm products has been drifting downward, even further reducing the instability of demand for farm products at the farm level arising from changes in income and employment.

In summary, it appears that the influence of the past major sources of instability in the aggregate demand for farm products in the United States has been reduced. Price-support programs have reduced the effects of shifts in both export and domestic demand for many products. Structural changes in the domestic economy have reduced the fluctuations in disposable income associated with nonfarm fluctuations in income and employment. These, together with an apparent downward drift in the income elasticity for farm products, suggest that the instability in the aggregate demand for farm products has been reduced substantially from earlier periods.

8 Milton Friedman, *A Theory of the Consumption Function* (Princeton: Princeton University Press, 1957).

The Effects of Nonfarm Cycles
upon Factor Markets for Agriculture

While the influence of cyclical nonfarm fluctuations in employment upon the demand for farm products appears to have weakened in recent years, this does not mean the fluctuations in nonfarm employment no longer are of importance to agriculture. On the contrary, because of their increasing influence on factor markets for agriculture, the influence of nonfarm cycles actually may have increased.

One of the most important effects of nonfarm business cycles has become their impact upon the rate at which labor leaves agriculture. In Chapter 4, it was pointed out that with a situation where the earnings of labor in the agricultural industry were below those of comparable labor elsewhere, the rate at which labor left agriculture was dependent upon the relationship between the salvage value of labor outside of agriculture and its expected future earnings in agriculture. Increases in nonfarm employment tend to increase the salvage value of labor "trapped" in agriculture in two ways. First, a reduction in unemployment levels increases the probability of a farmer finding nonfarm employment. Second, increases in employment levels usually bring an increase in real nonfarm wages. The combination tends to increase sharply the salvage value of labor outside of agriculture. This holds both for labor which leaves the industry completely via migration, and for work off the farm by farm operators who might wish to sell part of their labor off the farm.

Sjaastad has shown that the relationship between the migration rate from agriculture and unemployment is negative and surprisingly high.[9] On the other hand, the level of income in agriculture did not appear to explain any significant portion of the variance in migration rates. This does not mean that the income differentials do not affect migration. Instead, it suggests that the

[9] Larry A. Sjaastad, "Occupational Structure and Migration Patterns," in *Labor Mobility and Population in Agriculture* (Ames: Iowa State University Press, 1961), pp. 8–28.

disequilibrium in labor returns in agriculture and elsewhere in the economy is chronically large enough to induce migration, so that the rate of migration has been dependent largely upon employment opportunities elsewhere.

Fluctuations in nonfarm unemployment levels have a similar effect upon the income of farmers working off their farms on a part-time basis. Blank has shown that, whereas official estimates of nonfarm income to the farm population showed a decline of only 3 per cent from 1953 to 1954, Social Security data showed a decline in nonfarm wage income of farm operators of 20 per cent.[10] The decline reported by Blank was largely the result of a sharp reduction in the number of farm operators reporting nonfarm wage income as unemployment increased.

The increased importance of income from nonfarm sources to the farm population (now above one-third), and the importance of outmigration to average income per person in agriculture, mean that nonfarm business cycles still influence strongly the per capita income level in agriculture. Thus, in Table 2, we see that the per capita net income of the farm population in current dollars has advanced in every business expansion for which data are available—despite the apparent failure of the recent expansions to increase the demand for farm products. The purchasing power of per capita income has increased in five of the six business expansions for which data are available, and the real per capita decline in the 1946–48 period was less than the real decline in farm prices or cash receipts.

Conversely, the average per capita income of the farm population in constant dollars has declined in three of the five business contractions for which data are available. The modest rise in the 1944–46 contraction, even though farm prices and gross incomes rose, again suggests the vital importance of outmigration to income per person in agriculture and the effect of unemployment on migration.

Another factor has entered the picture which may tend to off-

---

[10] Uel Blank, *O.A.S.I. Data of the Farm Labor Force.* Unpublished Ph.D. Thesis (Michigan State University, 1960), p. 192. Blank points out that the method used to obtain the U.S.D.A. estimates automatically underestimates the fluctuations in nonfarm income of farm people.

set the cyclical impacts just discussed. Increasingly, farmers are dependent upon inputs purchased from the nonfarm economy. The use of these purchased inputs has increased substantially. However, for such inputs as steel products, chemicals, and petroleum products, the demand from agriculture is only a minor fraction of the total demand, and the income elasticity of demand for such products appears to be relatively high in the nonfarm economy. Given a less than completely elastic supply curve for such products, gains in nonfarm income tend to increase the price of these products, thereby inflating farm costs without inducing an offsetting increase in the demand and price of farm products. Bryant has shown that the impact of such price increases has been significantly greater since World War II than prior to it.[11] This explains why the purchasing power of cash receipts declined in three of the four postwar expansions, even though current dollar cash receipts increased. During postwar recessions most downward flexibility in nonfarm prices seems to have disappeared, so that while outmigration and nonfarm income sources of farmers decline, farm operators gain no relief from operating costs, and total income per capita in agriculture declines.

Thus, the present impact of the nonfarm economy upon agriculture appears about as follows: Expansions in national income *and employment* increase the demand for farm products relatively little, and they tend to induce price increases for purchased inputs used in agriculture. Gains in agriculture during business expansions, if any, depend upon the increased rate of outmigration from agriculture and the increased sources of nonfarm income available to farm people. Contractions in income and employment apparently reduce the demand for farm products little, if at all. They never seem to reduce the price of purchased inputs, and they sharply reduce the outmigration from agriculture and the nonfarm income of farm people.

It is easy to see what the best and worst circumstances could be for agriculture, but it is difficult to predict what actually will occur over future cycles. The best circumstances would be busi-

[11] W. Keith Bryant, *An Analysis of the Origins and Impacts of Inflation on Farm Input Expenditures,* Unpublished M.S. Thesis (Michigan State University, 1960).

ness expansions that sharply reduced unemployment rates, thus inducing outmigration and increased nonfarm income for farm people, without inducing price increases for purchased inputs used by farmers. The worst situation would be a major depression that would reduce the demand for farm products, outmigration, off-farm income of farm people, and would not reduce farm input costs appreciably. However, the situation of the last two business expansions may come close to being as unfavorable as the worst situation. In both the 1954–57 and the 1958–60 business expansions, the demand for farm products expanded little, nonfarm unemployment remained high, so that outmigration was slowed, nonfarm income of farm people gained little, and the cost of purchased inputs rose appreciably. This was particularly true in the 1958–60 expansion in which the nonfarm unemployment rate remained high. Thus, the nonfarm economy may contribute to income instability for farm people in ways which are not ordinarily considered, but which have become more important as the proportion of farm income derived from nonfarm sources increases and as the proportion of inputs purchased from the nonfarm economy rises.

Instability of Aggregate Supply

All changes in farm output should not be considered as shifts in the aggregate supply function, for despite assertions to the contrary, the aggregate supply curve for farm products is not completely inelastic, even though asset fixity in agriculture tends to make its short-run elasticity near zero when product prices are falling.

However, the conclusion that the aggregate supply function for farm products is totally inelastic has led some economists to conclude that all short-run cyclical fluctuations in farm output are the result of variations in the weather. Thus, they concluded, we tend to have bad weather during periods of falling farm prices and unusually favorable weather when farm prices are rising.[12]

12 See T. W. Schultz, *Agriculture in an Unstable Economy, op. cit.,* p. 41 and W. W. Cochrane, "Professor Schultz Discovers the Weather," *Journal of Farm Economics* (May 1953), p. 282, as examples.

Such fortunate coincidences seem nice, but somewhat doubtful.

Subsequent examination of the indexes of crop output over the business cycle suggested a positive confirmation between the business cycle and crop yields too strong to be coincidence.[13] The development of a weather index by Stallings [14] and its applications, showed that variations in the weather index did not account for the recorded changes in crop output over the business cycle. In fact, according to Stallings' index, weather was more often perverse than consistent with the business cycle. This being the case, the short-run changes in crop yields previously attributed to weather appear to be the result largely of factors other than weather. This is consistent with other data showing significant variations in the use of fertilizer and lime and in expenditures for capital items as business conditions and farm income fluctuate.[15]

Just because all fluctuations in farm output are not due to the influence of weather does not suggest that weather is unimportant to farm output. Stallings showed the coefficient of determination between his weather index to be .404 for the index of farm output, .435 for the index of crop production, .613 for the index of feed-grain output, and .681 for the index of crop production per harvested acre.[16] Thus, variations in weather are associated with variations in crop output in a manner consistent with expectations. The relationship is higher for individual crops (corn) than for groups of crops (feed grains) and higher for groups than for total output.

There is an interesting fact regarding the index of weather published by Stallings, which may be of some significance. For each of his weather indexes for individual crops and for groups of crops, the relative variance declines in each succeeding decade. This might be explained by: (1) actual absolute variations in the weather have been less in the past two decades; (2) Stallings'

13 D. E. Hathaway, "Agriculture and the Business Cycle," *op. cit.,* pp. 487–99.

14 James L. Stallings, "Weather Indexes," *Journal of Farm Economics,* **42** (Feb. 1960).

15 See D. E. Hathaway, "Agriculture and the Business Cycle," *op. cit.;* and Ralph A. Loomis and Glen Barton, *op. cit.,* pp. 14–15 for measurements.

16 *Op. cit.,* p. 185.

methods produced decline; or (3) the absolute level of variance has remained stable but the mean level has risen.

There is no evidence that the absolute variance in rainfall, temperature, sunshine, etc., has declined. However, Stallings' index was computed by measuring the variance of test plot yields from a trend value for the individual test plots. To the extent that the individual test plots had rising trends without increasing the variance in yields, the variance in the computed weather index would decline. Moreover, the rise in the sample size due to increased numbers of test plot data would also bring a reduction in variance.

Much of the effort in plant breeding has been to increase the adaptability of farm crops to variations in weather and to increase their resistance to adverse elements, including disease. Thus, it seems reasonable to assume, and Stallings' data seem to confirm it, that new technology of crop production has not only brought rising yields, but it has also reduced the relative and absolute effect of weather upon these yields.

There are additional elements of stability which would not be measured by the reduction in the variance in the weather index. Examples include irrigation equipment and drying equipment, which make possible more stable yields regardless of fluctuations in the weather. Stallings' index deals with field crops, and the output of fruits and vegetables has been subject to the widest variance in output due to the weather changes. However, for fruits and vegetables even more than for field crops, new developments have reduced the effects of adverse weather. Irrigation, frost control, disease control, and improved product handling after harvest have tended to reduce the weather-induced variations in *usable* crop output.

Thus, a combination of new seeds, new capital equipment, and improved practices have combined to reduce the impact of variations in weather upon the output of either individual crops or total crop output. This does not mean that individual farms, areas, or crops may not be subject to substantial unplanned year-to-year variations in output as a result of unusually good or adverse weather. It does mean, however, that the magnitude of these variations, even for individual farms, has probably been substantially reduced in recent years. Even so, for some crops and in some regions, variations in weather are still important sources of year-to-year variations in output and individual farm income.

Internal Instability in Agriculture

So far the discussion has centered upon external sources of instability which might create shifts in the aggregate supply of or demand for farm products, and in the supply and demand curves for individual products. All other things being equal, such shifts would create unstable farm prices and incomes.

In addition to these external sources of instability, the nature of the demand, supply, and output conditions in agriculture are such to create an inherent instability in prices and incomes within the industry.

The usual explanation of the variability of individual commodity prices in agriculture is the "cobweb theorem" explained by Ezekiel.[17] Given three conditions, this theorem postulates that there will be continuing price fluctuations for farm products. These conditions are: (1) that price in the market be determined by the supply available; (2) that producers' output in the next production period be solely determined by price in the current period; and (3) that production conditions are such that there is a time period between current prices and output response.

Given these conditions, it can be shown that departures from the equilibrium price will lead to subsequent oscillations in the commodity price, the magnitude and direction of the oscillations depending upon the relative elasticities of supply and demand for the product involved. If the elasticities of supply and demand are equal, the oscillations will be a uniform path around an equilibrium point. If the elasticity of supply is relatively higher than the elasticity of demand, then the oscillations will progressively move away from the equilibrium point. If the elasticity of supply is lower than the elasticity of demand, the oscillations will move progressively toward the equilibrium point. The length of the price cycles are dependent upon the length of the production period of the commodity.

Do the conditions necessary for the cobweb theorem actually

[17] M. Ezekiel, "The Cobweb Theorem," *Quarterly Journal of Economics,* 52 (Feb. 1938), pp. 255–280.

exist in agriculture? For farm products the time lag between current prices and the next period output holds, since the products
are the process of a biological process involving a varying length
of time. It also appears that agricultural prices are determined
primarily by the supply currently available.[18]

However, the usefulness of the cobweb idea has been questioned on another point. Why should producers, who act rationally in all other respects, base their output decision for the next
production period solely upon current prices, especially for a
commodity with a history of fluctuating prices? Also, even if future price expectations are based solely on current prices, with
resource fixities on farms is output in the next production period
solely determined by current prices?

Nerlove shows that the use of more than current prices to
determine producers' expected prices and the introduction of lag
in producers' ability to make supply adjustments substantially
reduces the price fluctuations to be expected, but is not likely to
completely eliminate them.[19] It also broadens the range of relative supply and demand elasticities over which prices could be
expected to converge after an initial outside disturbance. Therefore, while conditions are such that the existence of "explosive"
cobwebs do not appear common in agriculture, it also appears
that production, supply, and demand conditions are such to create unstable prices for many commodities.

Given the conditions necessary to produce a cobweb reaction
in product prices, one would expect to find such a pattern for
commodities where production conditions make the short-run
supply curve relatively elastic,[20] and for which the demand is

[18] You do not have to base this on their perishability as does Cochrane in *Farm
Prices, Myth and Reality, op. cit.*, Chapter IV. All that is needed is to define the
demand curve as including the demand for stocks as does Ezekiel, *op. cit.* This
tends to increase the elasticity of demand for storable products, probably making
them into converging cases. Thus, one way to reduce price fluctuations in perish-
ables is to make them storable.

[19] Marc Nerlove, "Adaptive Expectations and Cobweb Phenomena," *Quarterly
Journal of Economics*, 72 (May 1958).

[20] The production does not involve a high proportion of specialized inputs
which become fixed in the production of the individual commodity during falling
prices, nor does its production involve enough total inputs to make it highly inelastic when product prices rise.

relatively inelastic and storage is either expensive or impossible. Potatoes, dry beans, hogs, many annual fresh vegetables, and some field crops meet these requirements, and it is not surprising to see their prices vary substantially from year to year around the average price level for farm products. However, for many products which historically have shown such price variations, the introduction of prices known to the producer in advance of production has ended the dependence upon current prices as a guide for the next period's output and has tended to reduce the cobweb pattern.

INSTABILITY AND
UNCERTAINTY FACING INDIVIDUAL FARMERS

In an economic world subject to constant change, all entrepreneurs are subject to some degree of uncertainty in the prices and incomes they may receive for their endeavors. For agricultural firms this uncertainty comes from a variety of sources, and it has affected the organization of the industry.

The inelastic aggregate demand and supply curves for farm products mean that shifts in either one bring large changes in the aggregate level of prices and incomes. Historically, shifts in aggregate domestic and export demand have been large at times, creating significant short-run changes in farm prices and incomes. Recent events apparently have reduced the impact of these sources of instability.

Unplanned shifts in the aggregate supply curve also have occurred in some years due to variations in the weather. However, here again the aggregate effect of this source of instability appears to be declining with time as numerous new developments reduce the impact of variations in weather upon crop production.

Farmers do not produce farm products in the aggregate. They produce one or more products on an individual farm located in a specific place. Thus, an individual farmer's prices are determined by shifts in demand and output of the commodity he produces. The income of an individual farmer is determined by the output of his individual farm, the price of the particular output he produces, and his production costs.

Thus, the individual farmer is subject to instability of both

demand and costs from outside the agricultural industry, subject
to price uncertainty for his commodities due to changes within
the industry, and sometimes subject to substantial deviations from
planned output upon his individual farm. Firms in relatively few
industries face as many sources of uncertainty when they plan
their output mix and level, and the combinations of resources to
produce it most profitably.

Various governmental programs have been added that have
tended to reduce the price uncertainty for some farm products.
These programs in turn introduce another element of uncertainty for farmers, for they are subject to change via congressional
and administrative action. Thus, price-support levels can be
raised or lowered, and acreage allotments can be reduced or increased. Such actions usually are taken prior to the planting time
for crops, but where production involves the use of inputs having a life of more than one production period, as most inputs do,
uncertainty regarding future government programs can become
an important source of uncertainty to individual farmers. Whether
the uncertainty introduced by the programs exceeds or is less than
the uncertainty that the program is designed to alleviate, sometimes is a debatable matter.

THE ADJUSTMENT OF
AGRICULTURE TO UNCERTAINTY

In theory, there is no reason, given a perfect capital market,
for farmers to favor certain incomes over uncertain incomes, for
in years of good income, they would save part of their income for
use in bad years, and in bad years, if necessary, they would borrow
to maintain their consumption level consistent with their long-
run average income.[21] However, there are several reasons why a
preference among farmers for stable incomes is rational. First, uncertainty by definition means that the sequence of future events
is unpredictable, and given the varied nature of the sources of
uncertainty facing farmers, they have difficulty telling whether an
observed income change is a change in the long-run average in-

[21] See Milton Friedman, "The Reduction of Fluctuations in the Income of
Primary Producers; A Critical Comment," *Economic Journal,* **64** (Dec. 1954), for
an exposition of this position.

come, or a short-run fluctuation from the average income. Moreover, farming is a business largely tied to individual operators, and people enter and leave agriculture. While one's income may cease if he dies or retires, his debts are not canceled.[22] The capital market serving agriculture is imperfect, and a few years of low income for beginning farmers, or a run of such years for established farmers, may mean bankruptcy or liquidation of the enterprise as such. In order to forestall these presumably undesirable events, firms can be organized to either reduce the variability of income or enable the firm to withstand unfavorable economic events.

METHODS OF REDUCING
OR ADAPTING TO UNCERTAINTY

Several methods of reducing income variability to the firm are available to farmers. One is to adopt an enterprise, such as dairying,[23] which by its very nature is subject to less income variation. If this occurs on a farm having a low comparative advantage for the product, it tends to represent a less efficient allocation of resources than would be possible.

Another method of reducing income variations is by diversification of farm enterprises, that is, the adoption of multiple enterprises on the same farm. Diversification generally, though not always, tends to reduce income variance.[24] Of course, a reduction in income variance is not always the sole reason for diversification. For many farm enterprises complementarity in production exists, so that products can be produced more cheaply in multiple enterprises than individually. Moreover, diversification often provides more efficient labor utilization as different enterprises have different labor requirements at different times. Thus, a fruit farm with several varieties of apples, grapes, and pears might represent an attempt to reduce income variance, whereas a fruit farm

[22] Insurance would handle part of this problem.

[23] See E. O. Heady, *op. cit.*, p. 460, for a table showing the average year-to-year variability in prices for major farm products. Also note the substantial differences in the coefficient of variation of income for different type farms shown in Table 9, p. 45.

[24] See Heady, *op. cit.*, pp. 511–21, for the conditions and extent by which diversification will reduce income variance.

with strawberries, cherries, raspberries, peaches, apples, and pears might represent both a reduction in income variance and a more efficient utilization of labor resources on the farm.

Another form of diversification increasingly common in agriculture is part-time work off the farm by the operator or his family members. Such diversification may have any or all of the purposes usually attributed to diversification within farm enterprises. However, the evidence of Blank's research mentioned earlier—that nonfarm employment income of farm people was highly unstable —raises questions as to whether this form of diversification will improve income stability for most farmers.

Another device for reducing income uncertainty which has spread rapidly in certain areas of agriculture is that of advance contractual arrangements regarding the prices to be obtained by a given farmer for his output. Such contracts have long been common in certain canning and processing crops, subject to great year-to-year price fluctuations. They have been extended to broilers, eggs, turkeys, and to a lesser extent to meat animals. The contractual arrangements vary substantially from area to area and crop to crop, but some element of risk sharing is a common characteristic. A recent report on contract arrangements in six Midwest states showed: [25]

About three-fourths of the informal and risk-sharing contracts and about half the formal contracts were made by feed manufacturers; the remainder were made by feed dealers. Responsibility for bad debts was carried by the manufacturer in about three-fourths of the programs under all types of financing and was shared between the dealer and manufacturer in 11 per cent of the formal and risk-sharing programs. Over half the risk-sharing programs had no interest or service charges other than those included in the price of the feed while all of the other financing provided specifically for such charges.

In contrast with the contract programs used by the feed industry in other areas of the nation, the Midwest contracts provided relatively little sharing by the dealers and manufacturers in the livestock production risk. Only one of 18 contracts classified as risk-sharing assured the farmer of a specific annual income. The remaining programs were mostly "partnership" arrangements with two-thirds of these programs

[25] *Agricultural Letter,* Federal Reserve Bank of Chicago (Dec. 8, 1961).

including minimum loss provisions or production incentive payments and the remaining programs having provisions for both.

It certainly is more than coincidence that the most rapid development of risk-sharing contracts has been for farm products lacking price support and having large short-run price variations.

Crop insurance is another method of reducing income uncertainty—in this case, the uncertainty arising from variations in weather.[26] Swerling has suggested a scheme for income insurance that would reduce the income uncertainty facing an individual farmer to some degree by limiting the extent by which net income could decline from one year to the next.[27] However, the uncertainties which produce large variations in farm income are not insurable risks in the normal sense. Sharp changes in the general price levels of all agricultural commodities are a major source of income uncertainty, and these are not distributed according to known probabilities. For this and other reasons, the proposed scheme is not an insurance program in any sense of the word.

Farmers faced by uncertain prices and incomes also may take actions which enable the firm to withstand an adverse outcome. One such action is the maintenance of a higher degree of liquidity than would be warranted in the absence of uncertainty. Thus, a farmer may maintain a bank balance of some size even though he knows that the return on this capital would be substantially higher if invested in productive assets on his farm. A related action has been termed internal capital rationing by D. Gale Johnson.[28] In this case, a farmer refuses to borrow despite the knowledge that the investment would be highly productive, because borrowing would increase his vulnerability to adverse income outcomes. Both excessive liquidity and internal capital rationing may well reduce the efficiency of resource allocation on an individual farm and within the agricultural economy as a whole.

[26] See Harold G. Halcrow, "Actuarial Structures for Crop Insurance," *Journal of Farm Economics,* **31** (Aug. 1949), pp. 418–43 for a discussion of the problem of crop insurance.

[27] Boris C. Swerling, "Income Protection for Farmers: A Possible Approach," *Journal of Political Economy,* **57** (April 1959), pp. 173–86.

[28] D. Gale Johnson, *Forward Prices for Agriculture* (Chicago: University of Chicago Press, 1947).

Another way in which the firm can reduce the effect of uncertainty is by the maintenance of flexibility. This can take many forms, such as the keeping of dual-purpose cows or chickens or the purchase of multi-purpose buildings and equipment instead of specialized equipment. To guard against the effect of future technological change, a farmer may invest in a used machine rather than a new one. If, in achieving this flexibility, there is a loss in productive efficiency, as is often the case, then the efficiency of agriculture is reduced from the level that might exist in the absence of uncertainty.

The discussion has centered upon ways in which the individual firm can organize in order to reduce the adverse effects of uncertainty upon it or to enable it to withstand the effects of adverse outcomes should they occur. The extent to which individual firms will tend to make such adaptations depends upon a number of circumstances.

These adaptations are dependent in part upon the subjective attitudes of the farm manager. Some farmers by nature are gamblers and do not hesitate to enter enterprises involving high degrees of uncertainty, while other individuals shrink from such situations. Thus, some farmers stick to the enterprises with less uncertainty, even though they recognize that opportunities for greater profits might be available.

The willingness of farm operators to enter highly uncertain enterprises appears related to their asset position. A farmer whose asset position is weak, in that his equity is low, often avoids uncertain enterprises because if he entered one and the income results were adverse, he would be out of business. However, occasionally such individuals "go for broke" in the hope of achieving a favorable asset position quickly. It is probably most common that farmers with more favorable asset positions are more likely to engage in more uncertain enterprises, since they are in a position to withstand unfavorable outcomes. Thus, as the asset position of individual farmers, and the industry generally, improves, it is to be expected that farms will be less likely to make internal arrangements to reduce uncertainty or mitigate the effects of adverse outcomes, especially if to do so will lower their mean income level.

Uncertainty of prices and incomes also produces an external effect upon the industry, that of reducing the willingness of lenders to make capital available, or if it is available, the cost is high to cover the risk involved. This results in what D. Gale Johnson has termed *capital rationing,* which reduces the capital available so that it has a higher return in agriculture than elsewhere, representing an inefficient allocation of capital resources in the economy.[29]

Taken all together, the various adaptations made by farm firms to price and income uncertainty and the effects of uncertainty upon the capital market suggest a reduction of the efficiency of resource allocation within agriculture and between agriculture and the nonfarm economy. As a result of price and income uncertainty, resources in agriculture are combined in a way that produces fewer farm products than might be obtained from the same resources otherwise combined.

Changes in Uncertainty and Changes in Agriculture

The discussion thus far has dealt only with the effect of uncertainty upon resource organization due to the threat of uncertainty to the survival of the firm. But, uncertain prices have other effects upon resource allocation.

In price theory, prices are supposed to function as guides to resource allocations within firms, between firms, and between sectors of the economy. But, if future prices are uncertain, their usefulness as guides to resource allocation is substantially impaired. The extent to which the efficiency of resource allocation is reduced is dependent upon the divergence between expected prices and actual prices, the elasticity of factor supply—which determines how much resources will shift with changes in expected prices, and the extent to which resources become "fixed" in production of a particular product or industry.

Some idea of the impact of uncertainty upon agriculture can be obtained from observing what has happened when the uncertainty facing certain agricultural producers was reduced substan-

[29] D. Gale Johnson, *Forward Prices for Agriculture, op. cit.,* Chapter V.

tially. The inauguration of price supports for potatoes during World War II substantially reduced the price uncertainty facing potato producers.[30] As a result, there was a rapid specialization of potato production by areas and upon farms within areas. By 1959, 80 per cent of Irish potato production was on 15,000 farms.[31] The rate of adoption of new technology was increased, and the utilization of capital rose rapidly as both internal and external capital rationing were reduced. Per acre yield rose rapidly as a result of these changes. The researchers concluded that the net effect of the reduction in uncertainty, and the changes that followed, was a substantial reduction in the real cost of producing potatoes and lower average consumer prices.

Similar changes took place in the dry bean industry when price supports were introduced that reduced the price uncertainty facing the producers of this crop, which had been subject to a high degree of both price and yield uncertainty.[32] There was a rapid shift of production to areas and farms having high yields, as these farms were able to specialize without subjecting themselves to extreme income uncertainty. There was a sharp rise in yields per acre, and the real price of dry beans declined as a result.

Johnson found similar effects with the imposition of a price support and production control program for burley tobacco.[33] The rate of adoption of new technology was increased and additional capital entered. However, production control programs in the form of historical acreage allotments prevented the specialization that was a feature of the changes in potatoes and dry beans.

Mention has been made already of a number of factors tending to reduce price uncertainty in agriculture—including price supports, structural changes in the nonfarm economy, the development of risk-sharing contracts in the broiler, egg, and turkey

[30] Roger Gray, Vernon Sorenson and Willard W. Cochrane, *The Impact of Government Programs on the Potato Industry*, Technical Bulletin 211 (St. Paul: University of Minnesota, June 1954).

[31] *Census of Agriculture, Preliminary Release, op. cit.*

[32] D. E. Hathaway, *The Effect of the Price Support Program on the Dry Bean Industry in Michigan*, Technical Bulletin 250 (East Lansing: Michigan Agricultural Experiment Station, 1955).

[33] Glenn L. Johnson, *Burley Tobacco Control Programs*, Bulletin 580 (Lexington: University of Kentucky Agricultural Experiment Station, Feb. 1952).

industries, and the improved postwar asset position of most farmers. These have had the simultaneous effect of reducing short-run price uncertainty, reducing internal and external capital rationing, and enabling farmers to withstand better the adverse effects of uncertainty. The net result has been an unprecedented increase in specialization in United States agriculture and, for many products, a rapid reduction in their real cost of production.

Perhaps the most spectacular changes have been in the production of poultry products. The production of broiler meat approximately tripled from 1950 to 1960, and the broiler-feed price ratio declined by about one-half. The number of farms having chickens declined by one-half, and the number of farms having 3,200 or more chickens increased 125 per cent in the five years 1954–59.[34] Turkey production has followed about the same path, and by 1959, four-fifths of total turkey production took place on 3,000 farms.

Of course, not all of the increased specialization in agriculture can be attributed to a reduction in uncertainty. For some products new technology has provided increasing returns to scale, at least well beyond the size of units previously in existence, but even here a reduction in uncertainty has contributed to the willingness and ability of farmers to take advantage of the new developments.

To the extent that the reductions in uncertainty have resulted in increased efficiency of resource organization in agriculture, they have been desirable, but they have had some adverse effects also. The large output effects of these changes in inputs and production methods have brought prices well below those expected by many investors at the time of their investment. Thus, in the broiler industry and turkey industry, there apparently has been an over-investment in specialized resources which are now "trapped" in the industry and are earning returns lower than expected and lower than investments elsewhere in the economy. Reduction of uncertainty can lead to improved resource allocation within agriculture; but as long as the conditions set forth in Chapter 4 hold, a reduction in uncertainty is not sufficient to prevent a significant disequilibrium in the industry.

[34] *1959 Census of Agriculture, Summary for the 48 States,* Bureau of the Census, Dept. of Commerce (Jan. 1961), p. 3.

The Impact of Agricultural Instability
upon the Nonfarm Economy

It was noted in Chapter 1 that part of the support for measures to stabilize price and income levels in agriculture arose from the belief that income stability in agriculture contributed significantly to income stability in the total economy. To what extent is this belief justified? Will declines in farm income result in a reduction in nonfarm income? Answers to these questions are not readily available. Therefore, we must depend upon theoretical reasoning, marshalling whatever facts are available to support it.

If there is an increase in farm output, farm incomes will decline, given the inelastic demand for farm products. This will have the effect of reducing farmers' consumption expenditures and their expenditures for purchased inputs and capital equipment. However, the decline in farm prices means a rise in the real income of the consumers of farm products. Unless the propensity of farmers to spend for consumption and investment substantially exceeds the propensity to consume of nonfarm people, there is no reason to expect a decline in nonfarm income. Instead, we should expect a decline in the demand for goods produced for farmers and an increase in the demand for other goods. There is no reason to believe that these are completely different goods. Thus, there seems no basis to argue that the decline in farm incomes over the past decade has been an important destabilizer of nonfarm income.

Declines in farm income that arise from shifts in domestic demand due to changes in employment and income are somewhat different. Here, the decline in farm income is not automatically offset to some extent by a rise in consumer income. Reductions in farm income bring reductions in farmers' consumption and investment expenditures which in turn reduce nonfarm employment and income. However, in this case, the effects of changes in farm income seem more likely to be cumulative rather than causal, so we can say that letting farm incomes decline during a recession may increase the magnitude of the downturn, but this is not to say the decline in farm income caused the recession or that the best way to achieve an upturn is via programs to improve farm income.

If the decline in farm income is due to a decline in export demand that is not offset by a rise in the export demand for nonfarm products, then the decline in farm income may result in a decline in national income. The decline in farm income will reduce farmers' expenditures which will reduce income and employment in the nonfarm economy. There is no offsetting increase in real income elsewhere in the economy. Thus, declines in export demand due to shifts in income and employment abroad are likely to reduce the export demand for all products. The effects of shifts in foreign output of farm products are difficult to judge, because they may produce a decline in the export demand for farm products which is offset by increased export demand for nonfarm products.

If enough people believe that farm income is an important determinant of national prosperity, then conceivably changes in farm income might influence business expectations, investment, and, consequently, general levels of employment and income. In an economy where agriculture provided an important fraction of national income, this would be more likely, but in an economy where agricultural income accounts for about four per cent of national income, this would not appear to be rational behavior on the part of nonfarm businessmen. Business investment in recent years seems to have had little relationship to changes in agriculture.

Although it appears unlikely that income variations in agriculture will induce major nonfarm business cycles, this does not mean changes in farm income are unimportant to the nonfarm economy. Farmers' expenditures for capital items, variable inputs, and consumption goods do vary with income, as I have shown elsewhere.[35] Since farmers' expenditures for capital items tend to be concentrated in a few firms and industries and farmers' expenditures for both production and consumption goods tend to be concentrated in areas where farmers live, variations in these expenditures can have a large impact upon a local area and spe-

[35] D. E. Hathaway, "Agriculture and the Business Cycle," *Policy for Commercial Agriculture, op. cit.*

cific industries. The prosperity of these areas and industries does suffer when farm incomes decline, regardless of the reason for the decline. Therefore, it is not difficult to understand why representatives of these industries and areas support the stabilization of farm income, for their income is heavily dependent upon farm income. In our representative political system, the interest in economic stability within geographical areas may equal or exceed the interest in some national average or aggregate.

Instability and Equilibrium in Agriculture

We have traced effects of changes in the general price level, employment, and income upon farmers and have noted that these changes in the nonfarm economy affect farm prices and incomes. Is there any relationship between the instability in agriculture and the chronic disequilibrium in the industry noted in Chapter 4?

Most nonfarm industries also are subject to some instability in demand, arising from changes in employment and income. If such changes contribute to the disequilibrium in agriculture, why don't they also create similar situations in other sectors of the economy? The answer may lie in two related factors.

The first has already been discussed: the several characteristics of agriculture. The characteristics of supply and demand for farm products cause short-run increases in the demand for products to be translated into higher prices, so that the marginal value product equals or exceeds the acquisition cost of new inputs, which quickly flow into the industry. However, short-run declines in the demand for products do not bring an equal outmovement of productive resources because of resource fixity. Moreover, the inelastic demand and the slow increase in demand cause such disequilibriums to be both large and extended.

Business booms, wars, and threats of war have been known to result in substantial "excess capacity" in many nonfarm industries, but for most such industries the adjustment to such disequilibriums appears easier. First, a more elastic demand for a product makes the extent of the disequilibrium less; second, normal growth in demand usually returns the industry to an equilibrium in a relatively short time; and, finally, labor inputs seldom are "fixed," so that part of the adjustment can be achieved by relatively painless transfers to other industries. Where, as in some cases this is not true, the adjustments are long, painful, and continuous as in agriculture.

A second problem which may differ markedly for agriculture is that of forming expectations regarding probable future events influencing the industry. Again the inelastic demand and supply functions may make future expectations have a vastly different probability distribution than do those for other industries. Also, the competitive structure of the industry may affect its ability to form accurate expectations regarding the future.

This latter point seems of special importance regarding expectations of future changes in technology and production techniques. Most nonfarm industries finance the research in these areas and, they therefore control or have knowledge of probable future changes in production techniques. They also probably have, as a corollary, better estimates of the rate of adoption and aggregate output effects of such changes. Most technical and organizational changes in agriculture are developed and announced by outside organizations, and rarely, if ever, are they accompanied by estimates of their probable aggregate effects upon output, prices, and the equilibrium level of adoption. Apparently, most private organizations pushing "vertical integration" never warned the farmer participants they could expect future prices well below prices received before the change; and public agencies producing new technologies have been remiss in their discussion of the probable aggregate impact of the changes they have produced. In an industry subject to high degrees of resource fixity, the lack of such knowledge can produce much of the chronic disequilibrium observed over time.

Therefore, it appears that instability and uncertainty in agriculture probably has been a major contributor to the problem of disequilibrium in the industry. The structural characteristics of the industry are such that this instability has greater impacts than might be expected in other industries. While the reduction in price and income instability arising from external sources will reduce such problems, it will not remove them.

Summary and Implications

Farming is a business subject to uncertainty arising from a variety of internal and external sources. Shifts in demand, output, weather, production techniques, and institutions have subjected the individual farmer to a relatively high degree of price and income uncertainty. This has caused farmers to adjust in ways which have reduced the efficiency of resource allocation in agriculture. Moreover, uncertain prices make less than perfect guides for resource allocation, even if the capital market could be adopted to insure survival under income uncertainty.

A number of changes have occurred since 1940 which have reduced the price and income uncertainty facing farmers due to changes in the demand for farm products. The built-in stabilizers have reduced the effects of nonfarm business cycles upon the demand for farm products, and price supports for some farm products have reduced both price and income fluctuations. Private risk-sharing contracts have been developed to reduce price uncertainty facing the producers of many products. New technology in agriculture appears to have reduced the unplanned variations in output arising from weather.

As a result of these and other changes in agriculture, the problem of internal and external capital rationing in agriculture has been substantially reduced, if not eliminated. There has been rapid specialization of production of many farm products as a result of these changes and other developments. The allocation of resources within agriculture probably has been substantially improved as a result of these changes, but the rapidity with which they have occurred has further contributed to the commitment of additional resources to agriculture and the problems of low returns for "trapped" resources. Thus, some of the postwar reduction in uncertainty may have contributed to the problem of low returns to resources in farming because of the immobility of resources out of the industry.

Despite the improvements on the demand side, substantial instability and uncertainty still remain in agriculture. It now appears to be concentrated in the factor markets for inputs and in the uncertainty regarding future production techniques. Whereas an improved capital market and insurance schemes were of value in meeting the old problems, these appear to be of little value in dealing with the newer ones.

Chapter 6

Poverty in Agriculture: Those Who Are Poor but Not Always Underpaid

The returns to human effort in farming, with few exceptions, are lower than for comparable effort elsewhere in the economy. But this in itself is not evidence that all of the people engaged in agriculture are poor. In fact, the contrary appears to be true for those 800,000 commercial farms selling over $10,000 of farm products annually. Yet the evidence suggests that the agricultural industry contains a disproportionately large share of the low-income population of the United States and that the income levels of these persons cannot be accounted for entirely by the lower level of returns for human effort in agriculture.

A 1959 study of the low-income population showed that in 1957 rural farm families were 11 per cent of the families in the nation, but they made up 30 per cent of all families having money incomes of less than $2,000.[1] In other words, 40.5 per cent of all rural farm families had incomes of less than $2,000 in that year. There were an estimated 1.9 million rural farm families in 1957 that had annual incomes of less than $2,000.

The picture looks somewhat grimmer, if possible, if one looks at the incidence rates of low income in various occupational groups. They showed that 54 per cent of the families whose heads were farmers and farm managers and 60 per cent of the families whose heads were farm laborers and foremen were classified as low-income families in 1957.[2] No other *major* occupational group came close to approaching the incidence level of low income found in these two agricultural occupations.

The high incidence of low-income families in agriculture was not due to special economic circumstances prevalent in 1957 when farm income was low and nonfarm employment was rising. Data for 1948, a year of high farm income, showed the same high incidence of low-income families in agriculture.

The data suggest two things: (1) that the incidence of low incomes in agriculture is much higher than in any other industry, and (2) that, whereas the incidence of low incomes declined markedly for the economy as a whole and in virtually every industry in the postwar period, the *relative* incidence of low incomes in United States agriculture has not declined. Thus, the extremely high incidence of low-income families in agriculture cannot be blamed entirely upon the recent declines in aggregate farm income or solely upon the low returns to human effort in agriculture. Instead, the high incidence of low incomes in agriculture are due to the special problems of large groups within agriculture having characteristics that, when combined with low returns for human effort, produce low-income groups and areas.

[1] Robert Lampman, "Study Paper No. 12, Materials Prepared in Connection with the Study of Employment, Growth, and Price Levels for Consideration by the Joint Economic Committee, Congress of the United States," *The Low Income Population and Economic Growth* (Dec. 16, 1959), p. 7.

[2] *Ibid.*, p. 22. The calculations did not take into account the value of home produced food or housing for farm families. Taking these into account would reduce the incidence but not eliminate the high relative incidence of low incomes in agriculture.

Low-Income Farm Operators

The largest group of low-income persons in agriculture in terms of numbers are farm operators. The Department of Commerce Survey of Consumer Income for 1960 shows that an estimated 27.3 per cent (about 839,000) of the 2.3 million families whose heads were classified as farmers and farm managers in 1960 had annual money incomes under $2,000.[3]

Unfortunately, neither Census income surveys nor the Census of Population collect data on the characteristics of the farms upon which these low-income farmers and farm managers reside. Nor does the Census of Agriculture collect data on the net income of the operators of the farms upon which it lavishes so much attention. Thus, we must connect the two by inference from other data.

Some idea of the cause of the low-income farm problem can be obtained from the Census of Agriculture. Despite the more restrictive definition of a farm in 1959, the Census still counted as farms 1,638 million places that sold less than $2,500 of farm products and 618,000 places that sold between $2,500 and $4,999. The available data show that the average cash income from farming of this latter group was only $1,288, although it is often supplemented by reasonably high off-farm income (Table 1).

About one-half of the 1.64 million farms with annual sales of farm products under $2,500 were operated by part-time operators whose incomes from nonfarm sources exceeded their farm income; thus their low income, if it were low, was not solely due to farming. On the average, their incomes are much higher due to their off-farm earnings. About one-fourth of these low-production farms were operated by persons over 65 years of age, so that the farms might be viewed as part-retirement farms and are so classified by the Census of Agriculture. The average income from farming for this group is very low, and their average nonfarm income also is low, so that many have total money incomes below $2,000. In 1959, there were still 348,000 farms selling less than $2,500 an-

---

[3] "Income of Persons and Families in the United States—1960," *Current Population Reports, Consumer Income,* Series P60, No. 37 (Washington: Bureau of the Census, U. S. Dept. of Commerce, Jan. 17, 1962), p. 30.

nually where the operator was under 65 and farming was essentially the primary source of income. These people were on the bottom of the income ladder on both counts, in that both farm and nonfarm income was low; the result was an average cash income of under $1,000 for these families.

Table 1

Location and Average Income of Farms Having Specified Characteristics in 1959

Farms	TOTAL NUMBER OF FARMS	Geographic Distribution of Farms			Average Cash Income From		
		North	South	West	Farming	Off Farm	Total
					DOLLARS		
Selling $2,500–4,999	616,839	298,057	277,174	41,608	1,288	2,077	3,365
Selling $50–2,499	348,382	89,443	244,748	14,191	438	525	963
Part-Time *	882,371	295,790	501,148	85,433	176	4,283	4,459
Part-Retirement †	403,696	144,851	231,823	27,022	116	1,846	1,962

* Annual sales under $2,500 and the family income from other sources exceeded the income from farming.
† Annual sales under $2,500 and operator over 65 years of age.

Source: *1959 Census of Agriculture, Preliminary Reports*, for numbers of farms by class and region. Average income by class of farm from *Food and Agriculture, A Program for the 1960's* (Jan. 30, 1962), Table 5, p. 50.

The farms having these characteristics are not distributed equally throughout the country (Table 1). Almost one million of the 1.64 million farms selling less than $2,500 of products are in the South. That region contains 70 per cent of all the farms where farming is the major source of income, the operator is under 65, and the gross sales were under $2,500. It also contains more than one-half of the part-time farms and nearly 60 per cent of the part-retirement farms.

The effect of the concentration of low-production farms upon the level and distribution of money earnings of farmers and farm managers is shown in Table 2 for selected states. It shows that a high proportion of low-production farms in and of itself does not produce low incomes. But where such farms are the predominant source of income, as is the case in many areas, the result is an extremely low-income level for farmers and their families.

Poverty in agriculture is the result of a number of interacting factors, including that on most low-income farms there is a combination of few capital resources and inadequate human resources. Areas which have high concentrations of such farms are low-income areas.

Table 2

Distribution and Median Money Earnings of Male Farmers and
Farm Managers in Selected States, 1959

Total Money Earnings	Alabama	South Carolina	Connecticut	South Dakota	Utah	Arizona
	PER CENT					
$1 to $499 or less	30.5	28.2	8.7	8.6	7.3	10.9
$500 to $999	23.8	22.6	7.8	9.3	5.4	6.6
$1,000 to $1,499	14.2	14.1	8.6	12.8	8.9	6.9
$1,500 to $1,999	7.5	8.1	6.0	9.6	6.7	4.4
$2,000 to $2,499	7.3	7.1	7.1	12.3	10.5	4.9
$2,500 to $2,999	3.1	3.9	6.5	7.6	6.0	4.1
$3,000 to $3,499	3.7	4.2	9.2	9.1	10.5	5.3
$3,500 to $3,999	1.7	2.0	6.4	4.9	5.4	3.9
$4,000 to $4,499	2.0	2.4	7.5	6.4	8.3	5.5
$4,500 to $4,999	0.8	0.9	4.8	2.9	5.2	3.1
$5,000 to $5,999	1.9	2.2	10.4	5.8	9.1	9.3
$6,000 to $6,999	1.0	1.5	3.8	3.0	5.4	5.8
$7,000 to $9,999	1.3	1.4	6.8	4.1	5.9	9.3
$10,000 and over	1.3	1.5	6.3	3.5	5.5	20.2
Median earnings	$910	$983	$3,284	$2,393	$3,250	$4,288

Source: U. S. Bureau of the Census, U. S. Census of Population: 1960. *General Social and Economic Characteristics.* Final Report PC(1)-2C (Washington: U. S. Govt. Printing Office, 1961).

A number of studies have been made in recent years of the characteristics of such areas, the people in them, and the resources available to these people.[4] Much of this information has been sum-

[4] As examples, see Ronald Bird, Frank Miller, and Samuel C. Turner, *Resources and Levels of Income of Farm and Rural Nonfarm Households in Eastern Ozarks of Missouri,* Research Bulletin 661 (Columbia: University of Missouri Agricultural Experiment Station, March 1958); William H. Metzler and J. L. Charlton, *Employment and Underemployment of Rural People in the Ozark Area,* Bulletin 604 (Fayetteville: University of Arkansas Agricultural Experiment Station, November 1958); H. A. Henderson, *Resources and Incomes of Rural Upper East Tennessee People,* Bulletin 312 (Knoxville: University of Tennessee Agricultural Experiment Station, March 1960); John H. Southern and W. E. Hendrix, *Income of Rural Families in Northeast Texas,* Bulletin 940 (College Station: Texas Agricultural Experiment Station, October 1959); William C. McArthur and Fred B. Sanders, *Resources and Incomes of Rural Families in the Coastal Plain Area of Georgia,* mimeographed

marized in a United States Department of Agriculture bulletin by Inman and Southern.[5]

In general, with the exception of the Michigan study area, all study areas showed the pattern of extremely low income for those families that are largely dependent upon agriculture (Table 3). The incidence of low incomes was high among all population groups in the area, but it was highest for those most dependent upon agriculture.

Table 3

Proportion of Rural Families Having Net Family Money Income of Less Than $2,000, Study Areas

Study Area	TYPE OF FAMILY		
	Nonfarm	All farm	Commercial farm *
	Per cent	Per cent	Per cent
Northwestern Florida	54.0	57.1	59.8
Michigan Cut-Over	29.5	24.0	25.6
Mississippi Clay Hills	58.1	63.6	65.8
Missouri Ozarks	54.5	57.6	64.9
Northeastern Tennessee	36.0	48.1	58.5
Northeastern Texas	48.6	50.3	65.6

* Commercial farm families are defined as in the 1954 Census of Agriculture, namely, "In general, all farms with a value of sales of farm products amounting to $1,200 or more were classified as commercial. Farms with a value of sales of $250 to $1,199 were classified as commercial only if the farm operator worked off the farm less than 100 days or if the income of the farm operator and members of his family received from nonfarm sources was less than the total value of all farm products sold." The Texas and Tennessee studies used a slightly different definition, but the data are comparable.

Source: Buis T. Inman and John H. Southern, *Opportunities for Economic Development in Low-Production Farm Areas*, Agriculture Information Bulletin No. 234 (Washington: U.S.D.A., Nov. 1960), p. 10.

series MS 74 (Athens: Georgia Agricultural Experiment Station, April 1959); K. M. Gilbraith and L. A. Reuss, *Sources and Levels of Income of Rural Households of North and West Florida, 1956,* Agricultural Economics Mimeographed Report No. 59–4 (Gainesville: Florida Agricultural Experiment Station, October 1958). In addition to the above, similar data may be found in Fred B. Sanders, *Economics of Resource Use in Farm and Nonfarm Opportunities,* Bulletin NS 43 (Athens: Georgia Agricultural Experiment Station, July 1957); Irwin T. Sanders and Robert F. Galloway, *Rural Families in the Purchase Area of Western Kentucky,* Bulletin 647 (Lexington: Kentucky Agricultural Experiment Station, June 1956). Also see the two bulletins by Dorothy Dickens on "Levels of Living of White and Negro Farm Operator Families in Mississippi," *ibid.*

5 John H. Southern and Buis T. Inman, *Opportunities for Economic Development in Low-Production Farm Areas,* Agriculture Information Bulletin No. 234 (Washington: U.S.D.A., Nov. 1960).

One of the reasons for the low incomes on farms in the area is that the productive level of the natural resources in most of the areas tends to be low.[6] Most such areas were originally settled because of the attraction of some natural resource base, such as lumber or mines. When these resources were depleted, farming became a dominant occupation and the land, which in many cases was poorly suited for intensive agriculture, was not capable of supporting the population.

Another reason for the low incomes on farms in these areas is the low capital investment that is common on such farms (Table 4). Not only is the total capital investment low, but the proportion of total investment represented by land and buildings is generally higher than for high-production farms. Relatively high land prices due to population pressure account in part for this relationship.

Table 4

Average Total Farm Investment for All Farms and for Commercial Farms,
Families with Net Money Incomes of Less Than $2,000, Study Areas *

| Study Area | AVERAGE TOTAL INVESTMENT | | |
	All Farms	Commercial Farms	Percentage of Commercial Farms with Less Than $10,000 Total Investment
	Dollars	Dollars	Per cent
Northwestern Florida	10,899	15,720	41
Mississippi Clay Hills	7,751	8,485	70
Missouri Ozarks	11,152	13,781	41
Northeastern Tennessee	14,758	16,700	50
Northeastern Texas	9,334	12,900	56

* Data not available for Michigan and New Mexico areas.

Source: Buis T. Inman and John H. Southern, *Opportunities for Economic Development in Low-Production Farm Areas*, Agriculture Information Bulletin No. 234 (Washington: U.S.D.A., Nov. 1960), Table 10, p. 20.

Perhaps the most striking finding of the studies of low-income farm areas is the generally low level of human resources on such farms (Table 5). In most of the study areas, one-third to one-half

[6] *Ibid.*, pp. 8 and 9.

Table 5

Specified Characteristics of Family Heads, Rural Families with Net Money Incomes Below $2,000, Study Areas

Study Area	All Heads 65 Years of Age and Over	Females Under 65 Years	CHARACTERISTICS OF FAMILY HEADS — MALES UNDER 65 YEARS		
			With Physical Handicap	Less than 5 Years Schooling and No Physical Handicap	No Limitations Noted
	Per cent	Per cent	Per cent	Per cent	Per cent
Northwestern Florida	40	3	16	19	22
Michigan Cut-Over	54	0	11	1	34
Mississippi Clay Hills	32	8	1	17	42
Missouri Ozarks	32	7	12	18	31
North-Central New Mexico	34	8	—*	18	40
Northeastern Tennessee	30	9	9	16	36
Northeastern Texas	39	4	21	7	29

* Not ascertained.

Source: Buis T. Inman and John H. Southern, *Opportunities for Economic Development in Low-Production Farm Areas*, Agriculture Information Bulletin No. 234 (Washington: U.S.D.A., Nov. 1960), Table 13, p. 26.

of the heads of the families were over sixty-five; in some areas, a significant portion had physical handicaps. Moreover, educational levels generally are lower among farm people than nonfarm people, and the incidence of low levels of formal education is especially high in these low-income areas. Heads of families in these study areas who were in their productive working years, lacked physical handicaps, and had more than five years of education, were in the minority in every study area.

Thus the picture of the problem of poverty in agriculture among farm operators comes into better focus. Some low-production, low-income farms are found in every farming area of the United States. However, in some areas, notably the Northeast and North Central areas, low-production farms do not necessarily mean the families have low incomes; a high proportion of such farms are part-time farms where the family income is largely dependent upon other sources. There also are farms located throughout the United States operated by persons whose ages limit their physical capacity and whose current incomes generally are low, although their asset positions are not always low.

In the South, however, there is a concentration of low-production farms where the operator's income is low and the income from other sources is low or completely absent. These concentrated low-income areas have a combination of poor natural resources for farming, few capital resources, and lower levels of human resources than elsewhere in the economy. It is little wonder that the income of these persons is low.

The numbers of these low-production farms has been declining rapidly during the past decade. Adjusting for changes in farm price levels, the number of low-production farms in the United States declined by 1.8 million between 1930 and 1954.[7] About 60 per cent of this decline was in the South. Using the 1954 definition of a farm, the number of low-production farms declined another 790 thousand or 30 per cent from 1954 to 1959.[8] Again, both the absolute and relative decline was greatest in the South.

The decline in the low-production farms has been due largely

[7] Jackson McElveen, *Family Farms in a Changing Economy*, Agriculture Information Bulletin No. 179 (Washington: U.S.D.A., March 1957), p. 20.
[8] *1959 Census of Agriculture—Preliminary Reports, ibid.*, p. 3.

to an outmigration of the operators of such farms, either physically or in terms of occupation. Areas classified as serious low-income farming areas by the Department of Agriculture had a net migration rate of 37 per cent in the 1940–50 decade.[9] However, migration is a selective process, highly concentrated among the young age groups.[10] This leaves a highly distorted age distribution in many of these low-income areas and, to the extent that migration is selective regarding other population characteristics, may leave a population distorted in other characteristics which affect productivity.

The effect of several decades of physical outmigration upon the age distribution of the remaining population in low-income areas is shown by Table 6. It shows that these areas have a much lower proportion of their population in the productive age groups 20–64 and a much higher proportion under 20 or over 65. Moreover, even within the 20–64 age group, the proportion over 45 is generally higher.

Unfortunately, areas of low-production farms and low incomes tend to become self-perpetuating "depressed" areas. Farms in such areas often suffer from external capital shortages, and their incomes are never high enough to generate internal capital via savings. Birth rates tend to be high in such areas, and neither the individual families nor the areas have the resources to make possible a substantial capital investment in humans via education. In 1959, 47 per cent of all children under 18 in families whose heads were employed in agriculture were in families where the head of the household had an income under $2,000.[11] Also, the low-income levels on these farms put a high premium upon the children entering the labor force at the earliest possible age. These continuing low educational levels make migration less profitable and more difficult, and reduce the attractiveness of an area for nonfarm business location. The outmigration that occurs further

[9] Gladys K. Bowles, *Farm Population—Net Migration from the Rural Farm Population, 1940–50,* Statistical Bulletin 176 (Washington: U.S.D.A.), Table A, p. 17.

[10] D. E. Hathaway, "Migration from Agriculture—The Historical Record and Its Meaning," *American Economic Review,* 50 (May 1960), 379–91.

[11] "Family Characteristics of Persons: March 1959," *Current Population Reports, Population Characteristics,* Series P-20, No. 122 (Dec. 29, 1961), p. 3.

Table 6

Proportion of Population by Age Groups, Low-Income Study Areas and United States *

Age Group	North-western Florida Per cent	Michigan Cut-Over Per cent	Mississippi Clay Hills Per cent	Missouri Ozarks Per cent	North-Central New Mexico Per cent	North-eastern Tennessee Per cent	North-eastern Texas Per cent	United States Per cent
Under 14	34.0	30.4	27.4	30.5	38.0	29.3	32.4	28.7
14 to 19	12.3	11.5	13.3	9.9	12.6	11.9	9.4	8.7
20 to 24	3.5	2.4	4.0	3.0	5.5	6.0	3.7	6.3
25 to 34	8.2	8.1	8.1	8.3	8.6	11.1	8.3	13.9
35 to 44	11.4	13.7	12.7	12.5	9.6	11.8	12.4	13.6
45 to 64	18.9	21.5	22.9	22.5	17.0	21.9	22.8	20.2
65 and over	11.7	12.4	11.6	13.3	8.7	8.0	11.0	8.6
Total	100.0	100.0	100.0	100.0	100.0	100.0	100.0	100.0

* Study areas include only open-country population enumerated in the surveys. The data of the United States include all population for July 1957 as reported in U. S. Bureau of the Census "Current Population Reports," Population Estimates (15).

Source: Buis T. Inman and John H. Southern, *Opportunities for Economic Development in Low-Production Farm Areas*, Agriculture Information Bulletin No. 234 (Washington: U.S.D.A., Nov. 1960), Table I2, p. 24.

lowers the productive income base to support public facilities—and so it goes.

The extensive research by Nicholls and his colleagues shows that the emergence and continued existence of these low-income areas in agriculture is closely related to local urban-industrial expansion.[12] They found that local urban-industrial development had an important impact upon factor markets which substantially affected the productivity in agriculture. Most important, they concluded that, in the absence of local urban-industrial development, outmigration alone cannot overcome the differential disadvantage of these areas in productivity and farm income.

Hired Farm Laborers

Poverty among farm operators is associated with low-production farms, and the problem is concentrated largely in areas where a combination of factors contributes to low individual incomes and low incomes for the area. There is a group in agriculture, the farm laborers, whose average income position is below that of the low-income farm operator and who are not always associated with low-production farms.

Discussion of the income status of the hired farm labor force in agriculture is difficult and often heated because it is not easy to define what constitutes a member of the hired farm labor force. As pointed out in Chapter 2, the hired labor force in agriculture is defined differently by the Department of Agriculture than by the Department of Commerce.

The effects of the differences can be seen by comparing the Census estimates of wage and salary workers in agriculture with the Agriculture estimate of all of the people who worked as farm wage workers in 1959.[13] The Census labor force statistics show

[12] For a summary of this research, see W. H. Nicholls, "Industrialization, Factor Markets and Agricultural Development," *Journal of Political Economy,* **69** (August 1961), pp. 219–340.

[13] "Labor Force and Employment in 1960," Special Labor Force Report No. 14, *Monthly Labor Review* (April 1961, U. S. Dept. of Labor, Bureau of Labor Statistics); Sheradon T. Maitland, Robert Stansberry, Jr., and Reed E. Friend, *The Hired Farm Working Force in 1959,* Agricultural Information Bulletin, No. 238 (Washington: U.S.D.A., Economic Research Service, April 1961).

that 1.69 million persons were employed as wage and salary workers in agriculture in that year, whereas the Agriculture estimate is that 3.58 million persons worked for farm wages sometime during the year. Both figures exclude the foreign nationals who are allowed to enter to work as farm laborers. The Agriculture figures provide the best data about these workers, their problems, and provide insights into the reasons for their low income.

A large portion of the hired farm work force is casual or short-time employment.[14] Thus, 1.4 million of the 3.6 million who worked for farm wages in 1959 worked less than 25 days. These persons consisted largely of women and younger males, usually students. Seventy-eight per cent of the persons who worked more than 25 days for farm wages were males.

The average earnings of the 2.2 million farm wage workers working more than 25 days in 1959 was $1,038, coming from $829 of farm wages and $209 of nonfarm wages. This was the highest average ever recorded for this group. Despite these low earnings, there were more persons estimated in the group in 1959 than in 1952 (Table 7).

Table 7

The Number of Male Farm Wage Workers Working More Than 25 Days Annually, the Average Days of Farm and Nonfarm Employment, and the Average Daily Wage Earned Per Day Worked, 1949–59

Year	Number of Males Working Over 25 Days (thousands)	AVERAGE DAYS WORKED		AVERAGE WAGE PER DAY WORKED	
		Farm	Nonfarm	Farm	Nonfarm
1949	2,001	157	26	$4.10	$6.40
1951	1,718	165	32	4.85	7.55
1952	1,558	152	35	5.30	7.75
1954	1,544	158	27	5.80	7.70
1956	1,553	157	27	6.20	9.05
1957	1,673	143	22	6.25	8.55
1958	1,788	147	24	6.30	9.75
1959	1,690	157	26	6.25	9.75

Source: *The Hired Farm Work Force in 1959, op. cit.,* Tables I and 6.

[14] The data that are presented in the following paragraphs are taken from *The Hired Farm Working Force of 1959,* Agriculture Information Bulletin 238, *ibid.*

The low income of the hired farm workers cannot be attributed to their old age, to their location in depressed areas, or to their working on small low-production farms. In fact, the contrary is more often the case.

In 1959, only 4 per cent of those males working more than 25 days for farm wages were over 65 years old, and their median age was in the low thirties. Eighteen per cent were under 17 years of age. Actually, this younger group tends to lower the average earnings figures substantially, for males under 18 worked only one-half as many days as the 18–64 age group; their average daily earnings were just one-half that of the older group. Thus, the total wages of the 18–64 year group averaged $1,480 in 1959. Males over 65 worked more days than those under 18, and their daily wage was higher.

In general, hired farm workers tend to be hired by larger commercial farms, although this varies by region and type of farm. The 1954 Census of Agriculture showed that farms selling over $25,000 of product annually hired one-third of all the hired workers in 1954, and that such farms account for a very large fraction of the total farm wages paid. Hired workers on smaller farms, to the extent they exist, are normally seasonal help. Thus, in 1959, one-half of the farm operators reported some hired labor in the year; but two-thirds of those hiring labor reported a labor bill of less than $500.

The major reasons for the low earnings of farm wage workers are: (1) underemployment, and (2) concentration in work where their physical productivity is low, thus their daily earnings are low.

Only about 37 per cent of the 2.2 million hired farm workers working over 25 days were employed more than 150 days per year for farm wages. This was particularly true for women, where less than 10 per cent worked over 150 days as farm wage workers. This does not mean, however, that all of these people were voluntarily out of the labor force. Instead, it means that for many, especially migrant farm workers, they are unemployed during the period when not doing farm work.

The effect of days worked on earnings is shown by the average annual wages of those working over 250 days compared to those working fewer days. Males working over 250 days averaged $2,186 in 1959, compared to $1,322 for those working 150–249 days and $749 for those working 25–149 days. Since 60 per cent of all migratory workers worked less than 150 days in 1959, voluntary or involuntary unemployment is one reason for their low income.

Not only do farm wage workers tend to be unemployed, but they also are employed in work where their productivity is low. More than one-third of the male white and 60 per cent of the male nonwhite wage workers in 1959 were employed in hand labor. Their average total wages, both farm and nonfarm, were $1,383 and $887 respectively. White males employed with machines and livestock averaged $1,686, and nonwhite males working with machines and livestock averaged $1,084.

The American dream of the "agricultural ladder" of success no longer exists, if it ever did. It is no longer possible for a hired farm worker to accumulate enough capital from his earnings to become a tenant and, as a tenant, accumulate enough to become a farm owner. Instead, hired farm workers are generally in that portion of agriculture where physical productivity is low; they are in an industry where the returns to human effort are generally low. They are often unemployed because the nature of the work is highly seasonal; yet, they usually are unable to obtain nonfarm employment.

The inability of the hired farm workers to obtain part- or full-time nonfarm employment arises for a variety of reasons. Hired farm workers generally have low levels of education and few skills of the type that are needed in the nonfarm labor force.

In March, 1959, a United States Department of Agriculture study showed farm laborers had the lowest median years of school completed of any of the major occupation groups.[15] Twenty-nine per cent of the farm laborers in 1959 had completed less than 5 years of school. The median years of school completed by farm workers over 18 was 7.7, compared to 11.7 for the same group of all employed males.

A Texas study of migrant farm workers in 1957 showed that

[15] James Cowhig, *Education and Earnings of the Hired Farm Working Force of 1960,* Agriculture Information Bulletin No. 262 (Washington: Economic Research Service, U.S.D.A., May 1962).

31 per cent of them had no formal schooling and that 95 per cent of them had never gone to high school.[16] A New York study in that same year showed that the median grade completed was low among migrant workers, especially for those over 44 years of age.[17] The United States Department of Agriculture data show an average of 6.2 years for this group.

For most farm workers, their unemployment is not voluntary, nor do they have farm wage work as their permanent employment goal. The Texas study shows that male migrant workers were available for work on 89 of the 97 days during the year when they did not work. A Department of Labor study of nonmigrant farm workers in four areas shows that unemployment also was a serious problem for these workers because of the seasonality of farm work.[18] The New York study shows that the bulk of the migratory farm workers in that state would prefer other occupations to farm wage work and that most such workers had aspirations to leave the migratory labor work force.[19]

Unfortunately, leaving the hired farm work force has not been easy for many of the workers, because of the relative disadvantage they face in the nonfarm employment market. The United States Department of Agriculture data on the hired farm work force indicate that more than 40 per cent of the migrant workers in 1959 had first done farm wage work prior to 1950, thus had been migrant workers for a decade. About one-third of the nonmigrant farm wage workers had first done such work prior to 1950.

[16] William H. Metzler and Frederick Sargent, *Migratory Farm Workers in the Midcontinent Streams,* Production Research Report No. 41 (Agricultural Research Service, U.S.D.A. in conjunction with the Texas Agricultural Experiment Station: Dec. 1960), Table 4, p. 12.

[17] Emmit F. Sharp and Olaf F. Larson, *Migratory Farm Workers in the Atlantic Coast Stream; II. Education of New York Workers and Their Children, 1953 and 1957,* Bulletin 949 (Cornell University Agricultural Experiment Station and Agricultural Research Service: U.S.D.A., May 1960), Table 4, p. 16.

[18] *Unemployment and Partial Employment of Hired Farm Workers in Four Areas,* by the United States Department of Agriculture, Bureau of Agricultural Economics and United States Department of Labor, Bureau of Employment Security (Washington, D. C.: April 1953).

[19] Emmit F. Sharp and Olaf Larson, *Migratory Farm Workers in the Atlantic Coast Stream; I. Changes in New York 1953 and 1957,* Bulletin 948 (Cornell University Agricultural Experiment Station and Agricultural Research Service, U.S.D.A.: May 1960).

The United States Department of Agriculture study came to the striking conclusion that the educational level of male farm laborers had not improved over the past 20 years.[20] During the period in which the median years of school completed by the general population increased from 8.5 to 11.0, there was no apparent increase in the level of education of the hired farm labor force. Their low level of education places serious limits upon the nonfarm jobs which are open to such workers and the level of earnings in such jobs. Unpublished tabulations of the United States Department of Agriculture study show a strong relationship between education and average daily earnings for each age group.

The problems of these low-income farm wage workers are increasingly difficult because there apparently is a self-perpetuating cycle among the groups involved. Despite the continued mechanization of farm work, the number of farm wage workers working more than 25 days per year has not declined appreciably over the last decade, but the average days of farm work per worker did decline (Table 7). As a result, there was virtually no increase in the average wage per day worked on farms during the five years 1955–59. Both the number of days of nonfarm work and the average wage per day are highly sensitive to nonfarm employment conditions.

The low earnings and underemployment have not been sufficient to reduce the numbers of farm wage workers in recent years because new entrants to the group have equaled departures from it. Both the Texas and New York studies show that the children of migrant workers are well behind their counterpart age groups in terms of schooling and, in addition, the achievement per year of school attendance is lower for such groups because of their general economic and social background and transitory status. The situation is similar, but probably less pronounced, for the children of nonmigrant farm wage workers.

Thus, the lack of salable skills and education limits the entry of many children of farm laborers to nonfarm employment. They enter farm wage work at a time when the demand for such labor is declining because of mechanization, and they enter types of work in which physical productivity is lowest. The cycle of low

[20] *Ibid.*, pp. 6 and 7.

wages, unemployment, low earnings, and poverty continues for this group.

The fact that most hired labor in agriculture is employed upon large scale commercial farms where the operator's income is often good has led to repeated charges of labor exploitation. To some extent, these charges may be true. However, where it is true, it is possible primarily because of the supply and demand conditions for such labor in agriculture. Most often, the earnings of farm wage workers are low because they are engaged in work in which their productivity is very low and their earnings cannot, even on the most prosperous farms, greatly exceed their marginal value productivity to the employer.

Summary

The agricultural industry has the highest proportion of low-income persons of any major industry in the United States economy, regardless of the criterion used to judge income levels. Many of the people involved have levels of living well below the minimum standards for our society.

Such persons are found both as farm operators and as farm wage workers. The highest concentration of low-income farm operators is found in the South, and it is associated with depressed areas, low capital-man ratios, low physical productivity of many of the individuals, and low-production farms. Low-income farm wage workers are found throughout agriculture, and they are not primarily working on low-production, low-income farms. They are, however, engaged in work where their physical productivity is low, and their educational levels and employment skills generally are low.

Thus the low-income problems in agriculture have common characteristics: the people involved are all poor; all are largely dependent upon labor income; and all have low productivity for any one of several reasons. They are almost always poor—but not always underpaid in an economic sense.

PART THREE

THE PROCESS OF

POLICY FORMATION

THE PUBLIC at large and, more importantly, farm people hold values as to how things ought to be in agriculture. These, together with beliefs about how things are, bring support for certain goals to be achieved via public policy. The development of public policies that will contribute to the achievement of these goals is dependent upon the political process. It is this process and the effects that it has upon the policies evolved that are the concern of this section.

To some, this brief discussion of the political processes in agriculture and the major participants in it will appear an inappropriate digression from the substance of agricultural policy. These are the persons who assert we would have no farm problems if it were not for the politicians, and therefore, that, our discussions of farm policy should be concerned only with what is economically "right." They assume that eventually politicians also will see the correct solution and adopt it.

It is my view that either to understand agricultural policy or to participate in policy formation, it is necessary to understand the process via which it is formulated. These processes are not "neutral" in that the people who form policy have beliefs, values, and power, and the distribution of this power and influence and its usage has a great deal to do with the nature of the policy that finally evolves. Changes in the processes by which policy is formed might bring as large or larger shifts in policy as would major shifts in the economic situation of agriculture or major shifts in the beliefs and values relating to the industry.

Chapter 7

The Participants—
The Congress

A discussion of political processes must contain some implicit model of political behavior. The earlier discussion of values and beliefs has pointed out that various groups within and outside agriculture have sharply different beliefs and values regarding agriculture. The model of political behavior used assumes that the primary function of the political process is the compromising of these conflicting or competing values and the discerning of the relevant beliefs in a fashion that *maximizes the satisfaction of the relevant* groups in society.[1] Such a view of the political process is a rejection of the concept that it is essentially and largely a process which derives the "national interest" or the "public good." It is the view put forth by Truman in the *Governmental Process,* which said: [2]

The second major difficulty allegedly inherent in any attempt at a group interpretation of the political process is that such an explana-

[1] The relevant groups are those who are recognized by the policy makers as claiming and having some right to be heard on the issues being decided. The composition of such groups varies depending upon the policy and the situation.

[2] David B. Truman, *The Governmental Process* (New York: Alfred A. Knopf, 1953), pp. 51–52.

185

tion inevitably must ignore some greater unity designated as society
or the state. . . .

Many of those who place particular emphasis upon this difficulty
assume explicitly or implicitly that there is an interest of the nation
as a whole, universally and invariably held and standing apart from
and superior to those of the various groups included within it. This
assumption is close to the popular dogmas of democratic government
based on the familiar notion that if only people are free and have
access to "the facts," they will all want the same thing in any political
situation. It is no derogation of democratic preferences to state that
such an assertion flies in the face of all we know of the behavior of
men in a complex society. Were it in fact true, not only the interest
group but even the political party should properly be viewed as an
abnormality.

This does not deny there are many widely shared values in our
society or widespread consensus on many issues. However, the political process whereby farm policy is made is a process involving
groups with differing values, and the policies that are produced
are reached by striking a compromise among these groups or, conversely, by a stalemate between the groups, as has been the case
in recent years.

The process which will be described is a subtle one, not usually
carried on in a fashion where its operation can be documented in
a fashion satisfying to scientists. Moreover, having participated in
it to a limited degree, the author is suspicious of some of the material available for documentation because it is like the proverbial
iceberg—more is there than can be seen. In fact, part of successful politics consists of not doing anything as long as other participants know that if you had to, you could. Thus, many political
issues are compromised without ever becoming issues because the
parties involved have a good idea of what the final outcome would
be if the issue were joined openly.

The recognition of the political process and an attempt to define the groups, their interests, and the source and extent of
their influence, constitutes neither a condemnation nor approval.
Rather it is an attempt to explain the process, to examine some
of the pressures for change in it, and to evaluate their probable
consequences for the shape of future policy.

The Farm Bloc

The Congress of the United States is the major decision-making point in public policy although, as we shall see, it is far from the only group participating in the process. Unlike foreign policy, where the executive has major initiative and discretion, farm policy has tended to be kept closely under congressional control. This is because outside groups which attempt to influence policy formation in agriculture, especially farm groups, have felt that their influence is greatest if congressional power is large relative to executive power.

Most of the history of congressional action regarding farm policy centers around the somewhat illusory "farm bloc." Most historians identify the "farm bloc" as a group of senators and representatives from farm states who banded together, without regard to party affiliation, in 1921 to evolve public policies to aid agriculture. It consisted of an alliance of Midwestern and Southern politicians who were representing constituents who shared interests in certain policies for agriculture.

The date of demise of this group is difficult to chronicle. Benedict suggests that it disintegrated in the late 1920's and certainly by the late 1930's,[3] while McCune delightfully traces its activities up to and during World War II.[4] Swerling indicates that the farm bloc finally fell apart in the mid-1950's.[5]

There is general agreement on one point by all observers. There was in both houses of Congress during the 1930's and 1940's a group whose power in those bodies was sufficient to enact a series of farm price and income policies and to prevent enactment of legislation opposed by the group. The "farm bloc" acted in concert with or at the behest of the major general farm organizations, especially the American Farm Bureau, whose rise

[3] Murray K. Benedict, *Farm Policies of the United States, 1790–1950* (New York: The Twentieth Century Fund, 1953), p. 199.

[4] Wesley McCune, *The Farm Bloc* (Garden City, New Jersey: The Country Life Press, 1943).

[5] Boris R. Swerling, "Income Insurance for Farmers—A Possible Approach," *Journal of Political Economy*, **58** (April 1959), pp. 173–86.

to power paralleled that of the bloc—or perhaps was dependent upon it.

But time, nonfarm population growth and change, and the decline of the agricultural population have now substantially reduced the number of states in which farming is the dominant or even the major source of employment. This is less true in the House where districts can be and are maintained which are predominantly rural. But in both houses of the Congress there is no longer a majority group which can be rallied as a "bloc" representing farmers.

The effects of these shifts have been slow but far-reaching in their implications for the processes of policy making in agriculture, because the processes of policy making for agriculture were largely developed in this earlier period, and the techniques for influencing policy of both the Executive Branch and of outside groups was built around the "farm bloc" technique. Major shifts in the policy-making process require major shifts in techniques of the participants and, since such changes involve shifts in the power to influence policy, they are usually painful and not easily and peacefully undergone.

The center of these shifts, as indicated, is in the two houses of Congress, so we must start with an examination of the way in which farm interests in Congress are reflected now as compared to the earlier period of the "farm bloc."

Congressional Committees and Farm Policy

All deliberative bodies, in order to function effectively, must have some division of labor and some regularized procedure for channeling their activities in a manageable fashion. In the Congress, this is accomplished primarily through the committee system, under which a series of standing committees are established to divide the labor of handling the thousands of pieces of legislation that are introduced annually. For agriculture there are two committees of importance in each house, the standing committee of each chamber which deals with agriculture and the Committee on Appropriations.

Committee assignments within the Congress are determined largely, but not exclusively, by seniority—the length of elective service of the individual member. Other factors may include an implicit understanding that certain states should be represented on certain committees and the particular attitudes of the individual involved. But, if an individual member with enough seniority desires a particular committee assignment, it is unlikely to be denied him.

Within the committee system, seniority is also important, although its influence is more subtle. Generally, there is a further division of labor with the more senior members obtaining membership upon the most important subcommittees or, at least, those most important to their constituency. Also, within the committees, the individual members are not exactly equal, with seniority again providing an important measure of the weight carried by an individual member. This is especially true of committee staffing, control of hearings, and general control of the direction taken by the committee.

Seniority, of course, depends upon one's success in elections. Therefore, the greatest seniority is found in those areas in which one or the other of the political parties is dominant for substantial periods. Since the purpose of representative government is to represent, it is only natural that an individual congressman or senator will seek assignments upon committees most likely to deal with matters of importance to his constituents. For those areas which are predominantly rural or in which farmers are an important group, this means the agricultural committees and the appropriations committees—the latter being crucial, because they allow the individual to deal, to a limited extent at least, with matters of importance to all his constituents.

Historically, the areas that have been dominated by one of the political parties have been the South and the rural areas of the Midwest. The former have been consistently Democratic and the latter, almost equally Republican. Since these areas also are areas in which rural interests are important or predominant, the composition of the committees dealing with agricultural matters is easily understood.

THE SENATE

The effect of these various factors upon the make-up of the committees dealing with agricultural policy is shown by Tables 1 and 2 which indicate the composition of the important committees in the Senate that made decisions relating to agriculture in 1962.

Table 1

Composition of Senate Committee on Agriculture and Forestry in the 87th Congress, 2nd Session

Democrats (11)	Subcommittee Assignments	Republican (6)	Subcommittee Assignments
Ellender, Louisiana, Chairman	*	Aiken, Vermont	1, 3
Johnston, South Carolina	1, 3 †	Young, North Dakota	3, 4
Holland, Florida	2,† 3	Hickenlooper, Iowa	1, 4
Eastland, Mississippi	1,† 4	Mundt, South Dakota	2, 3
Talmadge, Georgia	2, 3	Cooper, Kentucky	2, 4
Proxmire, Wisconsin	1, 3	Boggs, Delaware	1, 2
Jordan, North Carolina	3, 4 †		
Young, Ohio	2, 4		
Hart, Michigan	1, 4		
McCarthy, Minnesota	1		
Neuberger, Oregon	2		

Membership of Subcommittees:
1. On Soil Conservation and Forestry
2. On Agricultural Credit and Rural Electrification
3. On Agricultural Production, Marketing, and Stabilization of Prices
4. On Agricultural Research and General Legislation

* Ex-officio member of all subcommittees.
† Chairmen of subcommittee.

In the Senate Committee on Agriculture and Forestry, six of the eleven majority members were from the South, and five of this six are senior to all other Democrats on the committee. This shows up in the subcommittee assignments, where only one non-Southern Democrat sits on the important Subcommittee on Agricultural Production, Marketing, and Stabilization of Prices. All of the subcommittees are chaired by Southern senators as long as the Democrats control the Senate.

Table 2

Subcommittee on Department of Agriculture and Related Agencies of the Senate
Committee on Appropriations, 87th Congress, 2nd Session *

Democrats (8)	Republicans (5)
Russell, Georgia, Chairman	Young, North Dakota
Hayden, Arizona	Mundt, South Dakota
Hill, Alabama	Dworshak, Idaho
Robertson, Virginia	Hruska, Nebraska
Holland, Florida	Case, New Jersey
Stennis, Mississippi	
McGee, Wyoming	
Humphrey, Minnesota	

* Ellender, Johnston, and Aiken from the Committee on Agriculture and Forestry were ex-officio members.

The Republican membership of the committee was dominated, in numbers at least, by senators from states in which the
rural vote was relatively important. Here again membership on
the subcommittee dealing with price supports was confined to
senior members of the party.

Most farm-policy measures involve the expenditure of public
funds, so the people that allocate these funds become important.
The regional influence upon farm legislation is intensified by the
composition of the Senate Committee on Appropriations and its
Subcommittee on the Department of Agriculture and Related
Agencies. Five of the six senior Democratic members on the subcommittee were Southerners. Of the remaining three, one was an
Easterner, and one each was from Wyoming and Minnesota—
states where agriculture was important. All of the five Republicans on the subcommittee were from rural states, and four of the
five were from major wheat producing states. It also is worth noting that there was overlapping membership between the Committee on Agriculture and the Subcommittee on Appropriations,
especially among Republicans.

Of course, the Subcommittee on Appropriations is only effective as long as the total committee goes along with it. However,
there appears to be little likelihood the full committee will reverse its subcommittee since it contained, among other things, the

chairman of the full committee and five of the first nine Democratic members of the full committee. Moreover, nine of the
seventeen Democrats on the full committee were Southerners
(with seniority), and six of the ten Republicans were from the
Great Plains or Mountain States.

The picture that emerges is clear to all those who wish to influence agricultural policy, including the executive branch of the
government. First, in order to obtain approval for either substantive changes in legislation or funds to operate any public program, the program must be approved by a group of senators
heavily dominated by Southerners and those from the Great
Plains. Second, the committees are controlled by senators coming
from states which have relatively specialized farms heavily engaged in the production of crops—particularly cotton, tobacco,
sugar, and wheat. States with large numbers of dairy producers
also are represented, feed grain-livestock producers to a lesser extent.

The handling of commodity problems by those who come from
states having substantial producers' interests in the commodity is
heightened by the informal arrangements whereby the chairman
of the committee relies upon a relatively few individuals for decisions upon specific commodities. Thus, only the Southern senators on the committee really have an effective voice in determining programs for cotton and tobacco, and those from the Great
Plains, a major voice in determining wheat policy. This has the
effect of reducing the influence of committee members from the
more heavily populated consuming states in commodity policy,
except for those few commodities, such as dairy, in which their
states also are major producing areas.

Another characteristic of the senior members of both the agricultural committee and the subcommitteee on appropriations is
their relative independence from their political party. This is not
to intimate that they are not loyal party members, but merely to
point out that their position in the party and in their respective
states is strong enough so that they do not find it necessary to follow the party where they believe its policies conflict with the interests of producers which they represent. In fact, in some cases,
the national party in their states is more dependent upon their

support in presidential elections than vice versa, which may allow these senators to have an influence on national party policy greater than that implied by the population of the state.

On the other hand, the more junior Democratic senators on the agricultural committee come from states in which effective party support may be crucial to their political future. Their position on farm-policy issues is more likely to be influenced by the national party position. However, both the formal subcommittee system and informal operation of the committee tend to keep their influences upon policy to a minimum, especially upon matters affecting commodities important in the states of the other committee members.

Much has been written about the old "farm bloc," which was said to have consisted of some legislators from rural states whose collective political power was sufficient to obtain legislation desired by farmers during the 1930's and 1940's.[6] This coalition operated without regard to political parties to produce much of the basic legislation now on the books. The rapid growth of the urban population and the decline in the farm population has reduced this group. Now, in order to pass major farm legislation in the Senate, the legislation must be acceptable to senators who are primarily dependent upon nonfarm voters. Conversely, in order to change the legislation now on the books, changes either must be approved by senators representing states where the interests of producers of a few commodities are highly significant, or the legislation must be obtained by amendment on the floor of the Senate. Agricultural interests are no longer strong enough to impose their will upon the entire legislative body but, at the same time, neither the nonfarm portion of the Senate nor either political party is in a position to obtain new legislation unless it is satisfactory to the committee chairman and the senior committee members.

THE HOUSE OF REPRESENTATIVES

Many observers have commented that the House of Representatives probably now represents rural interests more than the Senate does. This is because the growth of urban populations has

[6] Benedict, *op. cit.*, p. 182.

switched the balance of power in the election of senators to urban areas in most states. House members represent much smaller geographic areas, and the determination of these areas is under the control of state legislatures, where the nonmetropolitan areas have been largely in control. The result has been congressional districts that maintain the power of the nonmetropolitan areas in the House, relative to their population, by the maintenance of rural districts with lower population than most urban districts.

The House Committee on Agriculture is larger, of course, than its Senate counterpart, but its composition was even more strongly dominated by Southern and Midwestern Great Plains representatives than the Senate committee (Table 3). Fifteen of the twenty-one Democrats on the House Committee on Agriculture were from the South, including Texas and Oklahoma. Nine of the ten senior members were Southerners. Three were from Kansas, Iowa, and Idaho. On the Republican side, ten of the fourteen committee members were from the Midwest or Great Plains.

The House committee operates formally with subcommittees organized primarily on a commodity basis. All of the subcommittees except the dairy subcommittee were chaired by Southerners. Moreover, an examination of the membership of the various commodity subcommittees shows that, with few exceptions, membership on a subcommittee was limited to those from areas where the commodity production is concentrated. An exception to this is the dairy and poultry subcommittee, but this is not surprising since the major dairy areas were not heavily represented on the committee.

The composition of the Subcommittee on Foreign Agricultural Operations is interesting. It, like two others, was chaired by Mr. Poage of Texas, and it contained five Southern and one Western Democrats, and two Eastern, one Southern, and one Midwestern Republicans. In view of the composition of this subcommittee, it is not difficult to see why administrators of our foreign agricultural operations must see that cotton and rice move well under export programs if they are to receive sympathy for broader programs.

As in the Senate, the Committee on Appropriations in the House plays a crucial role in the formulation of farm policy, with

Table 3

Composition of the House Committee on Agriculture in the 87th Congress, 2nd Session

Democrats (21)	Subcommittee Assignments *	Republicans (14)	Subcommittee Assignments *
Cooley, North Carolina	†	Hoeven, Iowa	†
Poage, Texas	1, 4,‡ 8,‡ 9 ‡	Dague, Pennsylvania	6, 9
Grant, Alabama	1, 3,‡ 5‡	Belcher, Oklahoma	1, 5, 7, 9
Gathings, Arkansas	1,‡ 5, 8	McIntire, Maine	2, 3, 9
McMillan, South Carolina	3, 5, 6, 9	Teague, California	1, 3
Abernethy, Mississippi	1, 2	Quie, Minnesota	1, 2, 4
Abbitt, Virginia	5, 6,‡ 9	Short, North Dakota	3, 4, 6, 7
Jones, Missouri	4, 7,‡ 9	May, Washington	3, 4
Hagen, California	1, 2	Latta, Ohio	4, 6, 7
Johnson, Wisconsin	2,‡ 8	Harvey, Indiana	4, 9
Bass, Tennessee	6, 7	Findley, Illinois	2, 5, 6
Jennings, Virginia	3, 4, 6	Dole, Kansas	5, 7
Matthews, Florida	3, 4, 6, 9	Beermann, Nebraska	1, 2, 5
Coad, Iowa	2, 4, 5	Reifel, South Dakota	5, 7
Breeding, Kansas	2, 4, 7, 8		
Stubblefield, Kentucky	6, 7, 8		
McSween, Louisiana	3, 5, 8		
Inouye, Hawaii	7, 9		
Harding, Idaho	3, 4, 7		
Hogan, Georgia			
Purcell, Texas			

Subcommittees on: *

1. Cotton
2. Dairy and Poultry
3. Forests
4. Livestock and Feed grains
5. Oilseeds and Rice

6. Tobacco
7. Wheat
8. Conservation and Credit
9. Foreign Agricultural Operations

  * Not all of the subcommittees are listed. Those omitted generally do not deal with price and income policy.
    † Ex-officio member of all subcommittees.
    ‡ Subcommittee chairmen.

the Subcommittee on Agricultural Appropriations the key decision point. That subcommittee consisted of four Democrats and three Republicans, and the power of its chairman, Mr. Whitten of Mississippi, in agricultural policy is second to none. Three of the four Democrats were Southerners and two of the three Republicans were from rural Midwest districts. The full committee rarely, if ever, reversed its subcommittee, perhaps because the full committee also was weighted heavily by persons representing similar areas.

Thus, in the House of Representatives, as in the Senate, the relevant decision-making group that must approve changes in agricultural policy is drawn heavily from areas in which producers' interests are predominant. The relative strength of these producers is heightened by the particular division of labor within the subcommittees, which puts the decisions almost exclusively in the hands of the parties directly interested in the welfare of specific groups of producers and their allied interests. Even more than in the Senate, the decisions for change are less subject to control of national political parties for there are few members of the House Committee representing areas in which other economic interests substantially exceed the farming and allied interests.

In the House, as in the Senate, it is probably no longer possible to get a major farm bill passed without its being acceptable to many nonfarm representatives. The redistricting following the 1960 Census will make this even more true as the relative strength of the rural areas in the House is reduced. But, at the same time, neither is it tactically possible for outside interests to obtain changes in farm policy that are unacceptable to the producers' groups that are ably represented on the committees which must approve changes in legislation.

The Effects upon Policy Formation

Talbot has shown that the power of the committees is very great over farm legislation.[7] He shows that the committees on agriculture were the crucial factors, in that bills not reported by the committee essentially were buried, while those reported were usually passed. However, he cautioned that the latter point should not be taken as an indication that what the committee wanted the committee got from its respective chamber. Instead, it marks the political skill of the chairman in judging what can be gotten from the collective body.

[7] Ross B. Talbot, "Farm Legislation in the 86th Congress," *Journal of Farm Economics*, 43 (August 1961), pp. 582–606.

This supreme power of the congressional committee is not new. In fact, it is one of the oldest observations of political scientists regarding the United States Congress. What is relatively new, insofar as agricultural policy is concerned, is that the committees have become the major possessors of power of control of changes in farm policy whereas, in earlier days, the "farm bloc" led, if not dominated, the committee action as a group over and above it.

In a sense, the larger "farm bloc" gave a unity to agricultural policy which has been lacking since its demise. The political party, which provides unity on many issues in the Congress, is not yet dominant in farm policy although its importance is increasing.

The organization and operation of the congressional committees dealing with agriculture are now such as to virtually preclude general farm legislation.[8] Instead, what is called general farm legislation tends to be a series of commodity programs acceptable to the representatives of certain areas in which the particular commodity production is important. There appears to be little or no attempt within the committees to deal with farm policy as a whole or unified policy. This is heightened by the organization and actions of the Department of Agriculture which also tends toward commodity fractionation rather than general policy.

The impact of the continued move toward the development of farm programs, which are bundles of commodity programs, is great when the policy situation is one such as is now faced. The problem is one of a general disequilibrium in agriculture, not of a temporary one in a few commodities. Quite naturally, producers of an individual commodity and their allied interests want to make as little adjustment as possible. However, resources in farm production are mobile enough so that the effect of adjustment in one commodity is likely to result in the increased output of another, which adversely affects the incomes of the second group. Therefore, the second group will not accept a program for the first unless its interests are safeguarded. Thus, unless there can be agreement among widely diverse commodity groups, there can be no general farm programs, and there are unlikely to be

[8] This trend was first noted by Charles Hardin, "The Tobacco Program: Exception or Portent," *Journal of Farm Economics,* **28** (Nov. 1946), pp. 920–38.

major changes for specific commodities if these changes would affect adversely either the producers of the commodity directly concerned or another of the commodity groups strongly represented on the committee.

It was this intra-industry dissention that contributed heavily to the defeat of the control programs proposed in the 87th Congress. Even though there was strong pressure from the Executive to maintain partisan solidarity for the control programs, party ties were not strong enough to overcome the interests of certain commodity groups and areas in avoiding production controls which would impair further expansion in a commodity or geographical area.

Even if all of the groups in agriculture were agreed sufficiently upon a single goal and a desirable policy to achieve it, it is doubtful if the policy could be approved unless that goal was accepted by a large number of nonfarm representatives as consistent with their constituents' beliefs and values regarding agriculture. This adds a new dimension to farm policy which hitherto has been lacking, for it is only recently that the power of the farmers in Congress has receded such that they need outside acquiescence to implement national policies.

However, the need for nonfarm approval to implement policy changes does not mean that nonfarm interests can now dictate farm policy in Congress. As long as farmers have permanent legislation on the books which is preferable to the alternatives upon which nonfarm groups will agree, the farm groups will be able to maintain the status quo in policy for some time. This contributes to the maintenance of a policy under which reality falls far short of the aspirations of all groups concerned. However, to bring about a major change in policy will require either a significant change in economic conditions or a complete change in the distribution of political power of the relevant decision-making groups in Congress. Attempts at the latter will be discussed in the next two chapters.

Chapter 8

The Participants—
The Executive

It might be argued that a theory of interest groups breaks down when applied to the Executive Branch of government because the President answers to the entire nation, and his allegiance to what is conceived by a majority as the national interest is necessary to hold office. However, on many issues, this often turns out to mean serving the interests of enough different groups to receive a majority of votes in the Electoral College. Moreover, in agricultural policy and most others, it is an error to consider the Executive Branch as a unified group with a single position on policy issues. Within the Executive Branch there are several groups, each pressing somewhat different and often competing interests. A major part of policy formation centers around the ability of the different interest groups within the executive, one of which is the national political party, to obtain support from and influence with Congress from other groups in society.

Few people now believe that the function of the Executive Branch rests solely with the administration of policy and that the sole function of Congress is to make policy. There are farm interest groups which say that this is how it ought to be, but their position is due to their relatively greater influence upon the relevant decision points in Congress, not to lack of recognition of executive power to influence policy.

The policy-making power of the executive comes from several sources. First, despite its desires, it is impossible for the Congress to write legislation that specifically spells out all of the necessary administrative details in a given program. Therefore, the Congress delegates a substantial discretionary authority to the program administrators which allows relatively wide policy choices to the administrators. This does not mean that Congress cannot hold administrators responsible for their discretionary action. It does mean that there are relatively broad policy actions which administrators may take without adverse reactions from Congress.

A second influence on the policy-making process is exerted by the executive in the budget-making process. The budget represents the allocation of resources among different policy objectives, and few public policies can be implemented without financial resources. Here again the Congress has major control over the final outcome, but control over the development and presentation of the budget, and over its use after approval, place important policy control in the hands of the executive. In fact, the placing of the Bureau of the Budget in the Executive Office of the President probably strengthened the power of the executive vis-à-vis Congress as much as any other single action.

Another important aspect of executive policy making is the executive influence upon program formulation. Few major policies are considered without asking the opinion of the relevant government agency regarding the effects of the program, the problems involved in administering it, and the best way in which to achieve the desired policy objective. The federal government has a vast number of technical people and persons experienced in dealing with most kinds of programs. Such persons have a substantial influence upon both policy formulation within the executive and upon the decisions of the relevant groups in Congress.

Another source of policy influence of the Executive Branch is its channels of communication which provide information regarding the probable reaction of the public to a program. Federal agencies, especially in agriculture, have large numbers of personnel widely dispersed throughout the country. These personnel often serve as a channel of communication to inform decision makers what public reaction would be to certain policies. Since one of the major rationales for the existence of farm organizations also is that of communicating farmers' opinions on policies to decision makers, there is generally a violent adverse reaction on the part of farm organizations to such activity. Nevertheless, it is one of the major ways in which the executive influences policy.

Another way in which the executive influences policy is via information (or propaganda) directed toward various groups, hoping that these groups will be convinced and inform Congress accordingly. Here again, farm organizations or interest groups tend to view the function of informing their membership as their exclusive prerogative and resist strongly attempts by government officials to use government agencies as a media of communication from the Executive Branch to the public.

Perhaps most important of all sources of power in the Executive Branch is that inherent in the power of the presidency. This includes several important facets. The President is head of his political party and, as such, has much of the power that the party can muster, including the ability to enlist the support of widely-diverse groups upon issues deemed important. The President has the power of appointment for many federal positions, including his administrative officials at the top levels of government. And above all, the President has at his disposal his veto power, which even if not actually used, can by its threatened use substantially alter policy formation in Congress.

Executive Policy and the Distribution of Power

The ways in which the Executive Branch can influence policy can be identified, but not all of these powers are centralized in one man, or even in one office, even though they all rest ultimately upon the power of the President. This power to influence agricultural policy is widely distributed within the Executive Branch, and this creates tensions within the Executive Branch and alliances between parts of it and other groups having or hoping to have power to influence policy.

Much of the executive power to influence farm policy is centered in the Department of Agriculture. As such, it is presumably under the control of the Secretary of Agriculture, although even here the control may be tenuous and, at times, completely absent.

Virtually all of the discretionary power explicitly or implicitly allowed by the Congress relating to agricultural policy is delegated to the Secretary of Agriculture. Even this is shared, however, with the President as party leader when the decisions are likely to have important political implications or with some of his other subordinates when there are nonagriculture implications which are not of prime immediate political importance.[1]

The Secretary of Agriculture has immediate and almost ultimate control over the vast personnel of the Department of Agriculture, although it is sometimes difficult to know who controls whom. That portion of the Department of Agriculture which deals with price and income programs reaches into every county and state via a network of appointed county and state committees and elected local committees. These committees, in turn, have local authority over state and county program directors and fieldmen who, nominally at least, are civil servants, although they tend to change at the state level with changes in national party control.

At the federal level the price-support programs are organized along commodity lines since most of the programs are commodity price supports. However, as has been pointed out, increased specialization by area and farm is occurring in agriculture. Thus, at the county and state level most of the employees of the Department work with the producers of only a few commodities. These state people, in turn, tend to work with their respective commodity division at the federal level. Appointments to higher levels (which are commodity divisions) in the organization usually go to people from within the system who come from areas where the commodity is important.

Since the bulk of their work and contacts are with persons having specific commodity interests, the administrators of these

[1] The discretionary power of the Secretary of Agriculture will be shared much more with the White House as leader of the political party as the role of the party in farm policy increases and as it becomes necessary to obtain urban support and approval for farm policies.

commodity price-support programs tend sooner or later to identify themselves with farmers in general and the particular commodity producers specifically. It would be ridiculous to assume that these administrators are not conscious of the commodity orientation of the congressional committees which furnish their appropriations and substantive legislation. Therefore, these administrative groups find their position most comfortable by closely relating to and working with the producer and other interest groups that have a major interest in the commodity.

It is from these lower commodity-oriented administrative groups that the Secretary of Agriculture must draw his advice as to the problems, possibilities, and consequences of changes in policy and, to a large extent, advice as to how a given policy is operating. Moreover, it is through these same channels that the Secretary must try to communicate changes in policy or desired changes in policy to the affected producers.

As a result, the Secretary of Agriculture often has his policy limits set quite narrowly in relation to specific commodities by administrators who are his subordinates. There is little he can do about it because these subordinates often have close personal and political ties with the relevant persons in the Congress and in private interest groups. Thus, we have a strong interlocking group of congressmen, administrators, and commodity interest groups whose influence over public policy is substantial and is not based upon partisan politics. In fact, partisan politics tend to reduce these groups' influence, and this threat to their power creates conflict.

The substantial power of these program administrators to influence policy both via administrative decisions and via their influence in Congress has opened new vistas of influence to private interest groups and has substantially increased the relative influence of the limited interest groups. Most private groups that want to influence farm policy now have one or more representatives who once worked at the higher administrative levels in the Department of Agriculture. These men know who makes the decision and, more than likely, know the individual personally. As we shall see, the use of executive influence is a tactic of certain types of organizations more than others for obvious reasons.

The influence of the commodity interests within the Department makes the development of consistent, comprehensive agricultural policy difficult, if not impossible, at the level of the Secretary of Agriculture. To achieve policy co-ordination requires that the Secretary have a group that answers solely to him and which attempts to perform this function.

The history of such attempts shows that nobody loves the co-ordinator. The commodity-oriented divisions of the Department resent having their direct access to the Secretary and the Congress blocked, and they will circumvent the process if not attempt to destroy it. The Congress resents the organization: first, because the congressional organization encourages nonco-ordinated programs; second, Congress wants to co-ordinate if it has to be done; finally, the general farm organizations resent policy co-ordination in hands other than their own, and the commodity interest groups resent co-ordination which reduces their influence over policy relating to their particular commodity. It was this combination of forces that led to the demise of the policy-co-ordinating function of the old Bureau of Agricultural Economics, and there is no indication that the pressures are lessened today, or are likely to be in the future.

However, not all of the policy-making power in the executive is in the hands of the Secretary of Agriculture or his subordinates. The power of budget control and review lies with the Chief Executive and so does the ultimate control over the use of the discretionary authority of the Secretary of Agriculture. Often, the Secretary or his subordinates can circumvent the executive offices and go directly to the Congress to obtain funds and legislative authority, but to do so openly is dangerous, if not foolish.

Much of the power derived from budget control is lost to the White House when the legislation provides open-end obligations for expenditures, as does most of the legislation on the books since World War II. Here again, the power of position is great because the executive has no alternative but to incur the budget expenditures as long as the legislation stands. It was for this reason that the Eisenhower administration incurred budget expenditures for price supports amounting to about $25 billion in its eight years in office, and its successors may incur even more.

The policy-making power of the veto and of political party leadership are not lost to the President, although party leadership is not a very powerful tool in dealing with the congressional committees important to farm policy. However, there is substantial evidence that party leadership may provide an increasing source of power to the President over farm policy in the future.

The increasing growth of urban populations even in the most rural states is slowly shifting many of the former one-party states into the contested column.[2] This means that farm organizations and commodity interests that have developed strong and cordial relationships with individual members of Congress on a bipartisan basis may find these legislators missing following an election and, what is worse, find out their new representative feels his interest and political future lie with wider interests than the commodity groups' interests. Moreover, the need to deliver votes other than from farm congressmen in order to achieve a change in policy means that the party influence has and will continue to increase, for it is only the party structure that is capable of developing a broad enough base to pass farm legislation at the present time.

Hadwiger has shown that partisan politics has become increasingly evident in farm policy in recent years.[3] He also cites evidence that farmers themselves are becoming less addicted to a single party and more volatile in their shifts of party allegiance. This, if true, increases the importance of farmers to both parties because in closely contested elections a shift of even a small group could determine the outcome of the election.

The increased emphasis upon partisan politics and broader views by the White House puts the Secretary of Agriculture in the increasingly uncomfortable position of a broker between several groups which do not want each other's products. On one hand, the Secretary of Agriculture owes his position to Presidential appoint-

[2] The decision of the Supreme Court of March 26, 1962, which said the federal courts could intervene in the apportionment of state legislatures may speed this trend. Since the state legislatures determine congressional districts, substantial reallocation of districts may follow. This will hasten the time when what have been safe rural districts become contested.

[3] Don F. Hadwiger, "Discussion of Trends in the Political Position of the American Farmer," *Goals and Values in Agricultural Policy* (Ames: Iowa State University Press, 1961), pp. 231–37.

ment, and it depends upon the political fortunes of party politics. On the other side, the Secretary of Agriculture has a Department largely dependent for appropriations upon congressmen not dependent upon national party fortunes and whose positions largely reflect the interests of predominantly rural areas and specific commodities. In addition, the Secretary has subordinates whose influence and ties with Congress may exceed his own and who also tend to have their interest base in specific commodities and areas. Added to all of this he must deal with a variety of organized interest groups whose aim it is to maximize their influence in the policy-making process, often at his expense. History suggests it has never been possible to perform this miracle of brokerage to everyone's satisfaction since the federal government became deeply involved in programs designed to influence the income of farmers. If anything, the task is becoming more difficult, and it probably will continue to do so until the power structure of the formal policy-making processes of government changes significantly.

An interesting example of this conflict between commodity interest, nonfarm interests, and program co-ordination, and the way in which the Department of Agriculture enlists aid in the struggle within the Executive Branch, can be seen in the development of the 1962 legislative proposals. Some farm groups and commodity interest groups were pushing through the Secretary of Agriculture for higher-income goals for farm policy, which would involve either higher food prices or larger budget expenditures or both. However, political interests at the White House level were for programs which would not increase budget expenditures or food prices. Somehow the policy proposals of the Secretary of Agriculture mysteriously found their way to a newsman who published them in detail as tentative proposals. Their publication allowed the National Farmers Union and interested commodity groups to put their weight publicly behind the Secretary, which they did by complaining that the Secretary's program was too little! [4] Thus, the news leak can become an effective weapon in the struggle for influence within the executive since it enables outside groups to enter the discussion, whereas they could not do so as long as the issues remained an open secret.

[4] *National Farmers Union Washington Newsletter*, Vol. 8, No. 40 (Dec. 22, 1961).

Proposals to Change the Policy-Making Process

Dissatisfaction with the present distribution of power to influence agricultural policy has lead to a variety of suggestions to alter the formal decision-making structure of government relating to agriculture. Each of the proposals would affect the power of one or more of the major participants in policy formation and, therefore, tends to receive support or opposition based upon who gains or loses.

One recurring proposal is that a nonpartisan board be established which has the authority to determine agricultural policy. This has been proposed by the National Grange and by some business groups.[5] The Federal Reserve Board is the model usually cited as precedent. The Grange wants such a board to consist of bona fide farmers, whereas other groups want it to include farmers, representatives of farm-oriented businesses, and consumers.

The intended purpose of such a board is to remove agricultural policy from the short-run political pressures. However, it has been pointed out that to a large extent the relevant decision-making groups in the Congress and the Department of Agriculture are not motivated primarily by partisan politics. If the proposed board were chosen from the membership of the commodity interest groups, their access to and influence over farm policy would be strengthened. If it were not, such groups would oppose it.

Neither the Congress nor the influential groups within and outside the Department of Agriculture are likely to wish to disperse their power over farm policy which they have so carefully gathered over the years. Therefore, unless they felt assured that they could control the appointments to the board, they are unlikely to want it. Nor would the President really be likely to desire such a board; in essence, such a board would be tantamount to giving away whatever budget control he now has over farm policy and all of the control he now exercises via the political party. The

[5] See *Economic Policy for American Agriculture,* a Statement on National Policy by the Research and Policy Committee of the Committee for Economic Development (Jan. 1956), p. 29.

power of appointment is important, of course, but if the appointments are for long terms—exceeding those of the person making
the appointment—even this power is not available to a newly
elected President.

Since all of the groups involved undoubtedly would prefer
more rather than less influence over farm policy, none are likely
to push the establishment of an independent board which might
appreciably reduce all of their power. While shifts in the power
base are likely and probably desirable, it is not clear that this
proposal is a desirable shift, even if it were obtainable.

An innocuous version of the agricultural policy board has
been used by the executive since 1953 as a method of trying to
strengthen executive power vis-à-vis Congress. This is the Agricultural Advisory Commission, which is appointed by the President
to advise the Secretary of Agriculture on policy matters. Actually,
the Commission is largely used as a device whereby the Secretary
of Agriculture legitimizes and seeks support for his policies. It
serves as another channel of communication from interest groups
to the Secretary and via him to the President, and it provides
another group or series of groups apart from the general farm
organizations which the executive can rally to bring pressure
upon Congress.

However, the use of an advisory commission also holds some
danger for the executive and his exercise of power for, to some
extent, the Secretary of Agriculture may become a captive of his
Advisory Commission. If the façade of Advisory Commission participation in policy decisions is to be maintained, policy issues
must be posed to the Commission as open questions. Then, if the
advisory group chooses a policy other than that chosen by the
Secretary, he faces the unpleasant choice of letting them determine policy or ignoring their advice and possibly losing their
support and influence.

Moreover, the use of appointed advisory boards increases the
danger of the Secretary losing communication with all of the
interests wanting recognition in agricultural policy. Appointments
tend to go to individuals sympathetic to the Secretary's policy
position. The advisory group then endorses the position or some
variant of it, which increases the displeasure of excluded interest

groups. Their expressed displeasure, in turn, reduces the likelihood of future representation on the Advisory Commission. To some extent, the policy advice then becomes a bilateral dialogue between groups with similar interests, and the Secretary does not actually receive the views of all of the interest groups which have access to Congress. To the extent that the advisory group consists largely of persons representing commodity interest groups, there is a tendency for the influence of these groups to be increased.

Perhaps the boldest proposal to change the decision-making structure for agricultural policy was that put forth by the new Democratic administration in early 1961. It was proposed that the Secretary of Agriculture be given almost unlimited authority to formulate agricultural policies which would become effective, unless disapproved by a majority of either house of the Congress or by farmers voting in referendum for those programs involving controls over production and marketing. At the same time, it was recommended that a national farmer advisory committee be authorized for every commodity or group of related commodities, and that these committees should be charged with responsibility for considering and recommending commodity programs.

Such a proposal, if adopted, would drastically change the relevant decision making points and the relative access and influence of different groups to these decisions. In order for either house to reject a program, it would be necessary to obtain an interest group in Congress far broader than that now represented by the agricultural committees. Essentially, the only base for such a group would be the political party; and programs could only be rejected by Congress if urban representatives chose to join with rural representatives. On the other hand, it probably would be possible to obtain a majority of nonfarm representatives to defeat a proposal unacceptable to them. Thus, congressional control over farm policy changes would move largely from the agricultural committees and their chairmen to the respective policy committees and party leaders who, of course, are much more responsive to the President as the national party leader.

The proposed change would have similar effects upon the relative influence of different interest groups in agriculture. It would tend to strengthen the position of commodity groups relative to the general farm organizations although, on balance, the power of the commodity groups might be reduced because of the decline of the agricultural committees which are the present source of their power. It might, however, increase the relative influence of a general farm organization with a relatively narrow commodity base, such as the National Farmers Union.

It should not be inferred that all of the power of the farm interest groups in Congress would disappear, for the Department of Agriculture would still be required to obtain appropriations via the route now followed. However, the executive would be in a position to barter substantive policies for appropriations, thereby increasing the relative power of the executive.

Given the relative shifts in power in agricultural policy determination that were implied in the proposal and the effect that this would have upon the effective access and influence that different groups would have, it is not surprising that the proposal did not pass. After all, the very groups that would lose power in the change were those who considered the change, and there is no evidence that any group within or outside government which has influencing policy as its rationale wants to consciously reduce its influence.

Government and Local Control over Farm Policy

The 1961 proposal still contained the feature that is unique to farm programs—it required farmer approval for programs affecting them. It also called for a strengthening of the elective committee system of program administration at the county and local level.

This feature, of elected farmers administering the programs at the local level and of requiring producer approval of programs, has been a part of farm programs since their inception. In a sense, it implies a formal relationship between farmers and the Department of Agriculture which is not implied in any other federal program. Essentially, it implies that the Department of Agriculture is the farmers' department, organized primarily to serve farmers' interests and, moreover, that locally elected farmers will be willing and able to carry out administrative policies determined at higher levels.

The first assumption appears to be valid, at least in part, partially because this is how the relevant decision makers in Congress see the Department and partially because the Department becomes largely dependent upon its locally elected administrators as channels of communication regarding the acceptance and operation of policies and the probable reaction to changes in policies.

The assumption that locally elected administrators can and will administer programs affecting their neighbors' absolute and relative income position appears questionable. In situations involving the administration of programs which are restrictive in nature, there are indications that the local committee system may not function effectively. No one has suggested that national price control and rationing programs could be effectively administered by locally elected officials, yet the assumption persists that programs in agriculture of a similar nature can be so administered.

The development of locally elected administrators came early in the New Deal and was partially the result of the necessity of enlisting large numbers of competent people to man a rapidly expanding bureaucracy. They also were the logical extension of a philosophical view of extensive national planning in which the distinction between public and private policy was distinctly blurred. The use of locally elected committees in the process was essentially an attempt to maintain a democratic base in the process of extensive central planning.[6] It essentially establishes formal channels of communication and interaction between the federal government and the program participants which are apart from private farm organizations, political parties, and other private interest groups.

The farm organizations, especially the American Farm Bureau, have recognized that the establishment of these ties could mean

[6] See Milton S. Eisenhower and Roy J. Kemmel, "Old and New in Agricultural Organization," *Farmers in a Changing World, The 1940 Yearbook of Agriculture*, pp. 1125–37; and Ellery A. Foster and Harold A. Vogel, "Cooperative Land Use Planning—A New Development in Democracy," *ibid.*, pp. 1138–56, for the philosophy behind the farmer administration of national programs.

the development of an interest group which was in competition with the farm organizations. Thus, there has been and continues to be a tension between some of the general farm organizations and the mixed bureaucracy that administers farm programs. Hardin has traced the continuing battle between the farm organizations and the administrators of the farm programs in his excellent book.[7]

The Republicans, upon obtaining control of the Executive Branch in 1953, attempted to reduce the power of the locally elected administrators in farm policy formation and execution. They substantially reduced the formal participation of local committees in program administration via the use of appointed county office managers, restricted the terms of service on local committees, prohibited the service of elected officials of farm organizations, and limited the extent to which they could work. The purposes underlying these changes may have been to obtain a more responsive local bureaucracy or to please the American Farm Bureau, which regards the locally elected administrators as a threat to their power. In any case, the changes were not taken lightly by the committee system or by the Congress, and an extensive series of charges, counter-charges, and hearings resulted. In 1954, the basic law requiring the Secretary of Agriculture to administer the programs through elected local and county committees was amended to prohibit the Secretary from imposing limitations upon the terms which a committeeman could serve.

The farmer-administrator linkage between the Department of Agriculture and local farmers in every county in the United States both increases and diminishes the policy power of the Secretary of Agriculture. It gives him power because he has, through the committee system and the power to distribute funds, access to farmers via persons identified as members of the farm interest group in a local community. It can thus be an important group through which pressure can be brought to bear on Congress, and through which support for a particular policy can be sought. Conversely, as has been pointed out, the farmer-administrator group—identifying as they do with the farmers in their communities and the

[7] Charles M. Hardin, *The Politics of Agriculture* (Glencoe, Illinois: The Free Press, 1952). See especially Chapters 8 and 9.

commodities which these farmers produce—puts sharp limits upon the policy actions of the executive.

As long as farm policy tended to be nonpartisan in character, both in the Congress and in the executive, the existence of this farmer administration was probably consistent with the predominant views as to how farm policy ought to be made—the main issues being who would speak for farmers. However, farm policy at both the congressional and executive levels is increasingly becoming partisan in character, and partisan control over this extensive system of farmer-administrators raises some new issues.

Historically, congressmen of both parties dealing with farm policy have supported the system because they viewed it as representing the same rural interests that they represented without regard to party. It is doubtful whether they will continue to so view it if it turns out that the system is being used as a national system to promote highly partisan issues which may result in their defeat. Hardin has suggested that strictly partisan activities of the local farmer committees were difficult to document,[8] but this was not saying that none existed or will exist, especially in light of the increased partisan nature of farm policy.

The issue in partisan politics really is not the danger that the local committees will use public funds to coerce farmers into supporting one or another of the political parties. It would appear to rest largely upon the use of the local committees, with their widespread local contacts, as a source of persuasion that one party's proposals for agriculture are more nearly in the interest of farmers than the other's are. In other words, should public officials at the local level engage in the propagandizing for programs largely of a partisan nature? The farm organizations say no, partially because such actions may substantially reduce their own effectiveness in farm policy.

The issue at the present time has become broader than the farmer-administrator system of the Department of Agriculture. Much of the support for the Cooperative Extension Service also is from federal funds and all of it is from public funds. Beginning with their involvement in the 1930's, the Extension Service has been increasing its educational activities on public issues, espe-

[8] Hardin, *ibid.*, pp. 149–55.

cially upon farm policy. The National Farmers Union has long been critical of this work because of the historical ties between Extension and a rival organization, the American Farm Bureau. However, these formal ties ended after much anguish and politics and, in recent years, the Grange and the Farm Bureau both question the desirability of using publically supported agencies to "educate" farmers on farm policy issues. Here again, the issue is the use of public funds to discuss issues that have become largely partisan issues.

The Future of Executive Policy Making

If this brief description of policy making in the Executive Branch of government appears less than concise, it can partly be explained as being due to the fact that farm policy making by the executive is not a precise, simple process. Historically, it has been largely carried on by the Department of Agriculture which, with its interlocking farmer-committees and relationships with the "farm bloc" in Congress, could make farm policy almost without regard to the interests of other groups in the economy.

But the "farm bloc," as such no longer exists. It has been reduced to the congressional agricultural committees which now have the power to prevent policy changes in agriculture, but not the power to achieve them. Thus, the power to achieve policy changes has shifted increasingly to the political parties, and the focal point of the party is the President.

Since the Department of Agriculture still is closely allied to commodity groups via its farmer-committeemen and still must obtain funds and substantive legislation from the sectional, commodity-oriented agricultural committees of the Congress, its role in policy making is ambivalent. On one hand it wants to represent the interests of the political party and, in fact, will have to do so in order to obtain congressional approval of major policy changes. However, such representation will be strongly resisted by the congressional committees, by the farm organizations whose power to influence farm policy rests on other than a partisan foundation and, probably, by the farmer-committeemen organization.

It is almost inevitable that the Department of Agriculture, as the federal department with the largest budget—outside of the Defense Department—will become subject to increased presidential control, and this will increase the partisan role in farm policy. No President can afford to fail to gain some measure of control over policy formulation in an area involving such major expenditures and important impacts upon resource use in the economy. To the extent the President is successful, his party conflicts with the Congress and with the outside interest groups will sharpen and, for some time at least, so will those with the Department of Agriculture.

Chapter 9

The Participants—
The Farm
Organizations

The tradition of agrarian political activity is long and significant in the United States.[1] Such activity will not be the major subject of our present discussion, however, because farmer political pressures no longer erupt in the form of agrarian revolt that once was typical. Farmers are now organized into farm organizations—at least some are—and it is these organizations that are the instruments through which farm people attempt to influence farm policy.

Farm organizations have been a favorite topic for the many writers examining pressure groups, and they have been the object of praise and condemnation by numerous political scientists and newspapermen. Apparently this keen attention is due to their success in their avowed purpose of affecting the course of democratic government. However, in recent years, none of the large

[1] Discussion of agrarian political activity and its impact on national policy can be found in Everett Edwards, "American Agriculture, the First 300 Years," *The 1940 Yearbook of Agriculture*, pp. 171–277; in DeWitt C. Wing, "Trends in National Farm Organizations," *The 1940 Yearbook of Agriculture*, pp. 941–83; in Theodore Salutos and John D. Hicks, *Agricultural Discontent in the Middle West, 1900–1939* (Madison: University of Wisconsin Press, 1951); and Grant McConnell, *The Decline of Agrarian Democracy* (Berkeley: University of California Press, 1953).

general farm organizations has been satisfied with the course of farm policy. Have farm organizations lost their power, or what has happened to everyone's favorite example of "private interest groups"?

There must be many hundreds, if not thousands, of interest groups in agriculture, ranging from local breed associations to national farm organizations. All of these have a common feature in that the membership has some shared attitudes. However, some of these organizations differentiate themselves from other such groups by making claims upon society via government; and these groups can be termed political interest groups.[2]

There are numerous farm organizations which qualify as political interest groups, and quite a few of them have been very successful in pressing their claims upon society, in large part without receiving attention. Most of the attention has been on the general farm organizations and their attempts to influence public policy.

A general farm organization is "general" in the sense that the shared attitudes of the group involve broader issues than the interests surrounding a specific commodity. This tends to widen the geographic base of the organization and, as we shall see, in the past has increased their influence. On the other hand, commodity organizations tend to include only those with shared attitudes regarding the specific commodity and, as such, have a narrower range of issues on which to make claims upon the political system.

In a complex society and an even more complex political system, such political interest groups perform a variety of roles. One, which is extremely important in the political processes of agriculture, is that of providing information to the decision makers regarding the values, beliefs, and events in the industry. It is interesting that few industries are as dependent upon technological advances provided by persons not directly engaged in the business and, at the same time, no industry has less faith in the ability of nonfarmers to judge what is happening. Thus, there is a tacit agreement by nearly everyone concerned that farmers or spokesmen for farmers are the only ones who understand the

2 Truman, *op. cit.,* p. 37.

business. Of course, part of the reason that farmers and their organizations are the accepted source of information about events on the farm is because farm organizations have told everyone this was the case for many decades in order to maintain their position, power, and reason for being.

Another function of political interest groups in agriculture is to inform the individuals at decision making points regarding the relative strength of various competing claims or conflicting values. To the politician, not interested in political defeat, this provides an idea of the consequences of alternative actions and, thus, helps him to maximize whatever political ends he has in mind.

Of course, the prime purpose of political interest groups is to obtain recognition of their claims upon government via policy action. Essentially, this means the interest group must be in a position—via pressure or other means—to influence the political process or to convince someone who makes decisions that action adverse to the wishes of the interest group will have undesirable effects for the decision maker.

The effectiveness of political interest groups depends upon several factors. A crucial factor, especially in agricultural policy, is access to the various points where the political decisions are made. Moreover, having access, the interest groups must then have influence since nearly everyone can get to see his congressman or senator. The important question is, does the policy maker listen and, if so, is he likely to believe that adverse consequences will follow for him if he fails to take the advice?

Interest groups have an advantage on the last point because they always have access to their membership via communications to convince members that a given action is or is not in their interest. Moreover, they usually also have formal or informal arrangements with other groups which may similarly persuade their membership. Therefore, part of the success of an interest group is dependent upon its ability to enlist a public beyond its own immediate interest group which will act in accordance with the interest group's views on a given subject.

A major point in the understanding of the general farm organization rests in its individual histories. Their rise to power as major interest groups came at times when they represented the major or dominant interests in the areas in which they had their membership. Moreover, after their formation, their power rested with their ability to influence the "farm bloc" in Congress, which was organized without regard to political party and, to a certain extent, without regard to the key congressional committees dealing with agriculture.[3] Thus, every biographer of the older general farm organizations points out that during their early years every general farm organization claimed to be nonpartisan or bipartisan and, recognizing that their power was largely based upon a bipartisan "bloc" in Congress, they vigorously opposed any and all attempts at partisan control of farm policy. Since executive control was more likely to mean partisan control, farm organizations also have resisted any move to enlarge the power of the executive in policy making—insisting that policy making should be an exclusive function of the Legislative Branch.

Unlike the general farm organization during the period of the "farm bloc," the commodity interest groups never had a broad enough geographical base to hope to influence farm policy as individual groups. Instead, they perceived that their greatest influence came from forming coalitions with the large general farm organizations or, in some cases, within the general farm organizations. Moreover, roughly similar factors tended to create cohesion among the big three general farm organizations, for it was obvious to each that its maximum influence was derived from a coalition of farm interests large enough to influence the entire "farm bloc" majority in Congress.

Thus, what has been recorded as the height of agricultural unity during the 1920's and 1930's probably was a unity of interest in maximizing power and influence as much or more than a unity of shared interests. A careful reading of the position taken by the major general farm organizations during the 1920's and 1930's shows that this unity was limited to those issues upon which a shared interest could clearly be obtained via compromise and was never extended to all issues. It is to be expected that when it became obvious that the individual organization's power in Congress

[3] Benedict, *op. cit.*, points out that the farm bloc had its own committees and caucuses in the early days, whose decisions often were more influential than those of the relevant formal committee.

was no longer maximized by this unity, it would largely disappear, as has been the case in the postwar period.

A striking inverse is found in the political activities of organized labor. Organized labor clearly was a minority group in the early years and, as such, consisted of a large number of individual groups that attempted to maximize their individual political influence through the political parties. However, the economic shifts and the population shifts attendant to them have put organized labor in a position approaching that of farmers in the 1920's and 1930's, in that it is learning that its maximum power probably lies in a coalition of diverse groups that operates outside the parties, much as the farm bloc did in earlier years. Since World War II, we have seen an alliance of organized labor which is at best uneasy and threatens to disintegrate, yet which is held together in large part by the promise of greater influence over public policy. Similar to the farm organizations in earlier years, labor leaders are finding it increasingly difficult to endorse political parties and party policies since there is not a clearly shared interest among local members on this point. Labor leaders also are increasingly uneasy with party discipline that forces compromises which are not always in their interests, but which are believed by party leaders to be necessary to win a majority in an election.

Returning to the farm organizations, we have already noted the changes that are taking place in the decision-making groups important in farm policy in the Congress and the Executive. This in turn implies changes in the relative influence and tactics of farm organizations.

Another part of the interest groups' success rests upon the maintenance of internal cohesion regarding various issues. As we shall see, there are a number of economic and other factors tending to make this more difficult for some organizations, thus affecting the issues which they press upon government and the views they take regarding them.

Given these elements regarding the nature and source of effectiveness of the political interest group in general, let us turn to the organizations in agriculture which are the most effective political interest groups to examine the nature of the groups, their tactics, and their problems.

The American Farm Bureau Federation

The American Farm Bureau Federation began as an organization with the avowed purpose of acting as a political interest group—namely, as an organization designed to press the demands of certain farmers and affiliated groups upon government for increased aid via the Cooperative Extension Service or county agent. The very basis of its origin meant that those starting the organization held certain beliefs and values and were largely drawn from a certain strata within agriculture.[4] This was highlighted in a keynote address at the first national meeting in 1919 at which the national organization was founded. The speaker said: [5]

It is our duty in creating this organization to avoid any policy that will align organized farmers with the radicals of other organizations. The policy should be American in every respect—a constructive organization instead of a destructive organization.

We shall organize not to fight anyone or to antagonize anyone but to cooperate and to construct, managing the affairs of agriculture in a broad business manner, following the policy that most of the ills complained of by the individual will disappear when business is done in business ways.

The Farm Bureau still regards the major purpose of the organization as action, in that it is a group "united for the purpose of analyzing their problems and formulating action to achieve educational improvement, economic opportunity, and social advancement." [6]

The Farm Bureau had a membership of 1.6 million farm families in 1961. These members were in forty-nine states (except Alaska) and Puerto Rico. The membership is not based upon particular commodity interests or geographical sections of the coun-

[4] The background of the American Farm Federation is thoroughly discussed in Orville M. Kile, *The Farm Bureau Through Three Decades* (Baltimore: The Waverly Press, 1948).

[5] Source: Kile, *op. cit.*, p. 50.

[6] "Farm Bureau Policies for 1962," *Resolutions on National Issues*, Adopted by Elected Voting Delegates in the 43rd Annual Meeting of the American Farm Bureau Federation (Chicago, Ill.: Dec. 14, 1961), p. 1.

try, although about two-thirds of its membership was in the Mid-west and in the South.

The present membership of the Farm Bureau is much wider geographically than during the period of its greatest influence over farm policy—during the 1920's and 1930's, when its membership was largely concentrated in the states represented by the "farm bloc." In fact, the Washington representative of the Farm Bureau is given credit for organizing the farm bloc, and there is little question that the organization had the major influence in directing the bloc's activities during its heyday. This alone would suffice to make the Farm Bureau what it was—the undisputed claimant as the most powerful private interest group in agriculture.

The existence of membership in every state immediately suggests that the organization's shared attitudes were not based upon commodity or sectional interests. It is argued by several authors, and not denied by the Farm Bureau, that the shared attitudes of the organization were based largely upon class interests within agriculture.[7] This merely is to say that the bulk of the membership consists of the more prosperous commercial farmers and that the attitudes of the organization were based upon a unity of interests as they are perceived by such a group.

The broad geographical base of the Farm Bureau membership and the suborganization of state and county farm bureaus explains much of the success of the organization as an interest group. Widespread membership, concentrated heavily in the rural areas of the individual states, means that the organization has access to every United States senator and to most congressmen from rural districts. Also, because the organization has within it a large number of producers of different commodities, this gives it a much broader access and influence within the commodity-oriented divisions of the Department of Agriculture. The inclusion of numerous commodity groups also increases the access of the general organization to the specialized commodity groups and to the non-

[7] McConnell, op. cit., Chapter XIII, pp. 145–57; and Wesley McCune, The Farm Bloc, op. cit., pp. 165–92. Kile, op. cit., also points out that the Farm Bureau membership was above average in size of farm and had other characteristics suggesting that they were in some sense superior farmers.

farm groups which tend to become affiliated with the specialized groups. Thus, the broad geographical and diverse commodity membership historically has provided the Farm Bureau with a power base unrivaled among farm groups and probably among all pressure groups.

However, shifts in Congress, which have increased the control over changes in farm policy of commodity-oriented congressional committees and of the political party, have created serious problems of access and cohesion for the Farm Bureau which was built upon a base dependent upon the "farm bloc" type of agricultural policy.

The historical accident of American politics is such that virtually all rural areas in the South are normally Democratic, and most rural areas outside the South generally produce a Republican majority. This was earlier recognized by the leaders of the different farm organizations, and it meant for those organizations having a wide geographic spread, the vehicle of the political parties as an instrument of policy control was difficult. Both the ability to hold together a large national organization and the access of the organization have been dependent upon avoiding an open alliance with one political party, which would prevent a shared interest with farmers allied to the opposite party.

However, in recent years, a number of rural districts that have normally been one-party districts have become marginal districts politically. This, together with certain shifts in the executive, poses a dilemma for the nonpartisan farm organization. If the political party becomes the crucial decision group for farm policy, the greatest influence in that decision process is derived by open political support for one of the parties. However, for the Farm Bureau with its wide geographical membership, to do this would pose greater problems than for the other general farm organizations.

Another change in agriculture that increases the difficulty of a truly general farm organization is the increased specialization of farms. It is much easier to maintain a shared interest and cohesion in an interest group if most of the group have some overlapping interests and problems. It is increasingly difficult if the group consists of quite specific commodity interests, some of which are in sharp conflict. Also, cohesion is much easier to maintain if the major policy objective can be one upon which all of the group agrees, such as getting a larger share for agriculture. But, if the major policy issues become that of division of an income via public action, as control programs tend to, then internal cohesion is difficult to maintain among a widely divergent group.

The problem of increased specialization of farms and areas would not present a major problem if it had not occurred simultaneously with the shift from "farm bloc" control of agricultural policy in Congress to committee and party control over policy changes. Given "farm bloc" control over farm policy, the individual commodity interests were forced to form coalitions with the general farm organization, and the general farm organization, to a large extent, could discipline its internal commodity factions in a fashion that would force them to compromise on a general policy position.

This is no longer possible. The American Farm Bureau has been forced to accept policies on tobacco, cotton, rice, and sugar that are clearly inconsistent with its policy positions relating to government controls, price fixing, and for sugar, direct payments. This has been done in order to maintain the internal cohesion necessary for the maintenance of influence, for all parties concerned know that cotton interests now have a clear independent source of power via their representation on the agricultural and appropriations committees.

Faced with such a situation, the organization can either be content to lose some of its group—and power base—or to seek or to build new shared attitudes which bridge or transcend the natural divisions that arise because of changes in the economic and political structure of agriculture. This latter appears to be the direction taken by the Farm Bureau.

In the place of shared interests on the above issues, the Farm Bureau apparently has substituted such issues as the maintenance of the relative power of state and local government (states' rights), freedom, curbing the Supreme Court, and internal security. It should be noted that these are issues which both cut across party lines and are important to those persons and areas which are dominant on the key congressional committees relating to agriculture. Some of these issues affect the power base and influence of both the farm organizations and the elected representatives of rural areas.

These particular issues chosen by the Farm Bureau also open new channels of intergroup co-operation and close old ones. Any possibility of co-operation with organized labor, if it existed, is largely removed because labor's political power rests largely upon an increase in the relative political power of urban areas.[8] The possibility of co-operation with the other two general farm organizations is also ended because they have decided, for reasons to be expanded later, that their interests lie elsewhere.

The combination of events which eroded the influence of the Farm Bureau as a major source of power on *all* farm policy should not be construed as having had a similar effect upon specific policy issues where organizational unity can be maintained. Its large, widely distributed membership is still a source of strength on farm labor issues and upon the method to be used to achieve policy goals (direct payments versus price supports). It also has a dominant membership in the major dairy and feed grain-livestock states and, thus, can block quite effectively, both in the committee and on the floor, any action deemed adverse to these commodity groups. Its power to block legislation is enhanced by its alliance with farm-oriented business groups in many nonagricultural areas.

It appears the power of the Farm Bureau relating to farm policy now largely consists of a power to prevent legislative changes on those issues where it can maintain internal cohesion and/or develop effective coalitions within or outside of agriculture. But, as an organization, it is no longer able single-handedly to dominate either the agricultural committees or the Congress via its widespread membership and, thus, has lost most of its control over positive policy formation that this influence once provided. As a result, it also has lost much of its former influence over the larger commodity interest groups.

As yet, there is no evidence that the leadership of the Farm Bureau is attempting to make the maximum possible use of the political party as a method of access and influence in farm policy

---

[8] Kile, *op. cit.*, pp. 275–76, cites one such case in which the Farm Bureau enlarged its power base by the use of urban labor groups.

making. Despite the ascension of the political party as a force in agricultural policy, the Farm Bureau is opposing this trend. Perhaps this is inevitable because of their geographical spread and the apparent aversion of Southern farmers to the Republican party. The movement toward partisan activity might mean a substantial decline in membership in some areas, even though it could mean an increase in influence in future policy formation.

The National Grange

An understanding of the background of the National Grange, or National Patrons of Husbandry, provides substantial insights into its role and power in national farm policy. The National Grange as an interest group had as its rationale from the beginning, the development of a fraternal group within agriculture. As its biographer, Charles M. Gardner, has stated: [9] "The real power of the Grange is not found in its legislative or financial accomplishments, but in the social and educational development of rural life."

The fact that its initial shared interest was fraternal rather than political power did not prevent the Grange from becoming a major force in public policy in its early years. The beginning of the organization happened to coincide with a period of major unrest among farm people regarding the dominance and tactics of nonfarm businesses. The result was a rush to the new organization during its early years that is probably unparalleled in the history of interest groups. Started in 1867, by 1873 there were Granges in all states except Nevada, Connecticut, Rhode Island, and Delaware.[10]

The "Granger" movement, as it came to be known, was perhaps the most successful of the "agrarian movements" that marked American politics from the Civil War to World War I. It is credited with the passage of numerous regulatory measures designed to control the activities of nonfarm businesses.

Riding on the crest of this movement, Grange membership

[9] Charles M. Gardner, *The Grange—Friend of the Farmer, 1867–1947* (Washington: The National Grange of the Patrons of Husbandry, 1949), p. v.
[10] Benedict, *op. cit.*, p. 95.

reached its peak in 1875 of 858,000 persons, but this fell far short of measuring the persons participating in its activities.[11] By 1880, the membership declined to 124,000, its lowest point, as those interested in its political activities drew away leaving the interest group concerned mainly with its fraternal interests.

It should be pointed out that membership in the Grange is an individual rather than a family matter, although family membership is common because of the organization's strong emphasis upon family life. This means that its comparative membership must be deflated by the average family size of the membership in order to be comparable to the membership of the Farm Bureau and the National Farmers Union, which count family membership.

The membership of the Grange has grown from its low point and now constitutes over 800,000 persons.[12] It had membership in thirty-seven states, although its membership was concentrated largely in the Northeast, Washington, and Oregon.[13] Moreover, recent gains in membership have been concentrated in the areas of strength.[14]

The basic organization of the Grange as a fraternal rather than a political interest group and its geographical concentration has lead to several characteristics in influencing agricultural policy. First, it has been and continues to remain aloof from partisan politics that are incompatible with its shared fraternal interests. Second, it has long favored individual commodity programs, allowing the commodity groups within the organization to pick their own menu.

These two characteristics of the Grange have had an interesting effect upon their relative influence in farm policy. During the

11 *Ibid.,* p. 104.

12 *1960 Summary of Legislative Policies and Programs of the National Grange,* Introduction.

13 Kile, *op. cit.,* p. 367, claims two-thirds of the Grange membership was in the Northeast in 1947. The National Grange declined to furnish this author with state membership in 1960–61.

14 Pennsylvania, New York, and Washington were the top three states having subordinate Granges qualifying for certificates for having achieved more than a 10 per cent gain in membership in the first six months of 1961. See *The Address of Herschel D. Newsom, Master,* before the 95th Annual Session of the National Grange at Worcester, Mass., Nov. 13, 1961, p. 2.

1920's and 1930's the Grange served mainly as an ally of the Farm Bureau where their interests coincided, for the Grange by itself lacked the geographic base to influence the farm bloc. Thus, the Grange, while not unimportant, was never a dominant interest group in farm policy.

However, the very characteristics that then limited the influence of the Grange have recently increased its influence. Its structure now tends to parallel the major decision groups in the key congressional committees and in the Department of Agriculture, and it can and has become a rallying point for the various commodity-oriented interest groups that see the advantage of alliance with a national organization of great prestige which will serve as their spokesman without imposing either the discipline of a political party or of the general policy position of the organization on them.

Another evidence of the rise of Grange influence in farm policy formation might be the appointment in 1961 of the State Master from North Carolina as chairman of the Agricultural Advisory Commission to the Secretary of Agriculture. Here was an individual with the dual qualifications that appeared to fit the needs of the times: from the same state as the chairman of the powerful House Agricultural Committee and from an organization which allowed the maximum expression of individual commodity group interests.

Evidence for and satisfaction with the increased influence of the Grange in farm policy matters was shown by the National Master who said in his address to the delegates: [15] "Major progress achieved during the past year arises out of the fundamental fact that an increasing number of the genuine friends of agriculture have at long last come to realize the accuracy of the Grange position these many years."

The basic organization of the National Grange as a group whose shared interests are predominantly fraternal rather than political or commodity oriented may prove its long-run weakness in influencing policy in addition to its short-run strength. For, while its fraternal interests provide a base for allowing and supporting diverse commodity programs of a nonpartisan derivation,

[15] *Op. cit.,* p. 5.

neither its history nor its background is likely to enable it to operate effectively via the political parties as an instrument of farm policy control.

As its official biographer stated: [16] "From the very beginning of the Grange its basic law has contained a stern prohibition against the discussion, in Grange meetings, of political questions, the naming of candidates, or expressing Grange endorsement of such candidates."

This nonpartisan position was reaffirmed strongly by the National Master in his 1961 address.[17]

Thus, the increasing role of the National Grange in farm policy formulation may prove to be a transitory one, much as it was during the last decades of the nineteenth century prior to the rise of the other general farm organizations. As long as commodity groups and the commodity-oriented agricultural committees are the most influential forces in farm policy, the organization that can best represent and influence these groups will be in a position of importance, if not of very much power. However, it is not power based upon trying and succeeding in co-ordinating the commodity groups' conflicting interests, instead, it is power based upon a willingness to join with commodity groups and put the fraternal-based interest group's influence behind programs upon which the coalition can agree. This power is likely to be reduced sharply when and if the commodity interest groups realize that another interest group—say the political party—offers them greater potential influence over farm policy.

The National Farmers Union

Even more than the Grange, the Farmers Union had its roots in the old stream of radical agrarian reform. Started in Texas in 1902 by a farmer organizer of one of these groups—the National Farmers Alliance—the organization spread rapidly in parts of the South and upward through the Great Plains. Its initial program was largely co-operative marketing and education, but before long it also turned to the task of influencing farm policy.

[16] Gardner, *op. cit.*, p. 337.
[17] *Op. cit.*, p. 22.

Just before the depression of the 1930's, the Farmers Union had a membership of 935,837 members, heavily concentrated up and down the Great Plains.[18] However, beginning with the depression, the organization's leadership became increasingly active in political issues, sometimes on a partisan basis, which alienated some of its membership.

From the outset, the modern Farmers Union, which dates to its change from a largely co-operative group to a militantly political interest group, has been openly hostile to the Cooperative Extension Service and the Farm Bureau. Moreover, there was increased emphasis upon the idea "that farm prices are made in Washington (D. C.)" and that political activity should have as its end the influencing of prices and the maximum control over business which dealt with farmers.

Unlike the Farm Bureau, the Farmers Union never has opposed organized labor; more often, it has joined organized labor on many issues. This was undoubtedly because both regarded themselves as minority groups at the time, whereas the Farm Bureau with its influence over the farm bloc rarely needed coalitions with labor. McCune says that the formal coalition was founded in 1941 when organized labor contributed funds to enlarge the Washington office of the Farmers Union.[19]

In 1960, the membership of the National Farmers Union amounted to about 300,000 families.[20] About three-quarters of this membership is concentrated in the Great Plains (including Wyoming and Colorado) and Minnesota, Wisconsin, and Arkansas. No other state has as many as 10,000 members, and there are few members in the Southeast and Northeast.

The geographical concentration of the Farmers Union provides it a much more closely knit interest group than either of the other farm organizations. A major portion of the membership is engaged in the production of wheat, feed grains (mostly sorghum and barley), and range livestock. Moreover, its membership is concentrated in states where farm interests still are very im-

[18] McCune, *The Farm Bloc, op. cit.,* p. 194.

[19] *Ibid.,* p. 216.

[20] Letter and material supplied by Wesley McCune, Director of Public Relations, National Farmers Union, Nov. 17, 1961.

portant, if not predominant, politically. These are also states in which the interests of organized labor and farmers do not conflict greatly, because there are few industrialized urban centers in these states, unlike the areas of heavy Farm Bureau membership.

This combination of characteristics has led the Farmers Union to use tactics of influence quite different from its rivals. It has openly entered partisan politics and has been extremely successful in influencing the Democratic party on issues relating to commodities of importance to the membership. It also has successfully pressured most Republicans from the areas where the Farmers Union membership is large to support the interest group's position in defiance of national party leadership.

Another strategy of the Farmers Union has been to concentrate its influence heavily upon the administrative structure of the Department of Agriculture, where its access via the commodity-oriented structure has been good and its influence substantial. Given its relatively narrow geographic and commodity base, the Farmers Union never had the power to influence policy for the entire "farm bloc" in Congress during the period in which the "farm bloc" was the major force in congressional policy. Therefore, the Farmers Union joined the Farm Bureau on the farm issues where their interests coincided and worked with labor unions when they did not. However, the Farmers Union has never been an advocate of nonpartisan congressional control of farm policy, probably because the leadership recognized that the organization's maximum influence lies in co-operation with other groups.

The increased emphasis of the Farmers Union upon partisan politics as a method of influencing farm policy arose first in their open support of Democratic Secretary of Agriculture Brannan, who later became counsel for the organization, for his controversial Brannan Plan in 1949. This willingness to engage in partisan politics, at a time when the other major farm organizations were professing—if not maintaining—nonpartisan positions, substantially increased the influence of the Farmers Union within the Democratic Party, and this, together with their strong base to influence certain members of the commodity-oriented congressional committees, has made the Farmers Union a significant force in influencing farm policy in the past decade.

However, like the Grange, the increased influence of the Farmers Union may prove to be transitory. The Farmers Union's strength within the Democratic party is largely based upon the fact that it has been about the only farm organization that has been trying to use the political party as a source of influence over farm policy. It is already apparent that political parties, to be successful, must have much broader interest and power bases than the sparsely settled areas in which the Farmers Union membership is concentrated and that the interests of the larger, more populous states are likely to dominate within both parties. If and when farmer interest groups in these populous states should decide to use the political party as a method of influencing farm policy, it is probable that farmer interests in the larger states—with more electoral votes and where a switch in farmer party allegiance might prove decisive—will become most important in influencing party policy relating to agriculture. In other words, farmers who will "swing" votes in the states with large electoral votes will have the major influence in party politics, much as urban minorities now have.

As yet, the Farmers Union has not been successful in obtaining substantial and stable continuing membership in the Corn Belt, the Northeast, the Southeast, or the Pacific coast states where total population and partisan political power is great and farmers might prove decisive in closely contested elections. Nor is the Farmers Union likely to make significant gains in these areas without altering some of its programs and ideals that provide much of the shared interest for the present membership. Therefore, it faces much the same problem as the other general farm organizations in that it is difficult, if not impossible, to bridge geography, commodity interests, regional interest, and political history simultaneously.

Commodity Organizations in Agriculture

It is impossible to list all of the commodity-oriented farm organizations which are playing an increasing role in farm policy. However, those organizations which were active in the 1962 legislative session are illustrative of the groups involved and their interests.

One group influential in policy pertaining to wheat was the National Association of Wheat Growers. Its president reported its membership as 79,524 in 1962, with 56,000 of the membership in Kansas.[21] None of the Eastern soft-wheat producing states are represented. However, because it has membership in those states which are represented on the committees, its views on wheat are of importance.

The National Corn Growers Association was another such organization formed in 1957. Four of its directors served on the Feed Grains Advisory Committee to the Department of Agriculture which formulated the proposed program. However, its president refused to disclose its membership to the Senate Committee.[22] However, its officers and directors were reported to be largely from Iowa and Illinois.

An older and larger organization whose influence is great on policy relating to dairy products is the National Milk Producers Federation. Representing dairy farmers who are members of dairy co-operatives in all of the states, its approval is required in order to achieve major changes in legislation relating to dairy products.

These organizations are typical of the organizations which represent growers of specific commodities. The processes of policy formation are now such that these specialized groups have as much or more influence on the policy relating to their commodity than do the general farm organizations. Unlike the general farm organizations, however, these specialized groups generally are not concerned wth a co-ordinated total farm policy but only deal with one or two closely-related commodities. This leaves the task of policy co-ordination in the hands of other groups, mostly groups within the formal governmental structure.

The Future of Farm Organizations in Farm Policy

This discussion on the process of policy formulation in agriculture assumes the process has been changing since about 1940

[21] *Hearings Before the Committee on Agriculture and Forestry, U. S. Senate, 87th Congress, 2nd Session on S. 2876*, p. 83.
[22] *Ibid*, p. 112.

and that the changes are proceeding more rapidly now than in the past. Recent developments probably will speed the change even more. Changes in the processes of policy making involve the transfer of power to influence policy, and these transfers are rarely voluntary and painless.

The major changes revolve around the changes in Congress. The political power structure of agriculture was built around the farm bloc as a majority which was effective without regard to political party. But the farm bloc as a majority no longer exists, and its former power to initiate and pass legislation is gone. What remains are the sectional commodity-oriented committees with the power to block change, but which must share the power to initiate and pass legislation with the political party. How this power is to be distributed remains the subject of substantial controversy for all groups concerned.

Within the Executive, roughly the same tensions exist. The influence of commodity-oriented groups within the Department of Agriculture has been strengthened by the increased sectional and commodity orientation of the important congressional committees, creating tensions between the Department of Agriculture and the other portions of the Executive, especially the President.

The general farm organizations which rose to power on their ability to influence the "farm bloc" in Congress have different degrees of difficulty in adjusting to changes in the political structure. The American Farm Bureau has had the greatest difficulty because of its wide geographic dispersion, and because its shared-interest base was largely that of a class of farmers rather than either commodity or fraternal. The Grange has had less difficulty because its shared interest that provides internal cohesion is fraternal more than commodity or sectional. The Farmers Union, with its relatively narrow commodity interest base, also has been successful in this transition period.

The politics of farm policy continue to be interest group politics, but the relative influence of various interest groups is shifting; and the changes can be expected to continue. As the changes occur, the influence of nonfarm interest groups—those interested in the budget cost of farm programs, program impacts upon food prices and resource use, program impacts upon foreign policy, and welfare considerations within agriculture—will rise, and the influence of both the general farm organizations and of the specialized farm interest groups will decline relative to the past or present. This is not to say that the various farm groups were never interested in those issues of prime concern to the nonfarm groups, but merely to say that the relative weights assigned these various values relating to agriculture may differ substantially between producers and nonfarm groups.

The steady march of events points to the continued ascension of the political party as a major influence in farm policy in both the executive and legislative branches of government, because it is the only "interest group" having a broad enough base to compromise the diverse interests now demanding a role in farm policy, and it is the only group with sufficient power to bring about major changes in farm policy. Moves that increase the power of the federal government will strengthen the Executive and, thus, the party, for the President is the focal point as the leader of the party.

The increasing role of the political party does not mean that farmers will have no influence in farm policy. In fact, it might mean that farmers could have an influence far greater than their numbers suggest. If the parties become convinced that farmers' party allegiance is subject to change because of farm policy, and that farmers are a crucial marginal group in many states having a close political balance, farmers might have a major influence over party policy relating to agriculture.

However, the increase in the political party as a controlling medium for farm policy is almost certainly going to reduce the power and influence of the general farm organizations. All of them are based upon shared interests which cannot maintain the internal cohesion of the group on a national base. The role of the specialized commodity groups seems likely to increase at the same time, for the shared interests of the commodity producers may be sufficient to allow their leadership and the group to switch (or threaten to switch) party allegiance in order to influence party policies, and to allow the open endorsement of party candidates.

Essentially, it must be concluded that the time has passed when a national general farm organization can be the major determinant of farm policy, unless the organization can find a way to form a shared interest among its members that overrides their other interests. No national interest group outside of agriculture appears to have been successful in its quest to build an interest group that can override the national political parties as channels for policy determination in their industries. Those that have had that power for agricultural policy will fight vigorously to maintain it, but they appear almost sure to lose.

PART FOUR

POTENTIALS AND OBSTACLES OF SELECTED POLICY ALTERNATIVES

I̲N̲ PART TWO, three major interrelated economic problems of United States agriculture were discussed. They were: (1) the problem of substantial and sustained disequilibrium in agriculture, resulting in lower earnings for resources in agriculture than elsewhere in the economy; (2) the problem of instability and uncertainty facing agricultural producers; and (3) the problem of large numbers of persons in agriculture who not only obtain low returns for the resources they use in producing farm products, but who also have so few resources that their total income is below what is generally considered minimum standards in our society. The operators of the approximately 800 thousand largest commercial farms, which produce nearly three-fourths of our farm products, are faced primarily with the first two problems, although, where these operators are tenants or operators with low equity, most of the resources may be owned by someone else who receives most of the income. Except for part-time farmers, largely dependent on and earning satisfactory incomes in other industries, most of the other persons engaged in agriculture are afflicted by all three problems.

The problems are not new, nor have they gone unrecognized by economists, farm leaders, and policy makers. To some extent, the nature of the problems has changed over time, and, as pointed out in the immediately preceding section, the political power structure which formulates farm policies is changing. However, certain elements contributing to our farm problems are now better identified than in the past, especially those relating to the continuing disequilibrium in factor earnings in agriculture.

Given these essentials—the beliefs, values, and goals for agriculture; the economic characteristics which create a gap between aspirations and reality; and the groups which are intimately involved in policy formation—what are the policy directions preferred by different groups and why? An almost unlimited number of policies and programs can be and have been devised and proposed. Despite the multiplicity of proposals, it is possible to classify them into several broad categories. Since many of the proposals affect more than a single facet of the farm problem, it is generally necessary to discuss each proposal in light of the disequilibrium, the stability, and the poverty problem. The chapters that follow do so, and then the economic and other implications of the various proposals are discussed.

Chapter 10

The Market As a Solution to the Farm Problems

The United States economy has been and continues to be an economy that is largely market oriented; that is, market prices are the primary determinant of resource allocations and returns to these resources in the economy. This is true despite numerous examples to the contrary, the most numerous being the variety of services provided by all levels of government.

There are several reasons, relating to the values discussed earlier, for this continued preference for the market economy. First, the market system is an extremely efficient (inexpensive) way of transmitting information regarding individual and aggregate wants and preferences of consumers to resource owners in the economy, assuming that resource owners are in a position to act on the information they receive. Even planned economies usually find that some sort of a price system is the easiest way to transmit orders regarding resource use to local managers. Second, the market system avoids direct outside intervention in the affairs of the owner of the resources and gives him discretion as to their usage, albeit at a cost. Third, the rate of reward under the market system is dependent upon consumers' estimates of the contribution of marginal output to their total satisfaction, and while the income distribution forthcoming may not be consistent with values relating to equal opportunity, it is consistent with values relating to total contribution, as long as contribution is measured via consumer preferences for goods in the market.

For these and other reasons to be covered later, the market operating with a minimum of direct government intervention is a policy in agriculture preferred by a number of groups, including the American Farm Bureau Federation, many consumer groups, and many nonfarm business groups. Since most of the other policy proposals would use the power of government to alter the functioning of the market in some fashion, it appears appropriate to start an examination of various policy proposals by examining a return to the market economy as a solution to farm problems.

The Market As a Solution to the Disequilibrium Problem

It is desirable to review the concept of equilibrium in agriculture and its relationship to the values of society. In the context used herein, equilibrium in agriculture would be achieved when the quantity of resources engaged in producing farm products was such that the output of those resources would produce returns to the resources equal to their acquisition costs. In this equilibrium situation, rates of reward for resources (including human effort) producing farm products would be equivalent to the rates of reward for comparable resources elsewhere. Assuming that other industries met the same conditions, at this point total output in the economy (as measured by consumer satisfaction) would be maximized.

Disequilibrium is indicated by either of two occurrences: (1) a rate of return for one or more resources that is significantly below (or above) the return for comparable resources elsewhere in the economy; (2) output levels that exceed (or fall short of) the quantities which consumers will take at market prices and that will produce comparable resource returns. In agriculture, the disequilibrium is evidenced by low returns to productive resources producing farm products (especially labor) and, when market prices are supported to maintain incomes, output in excess of that which will clear the market (surpluses).

The disequilibrium problem in United States agriculture has arisen and persisted because of the simultaneous existence of several economic conditions in agriculture. They are: (1) a relatively low price elasticity for farm products; (2) a relatively slow growth in demand for farm products; (3) a high degree of uncertainty regarding future economic and technical change, together with rapid output-increasing changes; (4) the competitive structure of the industry, which inhibits the ability of the industry to handle its adjustment problems; and (5) asset fixity in agriculture so that resources committed to producing farm products continue in production despite earnings which may fall well below the expected earnings and acquisition costs.

There are two basic issues involved in the discussion of the use of market prices as a policy to solve the disequilibrium problem in agriculture. One is the extent of disequilibrium that would exist if the present intervention in the market for farm products (via price-support programs) was ended. The second is whether, in the absence of intervention, equilibrium levels of resource use and earnings can be achieved and sustained. Advocates of the market as a policy for agriculture assume that the current disequilibrium is small and largely due to the government intervention in the market. They also assume that equilibrium would be reached rapidly and sustained without government intervention.

THE EXTENT OF THE DISEQUILIBRIUM

Most of those individuals who have pressed for a removal of government market intervention have argued that the gap between the equilibrium price and the market price that would exist without government intervention is not large. This was the position taken by a group of economists writing for the Twentieth Century Fund and by the Committee for Economic Development in 1956.[1] This was the implicit assumption of the Republican ad-

1 See Murray B. Benedict, *Can We Solve the Farm Problem?* (New York: The Twentieth Century Fund, 1945); and *Economic Policy for American Agriculture*, "A Statement on National Policy by the Research and Policy Committee of the Committee for Economic Development" (Jan. 1956).

ministration from 1953 to 1960 and was implied in the position of the American Farm Bureau Federation during the mid-1950's. It usually was argued that the intervention of the government programs, by attracting too many resources into agriculture, was the main factor accounting for the observed disequilibrium in output at support prices. However, as the analysis in Chapter 4 shows, it is possible in a dynamic industry with a high degree of uncertainty to get additional resources entering the industry, even though some of the existing resources are earning and will continue to earn less than equilibrium returns (acquisition prices).

Several statistical studies of the level of farm prices and incomes that would prevail in the absence of price supports suggested that the gap between short-run market prices and equilibrium prices would be very large.[2]

Some of the key estimates from one of these studies are shown in Table 1. It was estimated that prices received by farmers for all farm products would decline by about one-fifth from 1957–59 average levels and that the net income of farm operators from farming would decline by more than one-third. The greatest price declines would occur among field crops, especially wheat, where producers' gross incomes would be reduced by one-half or more. The price and income declines for livestock producers would be less because of the relatively higher price elasticity of these products. Even so, the price reductions would more than offset increases in volume, so that gross income from livestock would decline.

A reduction in the price and income levels in agriculture of the magnitude envisioned in these estimates would result in a substantial revaluation of the capital assets in agriculture. The probable magnitude of this capital loss is impossible to estimate, be-

[2] *Report from the United States Department of Agriculture and a Statement from the Land-Grant Colleges IRM 1 Advisory Committee on Farm Price and Income Projections 1960–65,* Senate Document 77, 86th Congress, 2nd Session (Jan. 20, 1960); "Materials Prepared for the Joint Economic Committee, 86th Congress, 2nd Session, Washington," *Economic Policies for Agriculture in the 1960's* (1960); W. A. Cromarty, "Free Market Price Projections Based on a Formal Econometric Model," *Journal of Farm Economics,* 43 (May 1961), pp. 365–78; Arnold Paulsen and Don Kaldor, "Methods, Assumptions and Results of Free Market Projections for the Livestock and Feed Economy," *Journal of Farm Economics,* 43 (May 1961), pp. 357–64.

Table 1

Selected Price and Income Variables Projected for 1965 in the Absence
of Price Supports and Production Controls

Item	1957–1959 Average	Projected 1965
	(1)	(2)
	Dollars	
Prices:		
Cattle, per cwt.	20.60	17.08
Hogs, per cwt.	17.30	10.95
Milk, wholesale, per cwt.	4.19	3.67
Corn, bu.	1.10	.77
Wheat, bu.	1.84	.87
Soybeans, bu.	2.09	1.35
Rice, cwt.	4.87	3.49
Cotton, lb.	.31	.21
Total cash receipts from farm marketings, million	32,227	30,857
Total other income, million	4,966	3,737
Realized net income of farm operators from farming, million	12,215	7,202

Source: Col. I: U.S.D.A. statistics; Col. 2: *Economic Policies for American Agriculture, op. cit.,*
Tables 6 and 7.

cause there has been no comparable decline in the postwar period.
In the period 1920–23, when there was a substantial postwar adjustment of farm prices and incomes, the book value of real assets
in agriculture declined by some $21 billion, which amounted to
about one-fourth of the current value at that time. However, if
one capitalizes the $3 billion to $4 billion of the present income
stream to agriculture which seems to rest on government programs at 5 per cent, it appears that a complete abandonment of
government income support in agriculture might reduce the book
value of physical assets in agriculture by some $60 billion to $80
billion. This would represent a rather severe blow to those farmers who have invested their savings in farm real estate.

An observation is needed regarding these market price estimates. Most of them implicitly assumed that the productive resources in agriculture were fixed for the time period involved,
except for the Cromarty model, which contained an endogenous
supply function based upon historical statistics. Thus, the prices

that were projected were market-clearing prices, assuming that all of the resources in agriculture in the late 1950's had no salvage value elsewhere and that there would be no outmovement. This probably was a reasonable assumption for the short-run periods involved, but it does not follow that these projected price levels would persist indefinitely in a full-employment economy.

On the basis of these several statistical studies and other evidence relating to the immobility of resources out of agriculture, there appears to be little question that an abrupt return to a market economy for agriculture would generate prices and resource earnings well below current or recent levels and well below equilibrium levels. Whereas some farm organizations earlier took the position that the disequilibrium was small and a return to the market economy could be absorbed relatively painlessly, no major farm organization now pushes this view. Each farm organization has a different approach to the situation, but none now recommends a return to a market economy without some device (usually land retirement) to reduce output or otherwise mitigate the income declines that would be forthcoming.

Businessmen in rural areas are highly conscious of the sensitivity of farmers' consumption and investment expenditures to changes in farm income. Thus they also press for measures that will prevent declines in farm income. Since these two groups—farmers and businessmen in predominantly rural areas—are the majority of constituents in areas represented in the congressional committees on agriculture, it appears unlikely that an abrupt return to a market economy will become a policy for United States agriculture in the foreseeable future, despite the preference for such a policy among certain groups.

There are persons and organizations that press for an immediate return to a market economy for agriculture. A substantial, and perhaps growing number of nonfarm people believe that earnings in agriculture are not significantly lower than elsewhere in the economy; that the magnitude of the disequilibrium of resources producing farm products is not great; and, moreover, that it is due solely to government intervention in agriculture. These groups also assume that because agriculture is a "competitive" industry, the adjustment to equilibrium price and earnings would be relatively quick and painless. Therefore, they suggest that the disequilibrium problem in agriculture would be solved quickly and easily by an abrupt return to a market economy for agriculture. Many general economists, bankers, urban businessmen, and professional men appear to be in this group. However, even during the eight years of the Republican administration, when such persons were well represented in policy positions, this view was not accepted by the Congress. It is unlikely to be accepted soon, except for commodities where producers prefer no price supports to stricter production controls.

A second group consists of those who believe the present disequilibrium is large and that an abrupt return to a market economy involves painful adjustments. However, they also believe that the past and present price-support programs have been responsible for part of the current disequilibrium level of excessive resources in agriculture. Therefore, they suggest a return to market prices to guide present and future resource allocation and then suggest various programs to cushion the effects of the short-run income declines that would result. This is the position taken by the Committee for Economic Development in their 1962 policy statement on agriculture.[3]

Despite these nonfarm dissenters, there is a growing consensus among farm groups that the disequilibrium in United States agriculture is large and that an abrupt return to a market economy would increase it. Of crucial importance for policy purposes is the apparent acceptance of this belief by all of the important decision makers in national policy, including the congressional committees dealing with agriculture. This, together with its belated acceptance by the largest general farm organization, suggests that an abrupt return to a market economy for agriculture is not likely, despite the growing discontent among nonfarm groups with the costs of programs to prevent the disequilibrium from falling completely upon farm prices and incomes.

CHRONIC DISEQUILIBRIUM IN AGRICULTURE

While there appears to be substantial consensus among farm policy makers that the current disequilibrium in agriculture is

[3] *An Adaptive Program for American Agriculture,* "A Statement on National Policy by the Research and Policy Committee of the Committee for Economic Development" (New York: Committee for Economic Development, July 1962).

large, no such consensus appears on the more fundamental issue. This is whether if once an equilibrium were attained in agriculture it would be maintained in a market economy, or whether a substantial and chronic disequilibrium would reoccur.

On this issue there is no agreement among agricultural economists, whereas there is agreement on the size of the current disequilibrium. Cochrane assumes that a substantial disequilibrium would reappear and persist even though, as pointed out in Chapter 4, his mechanism to rationalize such behavior appears inadequate. However, as pointed out in Chapters 4 and 5, if the five conditions postulated for agriculture do exist simultaneously, then a chronic disequilibrium is not only possible, *but probable*. Its magnitude will depend upon the frequency and rate at which economic and technical changes occur and upon the extent of fixity of resources in agriculture.

Expressions by economists that the observed disequilibrium in agriculture is temporary run through most policy pronouncements of the past decade.[4] Initially, it was argued that the disequilibrium was in wheat production and perhaps cotton. Then it was argued the problem was transferred to feed grains via acreage allotments for wheat. Since the late 1950's, there has been a reluctant swing toward acceptance of the assumption that the disequilibrium may be large and general in agriculture, but only a minority have accepted the view that it is inherent in the economic structure of agriculture operating in the market economy.

Virtually all of the groups involved in policy formation assume that if the current disequilibrium in agriculture could be removed, then the disequilibrium problem in agriculture would be solved. With the possible exception of the National Farmers Union, none of the major farm organizations has accepted the view that the market economy will not maintain equilibrium resource earnings in agriculture even if once achieved or that subsequent disequilibrium might appear, in the absence of public action, which might be as large as the present one.

[4] As examples, see Murray B. Benedict, *Can We Solve the Farm Problem?, op. cit.;* Boris C. Swerling, "Income Protection for Farmers: A Possible Approach," *Journal of Political Economy, op. cit.;* Boris C. Swerling, "Positive Policies for American Agriculture," *Goals and Values in Agricultural Policy* (Ames: Iowa State University Press, 1961); and "Discussion" of above by J. Carroll Bottum, *ibid.,* pp. 335–37.

The belated discovery in the mid-1950's by the Congress and the Executive that the disequilibrium was large, did not represent an acceptance that it was other than temporary. This belief explains the reoccurring fascination of Congress and most economists with temporary programs of land retirement, which implicitly assume that if the current disequilibrium could be handled, there would be no long-run problem.

The almost exclusive concentration of policy on piecemeal commodity programs is also a reflection of the belief on the part of congressional policy makers that if the temporary disequilibrium in a few commodities can be solved, there would be no long-run problems. This, plus the commodity orientation of the congressional committees, has contributed to the passage of a series of temporary programs to reduce wheat, cotton, and feed-grain production, without the development of a program that encompasses the total problem of excessive resources in agriculture.

For three decades most economists and virtually all policy makers in agriculture have implicitly assumed that the market economy would produce an equilibrium in agriculture if the problems of short-run disequilibrium induced by depressions and wars could be handled. Thus, our policies have been of a nature to prevent short-run disequilibriums or to make their existence tolerable to farmers. It has been assumed that such temporary problems could be solved largely within the industry. It now appears that the agricultural industry will not maintain an equilibrium adjustment in resource use (and earnings) even if we are blessed by peace and prosperity. This will make the policy choices in agriculture more difficult than they hitherto have been, for policies which will deal effectively with a chronic disequilibrium problem are not those that will satisfy all of the values relating to agriculture.

The major battles in agricultural policy in the future will be over this issue. This will be true among both professional economists and makers of political policy. Among professional economists the issues will be: (1) will agriculture suffer from chronic disequilibrium in the market economy and (2) if so, what are the probable impacts of various policies to either reduce the tendency to chronic disequilibrium or keep it within "acceptable" levels? It is assumed herein that the answer to the first question is affirmative, therefore, the remaining chapters are devoted partially to a discussion of the second question.

Policy makers also will have to answer these same questions. They will depend heavily upon economists for the answer to the first, although they will be difficult to convince that the answer is affirmative. Policy makers will be forced to answer the second question in a broader context than generally used by economists, because the policies that are followed affect not only values, but also may change the political power of the policy makers themselves.

The Market and Instability in Agriculture

In Chapter 5, it was pointed out that the nature of the stability problem in agriculture is changing. The relationship between nonfarm employment cycles and disposable consumer income is much weaker, and the income elasticity for farm products is declining. The relationship between nonfarm employment cycles and nonfarm income of farm people is increasing, and, at the same time, the importance of nonfarm input prices in farm costs is increasing. Uncertainty from weather and other natural phenomena appears to be decreasing, and short-run uncertainty regarding the price to be received for many products has been removed by the development of price and risk-sharing contracts.

These changes in the structure of the nonfarm economy do not mean that the agricultural economy will be completely free of the problems of short-run shifts in the demand for farm products in the absence of public intervention. Part of the observed decline in income variation has been due to government action to remove the instability arising from changes in export demand, and there is no indication that stability in this area would occur in the absence of public policy of some type.

Also there are indications that the price elasticity for farm products has been drifting downward. This suggests that in the absence of some price or income stabilization measures, fluctuations in prices and incomes in agriculture due to unplanned shifts in output or aggregate demand might be even greater than in the past. There appears to be virtual unanimity on this issue, for no major farm organization, no policy maker, and few agricultural economists suggest a complete abandonment of public measures to stabilize farm prices and incomes or to help farmers deal with instability. The Farm Bureau would maintain price supports based upon the average of some past years, thereby suggesting a belief that the market economy can handle the aggregate disequilibrium problem, but not the short-run stability problem. Swerling makes the same assumptions, but he suggests income insurance to deal with the short-run fluctuations in income. Most suggestions are for extensions of such extra-market policy devices as marketing orders, marketing agreements, stabilization pools, and diversion schemes to deal with the problems of short-run stabilization of farmers' prices and incomes. The danger now appears that such devices, which may be appropriate to handling short-run stability problems, will be tried as solutions to the basic disequilibrium problem.

There apparently has been a substantial improvement in the capital market in agriculture, perhaps in part because of the public measures which have reduced the short-run price and income fluctuations, perhaps in part due to the public policies specifically designed to provide farmers with better access to capital and credit. In any case, there is no evidence of great pressures for either major additional public action in the credit area or for major reduction or removals of those now existing.

A part of the public action to reduce uncertainty facing farmers has been the development of extensive research and information programs on annual outlook for farm product prices. These programs were developed when changes in domestic employment and income caused major shifts in the demand for farm products and when forward price contracts for farm products were virtually unknown. Such programs have received and continue to receive the general support of the farm organizations and farm policy makers. The conditions upon which these programs have focused in the past have changed. The continuation of such programs is not questioned, but the appropriate focus of their attention is open to question. The improvement of outlook programs to help farmers deal with their major problems of instability and uncertainty will be discussed later.

Despite the observed decline in farm price and the income instability of the postwar period, there is general agreement that a variety of public policies is needed to supplement the market. There appears to be little controversy on this point, either within agriculture or elsewhere. Most of the recent discussion has been on the most appropriate device to achieve short-run stability and has not been on whether such policies are needed. There appears little reason to expect a change in this regard.

The Market As a Solution to the Poverty Problem

In this problem area, perhaps more than any other in agriculture, our historical policy has been that of nonintervention in the market economy, and policy proposals that deviate sharply from the market economy to reduce rural poverty have been and continue to be among the most controversial in agriculture.

The continued dependence upon the market as a solution to the poverty problem in agriculture is rooted both in our value system and in the political power structure in agriculture. Several values are involved. One is the value that an individual's reward should be related to his contribution to total output. A second is that there should be no outside interference with the operation of individual enterprises. A third is that there should be no outside interference with local political decisions.

There are a series of closely-related beliefs that also are important in this context. They are: (1) that an individual's assets (including personal education and skills) are largely the result of his past effort or contribution to output, and (2) that the unsupplemented market economy affords equal opportunity to all individuals in it.

These values and beliefs are important, because they predominate among many of those individuals who control or influence congressional policy decisions in agriculture. The agricultural committees in Congress are largely controlled by Southerners and by individuals from the Midwest where commercial farms are dominant. In the South, rural poverty is heavily concentrated among nonwhites. Outside the South, it is concentrated among the farm laborers. Neither group is effective politically with the members of Congress which control the agricultural committees.

None of the farm organizations draws any significant portion of its membership from the very low-income groups in agriculture. In fact, with the possible exception of the Farmers Union, the membership of the farm organizations is composed largely of farmers having the beliefs and values just described. As a result, there has been little pressure from farm organizations for policies to deal with the poverty problems in agriculture, and, at times, there has been and continues to be strong opposition to policies designed to deal with these problems.

The first federal program aimed largely at the alleviation of rural poverty was the Rural Rehabilitation Program that was incorporated into the Farm Security Administration when the latter was established in the mid-1930's. The attacks upon these programs, led by the Farm Bureau, resulted in the abolition of the agency and the demise of the programs.[5] The concern of the Bureau of Agricultural Economics with the poverty problems of nonwhite Southern farmers and the indication that many of the Bureau's researchers did not share the values and beliefs of the controlling political forces in agriculture resulted in substantial budget cuts for that agency during the 1940's. Charles Hardin has chronicled that battle and its issues carefully in his article "The Bureau of Agricultural Economics under Fire: A Study of Valuation Conflicts." [6]

As a result of these and similar experiences, there was little enthusiasm in the postwar period among members of the Department of Agriculture to develop and push policies to support or supplement the market economy in dealing with the poverty problem. In 1954, the Republican administration presented its Rural Development Program, which offered mild and innocuous supplements to the market—largely via educational programs to enable low-income areas to better evaluate their opportunities. They assumed that this information would enable the low-income areas to redress their personal and community income disadvantages via the market economy. Even this modest program was

[5] See Grant McConnell, *The Decline of Agrarian Democracy, op. cit.*, for a discussion of this battle and the issues involved.

[6] *Journal of Farm Economics,* **38** (Aug. 1946), pp. 635–68.

viewed suspiciously by Southern congressmen and the Farm Bureau and, as a result, never received any substantial funds.

Perhaps the most interesting and explosive policy issue relating to the poverty problem in agriculture has been the attempt of
the Secretary of Labor—starting with the Republican administration in the late 1950's—to use administrative authority to
establish certain minimum standards relating to the employment
and living conditions of migrant agricultural workers. Legislation to clearly establish the authority of the Secretary of Labor
in this area probably would have to pass the agricultural committee, which is impossible, but his appropriation and normal
substantive legislation are not handled by the agriculture committees. Therefore, the Secretary of Labor has been able to use
his administrative authority to raise housing and wage standards
for migrant workers, despite the violent objection of the Farm
Bureau and many rural representatives.

Even though rural areas contain the largest absolute and relative numbers of low-income population and generalized low-
income areas, most of the rural congressmen and the Farm Bureau
opposed the development of federal programs designed to deal
with these problems. The National Grange has never vigorously
pushed for such policies, and only the Farmers Union among the
farm organizations has consistently pushed for federal programs
to deal with the low-income problems in agriculture.

The Area Redevelopment Act, passed in 1961, is the first major
program aimed specifically at the problem of general low-income
areas. It was passed by urban representatives—in spite of, not
because of rural support—who were faced with problems of low
incomes and structural unemployment in urbanized areas. In
their 1962 resolutions, the Farm Bureau said: [7]

The Area Redevelopment Program, authorized by the Area Redevelopment Act (Depressed Areas Act), is designed to deal with
chronic underdevelopment situations. It is applicable to designated
urban and rural areas. . . .
We believe it is the primary responsibility of the people in an area
to develop their own resources. If the federal agencies move in to

[7] Op. cit., p. 47.

dominate this program it will discourage efforts of communities to help themselves. . . .

We doubt that federal expenditures of funds for rural development is a desirable or effective means of accomplishing this objective. We do not favor extension of the authorization for such expenditures.

A related policy area is federal aid to education, and the battle lines are roughly similar, although the issues are somewhat more complex. In this case, values regarding racial equality, and beliefs that federal programs would impose national values on racial issues are involved; values regarding local political control, and beliefs that federal aid would involve federal controls and standards are involved; and issues involving the balance of political power between rural and urban areas are involved.

Public policies to deal with the poverty problem in agriculture are likely to increase, and the value problems and political conflict consequently will increase. There is growing acceptance of the belief that equal opportunity in our society must include some minimum level of income or consumption. Also there is widespread feeling that equal opportunity is not meaningful unless everyone has some minimum level of education (in both quantity and quality) and skills; some minimum level of knowledge about employment opportunities; and unless there are some minimum prescribed rules regarding employment conditions and wage levels and some alternative economic opportunities. Public programs to insure these minimums will involve providing some individuals with incomes or prerequisites not related to their current output. It may involve outside prescription of minimum standards for many individual enterprises and, perhaps, political control over the determination and enforcement of these standards by other than local and state units. Therefore, if public policies are required to insure equal opportunity, these policies will undoubtedly reduce the attainment of other values by some persons.

THE EQUALIZATION OF INCOME AND ASSET DISTRIBUTION UNDER THE MARKET

The poverty problem in agriculture is not only that the people concerned are underpaid, but that they have so few resources—

human and otherwise—to sell. Moreover, many of them face a market situation where there is chronic underemployment of the resources they have. Will the market, without public intervention, operate in a fashion so that such individuals will gain relative to other groups over time, or will it operate so that their disadvantage is increased?

For those farm people whose low productivity and income is due to advanced age, or a combination of advanced age and little education, the answer is clear. The market will not operate in a way to increase their relative income nor will it provide them with new skills or education for obvious reasons.[8] This was recognized by the inclusion of farmers in the Social Security program in 1955, with special provisions favoring low-income farmers and the aged.

What about individuals in the generalized low-income farm areas, primarily in the South? Will the market economy, through outmigration of people and inmigration of capital, tend to improve the relative position of such individuals? Could they, as some suggest, if it were not for a strong preference for indolence and fishing, easily find employment which would substantially raise their income levels?

Research on this matter is growing, and the results suggest the answer is no. Probably the most comprehensive examination of the question has been by Nicholls and his colleagues in their project on Southern Economic Development and Agriculture. Nicholls' conclusions were about as follows: [9]

1. The wealthier industrialized counties studied had a much higher rate of capital formation than did the poorer counties, so that their capital advantage increased over time.
2. The industrialized counties had a relatively greater capital investment in the human agent, reflected in school attendance and median years of school completed, so that the relative advantage of people living in the wealthier counties increased in this respect.

[8] See Burton A. Weisbrod, "The Valuation of Human Capital," *Journal of Political Economy*, 64 (Oct. 1961), which points out how the value of human capital declines with advancing age.

[9] William H. Nicholls, "Industrialization, Factor Markets, and Economic Development," *Journal of Political Economy*, 49 (Aug. 1961).

3. Despite continued higher outmigration rates, the poorer counties were unable to equalize labor returns between the two areas during the past two decades, although there is evidence that differential outmigration had done so prior to 1900.

Nicholls' conclusion was: [10] "Finally, particularly for those areas which lack the attributes required for sound industrialization, public policy must provide for facilitating farm-labor and farm-capital mobility at rates far in excess of those which can be expected under complete laissez faire."

His results and conclusions are not surprising. Capital is attracted to growing, not poor or declining communities, and, moreover, higher incomes make easier the accumulation of a given absolute quantity of capital. What are irritating tax loads in wealthy communities—farm or city—to provide schools, roads, libraries, and health facilities which produce productive human beings, are impossible tax loads in poor communities. Income currently foregone and educational expenditures for school attendance of children in some families means foregoing desirable extras. For very poor families, it means foregoing what are generally regarded as essentials.

Our belief that the market economy, through trade, would not produce an equilibrating rate of economic growth in poor countries has led us to adopt an extensive policy of international aid programs. Similar beliefs, founded in fact, have led us to embark on policies to supplement the market economy in solving the problems of low-income individuals in our own economy. These have included the Area Redevelopment Act in 1961 and the Manpower Retraining Act in 1962. The former provides capital for private and public facilities and modest training programs for workers. The latter envisions a more extensive training program to provide marketable skills to individuals whose current productivity and income are low because of inadequate skills. Neither involves any appreciable competition with existing values, but other policy proposals would.

In the case of hired farm workers, particularly the migrants, the market economy may provide even less of a solution to their

10 *Ibid.*, p. 340.

low-income problem than for low-income farm operator families. This is a group whose financial assets are very small, and given the low returns to labor generally in agriculture, the industry offers them little opportunity to acquire income-producing assets. Moreover, a high proportion of this group are greatly disadvantaged in formal education and salable nonfarm skills, so that their opportunities in the nonfarm labor market are extremely limited.

The migrant farm workers appear to be in the worst situation in this respect. Whereas many of the nonmigrant farm workers may live in communities where their children have access to adequately financed schools, thus breaking the pattern from one generation to the next, the very migrant nature of their employment means that the families of migrant workers are likely to reach working age with the same or larger relative disadvantage in education and skills that restrict the opportunities of the current generation of migrants.

There is growing recognition, especially outside agriculture, that the income position of hired farm workers in agriculture is not likely to be improved substantially over time by the operation of the market economy. Policy proposals are being put forth to improve the position of this group. But, virtually every proposed public action would involve some outside intervention in, or regulation of, the employers' activities, and, as such, public action has been vigorously opposed by most farm operators who employ hired workers. The values involved are strongly held by the various groups concerned, and the result will be extended controversy over policy in this area.

Summary and Implications

The market economy is an appealing solution to many of the problems of United States agriculture, because it is consistent with important values and beliefs in our society. The price system is an inexpensive and efficient way to transmit information to resource owners regarding the desires of consumers; it relates rates of reward to current output; it is impersonal in its operation; and it avoids the majority-minority rights dilemma of political control.

Despite these favorable aspects of the price system, we have intervened in the market economy for farm products for more than three decades. This intervention has resulted from the belief that the price system would not produce results consistent with our values regarding income stability for farm people.

Until recently, most policy makers have believed that the market economy would produce equilibrium resource use and earnings in agriculture. A variety of recent economic studies have shown, however, that over the period immediately ahead, the level of prices and incomes generated by the market economy for agriculture would be so inconsistent with the values relating to income levels that some public measures are needed. There now appears to be widespread agreement on this issue among the groups important in agricultural policy formation.

Increasing theoretical evidence and scanty empirical evidence indicate that the economic structure of United States agriculture is such that the market economy may not provide equilibrium resource use and returns in agriculture in the long run. The unsupplemented market may generate a chronic and substantial disequilibrium in resource use and returns. This belief is not widely accepted, either by economists or by the groups instrumental in policy formation in agriculture. Much of the policy discussion of the years ahead will revolve around this issue, and the nature of the policies adopted will be strongly affected by the extent to which this belief is accepted by farm people, farm leaders, and policy makers in agriculture.

Whereas there has been continuous and varied policy intervention in the market economy to deal with the stability and resource earnings problems in agriculture, there has been very little public intervention to deal with the poverty problems in agriculture. Here, the value problems are especially crucial, for virtually all of the solutions involve income and asset redistribution and change internal political relationships, and, in addition, the poor in agriculture are not influential in the processes that form farm policy. Recently, the beliefs that the market economy would not solve the poverty problems in agriculture have been increasing, especially among nonfarm groups. As a result, several policies to deal with these problems have been passed and others have been proposed, but these policies have gone through different channels than does farm policy normally. Policy actions in this area probably will continue to be initiated outside of the groups normally associated with farm policy formation, and they are likely to continue to be opposed by important segments of United States agriculture.

The belief that the market economy will not produce results sufficient to satisfy the value systems of farm people and of nonfarm society regarding agriculture has already led to a number of public policies to deal with the economic problems of agriculture, and others have been proposed but not adopted. The chapters that follow will examine the economic, social, and political implications of several broad categories of policies which have been used or proposed.

Chapter 11

Policies to Change
the Demand for
Farm Products

Policies to change the structure of demand for United States farm products are the oldest of our policies of market intervention, and such policies have been the most extensive, expensive, and enduring. There are several reasons for the extent of these policies. First, most of our past problems of stability were outgrowths of major temporary shifts in the domestic or export demand for farm products, or they were the outgrowth of unplanned shifts in supply in the face of a highly inelastic demand. Second, until recently the disequilibrium problem in agriculture has been viewed as a temporary one arising from a downward shift from some extraordinary level of demand—a postwar adjustment. For a decade following World War I, there was the problem of postwar adjustment in agriculture, and talk of a temporary postwar adjustment following World War II still persists in some quarters.

The agricultural policies that have attempted to concentrate on the demand for farm products as a solution to the farm problem have taken three general forms: (1) to change the aggregate product demand curve facing producers at a specific time; (2) market differentiation to take advantage of differential elasticities of demand in different markets; and (3) programs to increase the consumption of farm products. Having had some experience with each type of program, we can discuss them both in terms of their general implications and of this experience.

Price Supports and Storage Programs

A program of purchases and nonrecourse commodity loans has been the basic foundation of United States farm price and income policy since the mid-1930's. While these programs do not alter the underlying consumer demand for farm products, they have operated in such a way as to provide an outlet for that portion of farm output that would have otherwise cleared the market only at much lower prices.

Even though these loan and purchase programs have been limited to relatively few commodities and in some cases the eligibility for loans has been restricted to producers residing in certain areas or complying with acreage allotments, these programs have provided price and income protection to almost all resources in agriculture. This is because these programs have provided an outlet for a portion of farm output at price levels above those that would have prevailed if all of the output had cleared the market. Thus, the accumulation of feed grains under the support program has protected the income of livestock producers by providing an outlet for these feed grains other than feeding it to livestock, thereby preventing an increase in livestock output and a decline in livestock prices.

Purchase and loan programs imply either a storage program or a disposal program that uses other than normal market channels. Thus, in United States experience, loan and storage programs have become inseparable and they should be discussed in terms of this experience.

SHORT-RUN INSTABILITY

Price support and storage programs for farm products, as they have operated in the United States, have provided forward planning prices for the commodities concerned, at least for the production period immediately ahead. This, as discussed in Chapter 5, has important implications for resource allocation within agriculture and may contribute substantially to more efficient resource use in the industry.

The price support and storage program was inaugurated to deal with what was conceived as a problem of short-run instability in agriculture arising from three sources—fluctuations in domestic employment and income, shifts in export demand and unplanned changes in farm output.

Questions may be raised regarding the use of price supports and storage programs to stabilize farm price and income in the face of declines in employment and income which reduce the demand for farm products. An exclusive dependence upon price support and storage programs to deal with shifts in demand arising from changes in nonfarm income and employment will result in the use of public funds for programs which will be adverse to the interests of consumers. This is because the program would result in lower consumption if employment and demand declined, without a decline in the relative utility for farm products. Therefore, unless it can be shown that such declines in demand are to be followed immediately by very large increases in demand, such as occurred in World War II and the Korean War, a price support and storage policy will provide a solution to the short-run instability problem in agriculture arising from unemployment, only at the expense of consumers.

This has been among the reasons leading several economists who have examined the problem of dealing with the instability arising from short-run shifts in domestic demand to recommend that compensatory payments to farmers be used to deal with such problems.[1] Further examination of this policy proposal will follow in another chapter.

The use of price supports and storage programs to offset temporary fluctuations in export demand avoids some of the considerations involved in domestic demand, because such fluctuations usually are due to changes in other sources of supply. Therefore, such a policy—with supports at or near an average market price level—offers advantage to farmers, and possibly to domestic

[1] See T. W. Schultz, *Agriculture in an Unstable Economy* (New York: McGraw-Hill Book Company, Inc., 1945), and D. Gale Johnson, *Forward Prices for Agriculture* (Chicago: The University of Chicago Press, 1947).

consumers, without any real cost to foreign consumers. Domestic consumers may gain from such stabilization if the resulting price stability substantially increases the efficiency of organization and resource use in agriculture.

The strongest case can be made for the use of a price support and storage program to deal with the problems arising from un-planned changes in farm output. If the demand for the product is inelastic, such a program will stabilize prices, stabilize pro-ducers' incomes, and maximize social utility, simultaneously.[2] Since such a policy for feed grains would stabilize the price of a major input in livestock production, it also should add to output and income stability for the producers of livestock products.

Price support and storage programs, if properly conceived and operated, can contribute to a solution of the short-run instability problems in agriculture; and, as we have seen, income variation on most types of farms has declined during the period in which such programs have been effective. There are problems in using price supports as the solution to shifts in domestic demand arising from cyclical changes in employment, but such shifts appear to be a decreasing source of income instability for agriculture; so that there probably is less need for concern regarding this issue.

Farm product price supports based upon prices paid by farmers offer only a partial solution to the problem of price instability for purchased inputs by adjusting supports with changes in farmers' costs. There is no way in which price-support policy in agriculture could deal with fluctuations of nonfarm income of farm families that arise entirely from outside the industry. Thus, more than one-third of the income of farm people is entirely outside the con-fines of commodity prices.

PRICE SUPPORTS AND DISEQUILIBRIUM IN AGRICULTURE

The literature of agricultural economics is full of warnings that price supports, if maintained at price levels above equilib-rium prices, would attract and hold excessive resources in agricul-ture. "Surplus" output and stock accumulation would automat-

---

[2] See D. Gale Johnson, *ibid.*, Chapter X; and Robert L. Gustafson, *Carryover Levels for Grains*, Technical Bulletin No. 1178 (Washington: U.S.D.A., 1958).

ically follow. This literature implicitly or explicitly assumes that the average market-clearing price level also is the equilibrium price level—where factors in agriculture would be earning incomes comparable to returns to factors elsewhere. A common prescription usually follows such an analysis. If price supports are lowered, either slowly or rapidly, to market-clearing levels, equilibrium output and income would be achieved in agriculture. This was the program of the Republican Administration from 1953–60; and, with some land retirement to absorb the initial shock, it is the program advocated by the American Farm Bureau since the mid-1950's.

Obviously, price supports at the market-clearing levels are no solution at all to the disequilibrium problem if the market level is consistently below the level that will produce comparable incomes for productive factors in agriculture.

On the other hand, the experience of recent years has given ample evidence of the problems arising from attempting to use price supports at above market-clearing levels as a method of preventing the effects of the disequilibrium from falling upon farm income. Despite heroic surplus disposal efforts and somewhat less heroic efforts to control farm output, increasing quantities of virtually all major price-supported commodities were accumulated by the Commodity Credit Corporation, the government's price-support agency. As a result, by 1960 the cost of transporting and storing the accumulated products and the interest on the investment therein became a major burden on the federal budget, reportedly exceeding a billion dollars annually. By the early 1960's the Department of Agriculture reported that it would be required to spend $1.25 to store each bushel of corn acquired under the support program—certainly an extraordinarily expensive way to deal with the disequilibrium problem in agriculture since none of these expenditures subsequent to the initial acquisition of the commodity go to improve farm income.

The returns to most resources in agriculture, especially labor, have been below equilibrium levels over the past decade. Does it follow from this that price supports above market-clearing levels will have little or no effect upon output of supported products, so that price supports can be raised if equity or political considerations suggest higher incomes in agriculture? This was the reasoning behind the increased price supports for numerous products in 1961, and the results of this action suggest the reasoning was erroneous.

Even if some resources in agriculture are "fixed" because their salvage value in other industries is well below current earnings, it does not mean that all resources have a marginal value product well below current acquisition costs. An increase in corn price supports, from $1.00 per bushel to $1.20 per bushel, may increase the marginal value product of fertilizer enough to cause more to be used, even though the labor and durable capital involved in corn production may still have returns insufficient to cover acquisition costs. Thus, even if the $1.20 per bushel is just at or slightly below the price which would provide equal factor returns in agriculture, the output of corn is above equilibrium levels because it represents an above-equilibrium input of labor and durable capital together with an equilibrium input of fertilizer.

This is the basic dilemma of using price supports to deal with the disequilibrium in agriculture. Price supports at market-clearing levels do not improve the low returns to the productive factors. However, the use of price supports at above market-clearing levels—even if below levels which will provide equilibrium incomes for all productive factors—will result in stock accumulation by the government. The higher the support level the greater the additional resources which will be attracted, because their higher marginal value product further exceeds acquisition costs; moreover, the higher the support level the more the marginal value product of trapped resources exceeds their salvage value, preventing their outmovement. Higher supports thus may mean higher output and greater "surplus" or stock accumulation problems and still not achieve equal incomes for most productive factors in agriculture. This has been the situation in United States agriculture since about 1950.

 The use of a price-support program to deal with the disequilibrium creates strong political pressures for its continuance. The private storage of government surplus stocks of farm commodities is a large and profitable business. The production and sale of nonfarm-produced inputs for agriculture also is a substantial business. The provision of farm supplies and consumption goods is the major business of many merchants in smaller rural communities. All of these groups benefit directly or indirectly from price-support programs used to deal with the disequilibrium problem in agriculture. Therefore, these groups tend to favor price-support programs which maintain their personal prosperity, and this pressure is important politically to the elected representatives from such areas. These same groups generally oppose strongly those measures which will effectively reduce the productive inputs in agriculture (including labor if it involves migration), because they, individually, are better off with high farm output and gross farm income than with lower farm output, high returns to labor in agriculture, and higher net farm income.

Ironically, farm organizations, through their cooperative affiliates, have become major suppliers of purchased farm inputs and storers of surplus commodities. The leaders are torn between their role as representatives of farmers' interests as producers and the organizations' interest as suppliers. The result is that some farm organizations are pushing for policies that will continue excessive levels of farm output and the attendant problems of surplus disposal, rather than to concentrate upon programs that would move toward an economic solution to the farm problem.

Market Discrimination Policies As a Solution to the Farm Problem

Market discrimination or market diversion programs are among the most commonly used policies throughout the world in attempts to deal with the problems of farm income level and stability. Two conditions must exist in order for such a policy to be effective. They are: (1) there must exist two or more market outlets which can be separated, and (2) the price elasticity in one of these outlets must exceed the elasticity in the other. Given these conditions, it can be readily shown that, depending upon relative elasticities, a diversion of some of the products from the less elastic to the more elastic market will maximize producers' revenue.

The list of such programs in the United States is long. Fluid milk is the most important example. Presumably, the demand for bottled fluid milk is less elastic than the demand for manufactured dairy products, especially when considered from a single milkshed. Therefore, milk marketing orders are established which limit the quantity of milk that can be marketed within the affected area in fluid form, and quantities produced in excess of this are diverted to manufacturing outlets.

Similar schemes have been used for citrus fruits, fresh vegetables, potatoes, tree fruits, and various other farm products over the years. Most of the products involved have been perishable, at least in the primary market. The total agricultural resources involved in their production have been small (except for dairy products), and the nature of either their production or marketing process has limited entry or rapid expansion of production.

In the postwar period, a form of market discrimination has been extended to other major agricultural commodities involving much larger quantities of productive resources. Stripped to its essentials, our export subsidy for wheat under the International Wheat Agreement and certain aspects of our Public Law 480 sales of wheat are programs which attempt a complex market discrimination policy for wheat. The intent is to divide the market for wheat into three sectors—domestic demand for food wheat, commercial export sales for dollars, and export sales for foreign currency. All of our numerous export subsidy programs for farm products and sales for foreign currency are of this nature.

Our export subsidies, however, have operated in such a way as to differ from a "true" market discrimination program in one important aspect. Under our price support and export subsidy programs, producers have received the domestic price on all of their output, with the losses on the products exported at lower prices coming from the United States Treasury rather than from producers' revenues. Thus, the question as to whether such programs really would enhance producers' incomes in the absence of government subsidy has not been squarely faced.

Two questions need to be answered regarding such programs. Are the necessary conditions for the success of market discrimination policies met, particularly in commodities heavily involved in the export market? If the necessary conditions for such policies are met, are these policies appropriate to deal with the economic problems of United States agriculture?

The first of the necessary conditions is that there be separate markets for the product in question. For citrus these have been the fresh and juice markets, for grapes the fresh and wine or juice markets, and for milk the bottled fluid and manufacturing markets. Even for these, the problem of maintaining separate markets is great, if not impossible. In citrus fruits, the frozen juices and concentrates turn out to be substitutes for the fresh product.[3] Reconstituted dried skim milk appears to be a substitute for some consumption of fluid milk.

For commodities exported in the same form as they are consumed domestically, the problem of maintaining a separate and higher domestic market price is even more difficult. In fact, it can only be achieved through the use of some kind of tariff or import control policy.

The attempt to operate a market discrimination policy for cotton has been most enlightening in this respect. Under our export subsidy program for cotton, foreign mills can buy United States cotton at prices several cents per pound below those paid by domestic mills. Since our mills also receive an export subsidy on the cotton equivalent of finished goods, they suffer no disadvantage in export markets. But their disadvantage in the United States market is large, and imports of finished cotton goods, especially from Japan, rose sharply following the adoption of the export subsidy. Demands for tariffs or quotas on such imports followed immediately. In this case, an informal quota system was adopted, but even this is hardly consistent with our national policy position that the free world should maximize its potential gains from specialization and trade in products where the greatest comparative advantage is found.

Problems of a similar nature, but less in magnitude, arise in virtually every product in which international market discrimination is attempted. The only feasible way to successfully isolate our domestic market is by some kind of import restrictions, which clearly are inconsistent with our general long-standing policy

[3] Roy J. Smith, "The Lemon Prorate in the Long Run," *Journal of Political Economy*, 59 (Dec. 1961).

position on international trade. Therefore, the condition of separate domestic and foreign markets for farm products can only be maintained with some loss of our general bargaining position regarding overall international trade policy.

Cotton also provides an outstanding example of the problem of meeting the second condition necessary for market discrimination policies to work—that of having a less elastic primary market. Inelasticity depends upon the lack of close substitutes in consumption, and cotton policy makers have belatedly discovered that synthetics are good substitutes for cotton. In 1940, the per capita domestic consumption of cotton was 30.0 pounds and of man-made fibers was 3.5 pounds. In 1960, the per capita domestic consumption of cotton was 23.2 pounds and of man-made fibers was 10.6 pounds. At least a portion of this substitution must be due to the price-support level for cotton.

Leaving aside the question of the actual demand elasticity in the domestic market, what is the relative elasticity of demand for United States exports? The elasticity of demand for a particular country's export is directly related to the elasticity of total demand for imports of the commodity and inversely related to the proportion of the country's export to the total exports. If, however, most of the exports are under government programs and every country is determined to maintain its relative share of world trade, then the increased elasticity implicit in providing a fraction of the total demand for imports is lost. Since we are approaching the market-share concept in world trade in the major farm commodities, it may be that each of the major exporting nations, which includes the United States, faces an export demand for its products which has approximately the same elasticity as does the total demand for imports of the products concerned. Thus, the commercial export demand for our farm products may not be as elastic as we have presumed.

A second set of issues is involved in the special sales for foreign currency under Public Law 480. Presumably, this market is separable from normal commercial export sales, and the demand in it is more elastic than in either the domestic market or the commercial export market. Although the program is designed to achieve "additional" sales, there is some evidence that it has resulted in sales which were substitutes for either United States commercial exports or the exports of other countries.[4] This has been particularly true for cotton and tobacco.

There is no way of judging as to the demand elasticity for our farm products in this market. As long as we sell increasing quantities of United States farm products for foreign currencies and these currencies are carried on our books at some fictitious stable exchange value, the impression is given that the demand in this market is almost infinitely elastic. The only real measure would be the actual purchasing power of this accumulated currency in terms of real goods and services. Successive measures of this purchasing power with different quantities of it available would provide a test of the elasticity of this market; for if this purchasing power declined rapidly as the accumulation of currency rose, this would be a rapid decline in real price as sales rose, and the demand would be inelastic.

T. W. Schultz has suggested that the value of foreign currency accumulations under Public Law 480 is but a fraction of their "book" value and, moreover, that further such accumulations have a zero, if not negative, value to the United States.[5] This suggests that in reality the demand for our farm products in this market may be relatively inelastic.

Generally, the producers of products involved in our international market discrimination programs have not had to face the question of whether such programs would operate to increase producers' gross revenue. This is because the government has provided producers with the primary market price for all of their production, by providing price supports and export subsidies. In the case of the sales for foreign currency, exporters are paid in dollars by the Commodity Credit Corporation (CCC), which in turn is reimbursed by annual appropriations for the losses (or part of them) incurred on such sales.

This particular version of market discrimination policy came

---

[4] See Nicolas Ardito-Barletta, *History and Analysis of the Use of U. S. Surplus Agricultural Products for Foreign Aid,* unpublished thesis for the degree of Master of Science (North Carolina State University, Raleigh, 1961).

[5] T. W. Schultz, "Value of U. S. Farm Surpluses to Underdeveloped Countries," *Journal of Farm Economics,* 42 (Dec. 1960).

into being as a result of the unpleasant consequences of attempting a price-support program at prices well above market-clearing levels. The result was a substantial decline in exports, serious stock accumulation, and an "umbrella" over world prices which encouraged increased foreign output to replace our reduced exports. The obviously impossible economic consequences of following that policy indefinitely—implying a virtual abandonment of the export market—led to the gradual adoption and expansion of an international market discrimination policy for most major exported commodities.

While the adoption of market discrimination policies have had the advantage of reducing or of keeping stocks below levels they otherwise would have attained, as they have operated they have had some obvious disadvantages. The first—the import problem—has already been mentioned. The second is that the cost of the export subsidies and other losses that are required to make sales abroad while producers received the domestic price on all production has been very large, and the budget impact has, therefore, been unpleasant.

In fiscal year 1962, the Commodity Credit Corporation losses on the exports under Public Law 480 amounted to about $2 billion. In addition, payments to exporters on "commercial" sales exceeded $700 million. These expenditures, on top of the roughly $1 billion spent for storage, handling, interest, and transportation charges on stocks that were previously accumulated under the price-support program, helped to account for the $5.6 billion expenditures of Commodity Credit Corporation in fiscal year 1962.

These high expenditures for export programs, with prospects of continuing indefinitely, and the inconsistency of the export subsidy programs with our foreign policy have led many to suggest that a straightforward market discrimination program be adopted. The National Grange has long advocated such a program for wheat, terming it a *domestic parity* program. Under it each grower would be allocated a proportional share of the domestic market (based upon past output) and he would receive a higher price for this portion of his output. The remainder of his output would be used for export or feed and would return the grower a lower price.

The higher domestic price would be achieved by issuing certificates to the growers covering their domestic allotment and requiring processors of wheat for domestic food use to acquire sufficient certificates to cover the wheat so used. Presumably, wheat for other uses would be priced at market-clearing levels.

Subject to the approval of the wheat producers, a modified version of this approach will be applied to wheat starting with the 1964 crop. Under the program, each eligible producer will receive marketing certificates covering his portion of the domestic allotments and some fraction of expected exports as determined by the Secretary of Agriculture. The grower will receive a primary price for that quantity of his output covered by the certificates via the sale of wheat and certificates. Any additional output that the grower sells will return him a much lower price.

While this marks a substantial change from previous policy, it still does not require that producers depend upon prices in the export market for their income from that portion of their output. Instead, in order to maintain producers' incomes, some portion of exports will be taken from producers at primary market prices with losses via export subsidies coming from the Treasury.

The use of similar market discrimination or multiple price plans has been suggested for cotton and rice, which also are heavily dependent upon export markets and have required substantial export subsidies under our domestic price support program. In light of this continued interest in such programs, let us examine their implications for dealing with the farm problems.

MARKET DISCRIMINATION AND INSTABILITY

Market discrimination programs were developed for and have been widely used to cope with the income problems arising in farm commodities subject to wide variations in unplanned output or to large seasonal variations in output. Tree fruits, especially citrus, and grapes are examples of the former, and dairy products of the latter.

Faced with a highly inelastic demand for fruit in the fresh market and substantial year-to-year variations in output due to weather, disease, and other causes beyond the producers' control, the use of market discrimination programs that divert some of the crop to a more elastic secondary use can significantly reduce the year-to-year variance in income of producers.

Originally, the common reason for milk orders was the problem arising from large seasonal fluctuations in output in the face of a relatively stable demand for fluid milk. In the absence of the diversion program during the season of high production, the producers' price for all milk would fall to the level of the price of manufacturing uses, resulting in large seasonal variations in price and income and a lower total income.

Under the domestic market discrimination programs that have operated, the price received by individual producers has been a blend price derived by pooling the receipts from the primary market with those from the secondary market. Thus, under such programs, the blend or average price and the marginal price *to the individual producer* are the same. This results in a situation in which the value of additional output to the producer exceeds the value of the additional output in the secondary market. As long as the revenue from this blend price exceeds the revenue from producing alternative products, there is a powerful incentive to increase output, driving down the blend price to all producers whether or not they expand output. This is no problem if one assumes a completely inelastic supply with the quantity diverted to the secondary market uniformly distributed as a result of un-planned changes in output. However, where supply is not completely inelastic and the diversions are the result of changes in planned output, producers who fail to maintain their relative share of increased output will suffer a decline in average and marginal price and, therefore, a substantial loss in total revenue. This problem is related to the effectiveness of a market discrimination program to deal with the equilibrium problem in agriculture and will be discussed shortly.

These programs are not particularly adapted to dealing with stability problems arising from shifts in demand due to changes in income and employment. Such changes normally would affect all of the markets involved, and a market discrimination program thus would provide little income protection to producers in such a situation.

If the markets can be successfully separated and the relative inelasticity of the primary market can be maintained, market discrimination programs can reduce the instability of producers' incomes arising from significant year-to-year variations or seasonal variations in output. However, the number of farm products for which a separate, more elastic secondary market can be established and maintained is limited. Some of the long-standing programs appear to be failing on this count.

MARKET DISCRIMINATION AND THE
EQUILIBRIUM PROBLEM

The apparent success of market discrimination programs in increasing producers' incomes under conditions of widely varying annual or seasonal production has led many persons to conclude that such programs might offer hope as a solution to the problem of disequilibrium earnings for resources in agriculture. A wide variety of multiple price plans have been proposed. Will they work and, if so, under what conditions?

The market discrimination programs that have operated have experienced difficulty in those cases where they have attempted to use the program as a device to increase returns to producers of some commodities substantially above returns for resources elsewhere in agriculture. Smith points out that, under the lemon prorate program, production has risen steadily in the postwar period, requiring a steadily increasing diversion to the secondary market, which provides very low returns to the growers.[6] In 1958, 58 per cent of the crop was diverted to the secondary outlets. As a result of the rising proportion diverted, the blend price has declined until it is not appreciably above the average price that growers might expect in the absence of a market discrimination program.

These results are to be expected as long as the average price received by growers is high enough, so that the marginal value product of resources in producing the crop is above that in producing other crops, and the value of the resources in this use is above their salvage value outside of agriculture. As long as a market discrimination program is operated so that the marginal

6 Roy J. Smith, *op. cit.*

price for additional production, from either new producers or existing producers, is equal to the average price and the above conditions hold, there will be an increase in output sufficient to bring the average price down to the point where the return from producing the commodity in question is approximately equal to that of alternative crops. In the case of tree fruits, there is an especially long time lag involved in this adjustment because of the time required to enter production.

The market discrimination for dairy products has had about the same results, although somewhat different factors have prevented it from becoming as obvious. First, the high transportation cost for fluid milk allows some local fluid markets to maintain higher prices for primary products. These, however, are not always sufficient; and they sometimes are buttressed by health regulations which refuse inspection outside certain areas and thus exclude producers who would offer milk in a given market at the blend price, despite the transportation costs. In addition, in some markets handlers refuse to accept new suppliers despite the latter's willingness to enter the market at existing blend prices. Also, in some markets pricing provisions offer new entrants only secondary prices for some initial period after entry. Finally, and of crucial importance, the national price-support program for manufactured dairy products has made available a perfectly elastic aggregate demand for manufactured products at well above market-clearing levels. If the price support for manufactured dairy products were ended, it is clear that the blend price for milk in fluid markets would decline. Moreover, it is doubtful whether the other devices would prove sufficient to maintain blend prices significantly above manufacturing price levels.

This difficulty of using a market discrimination program to solve the equilibrium problem in agriculture has led to several proposals which are essentially barriers to entry—one to the primary markets, the other to the production of the product. Some groups now selling in fluid milk markets have proposed that the present primary (bottled fluid) milk market be allocated to existing participating producers on the basis of their historical participation. Then, producers could produce above and beyond their primary market share, but if they did, they would receive only the secondary price. This would mean that the average price and marginal price would be equal for quantities up to the producers' primary market share, but his average price for production in excess of his primary market share would be a blend price, and the marginal price for production in excess of his primary market share would be the market price in the secondary market.

If the price in the primary market can be maintained at levels well above those in the secondary market, such a scheme will increase the incomes of producers who obtain the primary market allocations. In effect, the program would create an income-producing asset in the form of the rights to the primary market. Will such a program bring the returns to resources engaged in producing milk to an equilibrium level?

As long as some resources have a salvage value—either in other agricultural production or outside agriculture—that is less than their current returns, the owners of these resources will gain by bidding the value of the right to produce for the primary market up to the point where the value in use of resources producing for the primary market is the same as in producing other products. In other words, the higher income from the primary market will be capitalized into the value of the rights to this portion of the market.

A somewhat different proposal was made by the Department of Agriculture in the Food and Agricultural Act of 1962. It would have established marketing quotas for individual milk producers, with marketings in excess of quotas subject to penalties sufficient so the net price would reflect approximately market-clearing prices. This was an attempt to avoid the high budget cost of an unlimited price-support program for dairy products, which amounted to nearly $600 million annually in fiscal years 1961–62. While the details differed, the economic principles were the same. It was a program which would discourage an expansion of production at the support level by imposing a tax upon production above quota levels sufficient to approximately equate the net mvp to the producer with the marginal value of his output in the market.

There have been a variety of proposals which would apply some variant of this market discrimination proposal to exported commodities, with the rights of access to the primary (domestic) market limited to those having some marketing certificate allocated on the basis of historical production. What can be said about the economic effects of such programs?

First, they would increase the income of participating producers over levels that would be obtained in the absence of price supports, export subsidies, or similar programs. To the extent that the expected income from the primary market exceeded the expected income from the next best alternative available to the owner of the resources, this expected income would be used to bid for the rights to the primary market. This would take place until the expected net marginal revenue from access to the primary market was just equal to the marginal revenue from the producer's next best alternative. This amount that producers would pay to acquire rights to the primary market or the amount they would forego in order to continue to hold these rights would become the capitalized value of the marketing certificates. Thus, in the long run the real net returns to the conventional inputs probably would not be increased beyond what they would be in the absence of the market discrimination program.

This, however, does not mean that income streams to the holders of the marketing rights and to the communities in which they live will not be higher. Actually, to a farmer who receives an initial allocation of the marketing certificates, it makes little difference whether his higher income is due to improved earnings on his conventional resources or upon his earnings from the new asset that has been created. Therefore, the initial recipient of the quotas is better off than he would be in the absence of the program, because his income will be augmented even though the real rates of return on his resources will not.

Producers entering production after the initial distribution of the marketing rights are neither helped nor hurt by the program as long as their expectations regarding the income effects of the program at the time they purchase the marketing rights are realized. If, however, because of program changes, their actual income having acquired the rights is higher than expected, they receive a windfall gain; and if their actual income is lower than expected, they suffer a loss. The possibility of the latter will tend to cause the discounting of the values of such programs, so that the capitalized values usually will not equal the actual value of the income differential.

As far as the community in which the producers are located, it makes some difference whether the income is due to higher returns for conventional inputs or to income accruing to the rights to market in a primary market. In the former case, the value of such inputs would rise providing a broader economic base for the community, in addition to the community benefits from the larger income flows. In the latter case, the community benefits are entirely those accruing from the higher income flows.

Even though the initial recipients of the capitalized marketing rights are benefited, those that later acquire them are not disadvantaged; and the community in which they are located benefits to some extent, though the real income of the economy is not increased by such programs. The higher income streams produced by such programs are the result of income transfers from consumers in the primary market and not the result of increases in real output in the economy.

The use of this type of market discrimination program offers one economic advantage over an unlimited price-support program. New resources entering production face a marginal return which is determined by their marginal value product in the secondary market. Thus, a program of this type would attract fewer additional new productive resources than would an unlimited support program or a market discrimination program offering a blend price for all production. Moreover, such a program would not maintain the marginal value product of resources producing for the secondary market at artificial levels well above their salvage value elsewhere, so that some of the necessary outmovement of excessive resources would be more likely to occur.

The use of market discrimination programs apparently is consistent with our values relating to receiving one's income in the market and having income dependent upon output. Similar programs are common elsewhere in the economy and, as would be the case in agriculture, their success is largely dependent upon government enforcement of market segregation or government sanction of private enforcement. In all cases, there are serious equity problems involved in the distribution of access rights to the primary market, but this is common to all programs which involve income redistribution, including the ones we have had.

For commodities where such market discrimination programs might be feasible, one major obstacle looms. The income of producers—although it would be better than with no program—would be lower than received under an unlimited support program of the type operated in the past. However, indications are that the continuing stock accumulation and the attendant costs of storage and disposal are so high that the nonfarm public, via its influence upon the executive branch, may force a change from unlimited support programs.

There would appear to be relatively few agricultural commodities for which a domestic market discrimination program is technically possible, due to the inability to maintain separate markets for most farm products. For those products for which separate markets can be identified, either domestic or foreign, the problem of maintaining the market's separability and of substitution is large.

The use of such programs for major export commodities would be possible, and the economic effects on other exporting nations should be preferable to our past policies of export subsidies—sometimes of undetermined amounts—even though import restrictions would be necessary. With export subsidies we actually may be selling our products abroad at less than their marginal production cost. This may appeal to our producers and to importing countries, but it does not appeal to competing producers, nor is it a wise allocation of world productive resources to do so. However, a market discrimination policy that made a fixed allocation of our domestic market and allowed unsubsidized exports at market-clearing prices would not represent unfair competition between our Treasury and foreign producers as does the export subsidy. Our producers would receive only the world price as their marginal price for products in excess of their domestic allotment, and this would not offer incentives for continued disequilibrium output even though their total returns would be maintained above disequilibrium levels.

Helen C. Farnsworth argues that a multiple price program will stimulate wheat production as much as a flat price-support program and constitutes unfair competition to foreign producers.[7] Neither point seems to be valid under the program outlined. In Figure 6 below, let p_1 be the domestic quota price and p_2 the world market price. The cost curves include only the opportunity cost or salvage value of fixed assets and the acquisition price of variable inputs. The producer's domestic quota is Q_1. With unlimited price support at price p_1, output would be Q_3 and exports would be sold for less than marginal cost of production. Under a multiple price system, production would decline to Q_2; the decline depending upon the slope of the marginal cost curve. The only situation in which the program would affect output is if the world price were below average variable cost, where without the program, production would cease, but with a program, production would continue as long as marginal cost were covered. It is doubtful if the world price for our export commodities would fall below their average variable cost.

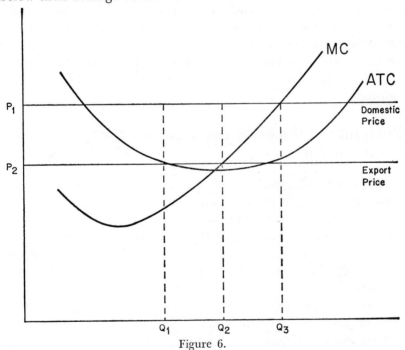

Figure 6.

Commodity output under a single and multiple price program.

[7] Helen C. Farnsworth, "Wheat under Multiple Pricing: A Case Study," *Policy for Commercial Agriculture, op. cit.*

In summary, market discrimination programs have been used successfully to deal with the problems of income variability for products subject to wide annual or seasonal variation in output. They have not been successful in attempts to use them to deal with the problem of disequilibrium in resource allocation and earnings in agriculture. To achieve even partial success in dealing with this problem will require that access to the primary market be rationed or allocated among producers, and these allocations will acquire a capitalized value. Thus, over time, income streams to producers might be improved, but returns will not be increased to factors having a wide divergence between acquisition cost and salvage value. Total resource use in the economy would be improved only modestly, the improvement largely resulting from the fact that new productive resources would enter only if their value in production at prices in the secondary market exceeded their acquisition cost. Market discrimination programs essentially are income transfer programs, not programs that increase total real output in the economy. While they may be preferable to income transfer programs of the type we have followed—both as to method of transfer and auxiliary costs—they do not provide a solution to the disequilibrium problem in agriculture.

Programs to Increase the Demand for Farm Products

Price-support programs open to all producers are devices that make the aggregate demand schedule completely elastic to producers at the support level, but price supports do not change either the shape or position of the underlying consumer demand curves for farm products. There is another series of programs that are designed either to shift the level of the demand for food or to change the shape of the demand curve, or both. Subsidized consumption programs, programs to expand the industrial use of farm products, and export sales of farm products at subsidized interest rates or with interest free long-term loans are of this nature.

A number of domestic food programs that subsidize the consumption of farm products are being used in the United States. These include school lunch programs, school milk programs, and food stamp plans.[8] Eight pilot food stamp programs were inaugurated in 1961, including about 140,000 needy persons.[9] About 13.5 million, or one-third, of the nation's school children participated in the school lunch program. The federal government contributed $94 million in cash, $133 million in commodities, and $82 million under the special milk program. State and local sources contributed $230 million and payments by participating children amounted to $595 million.

The first-year experience under the trial food stamp plan illustrates the effect of this type of program.[10] The retail value of the stamps issued averaged about $2.8 million monthly. Participants paid about $1.7 million monthly for the stamps, so that the monthly subsidy cost was slightly over $1 million. Special surveys showed that food sales increased by about 8 per cent and that between 85 and 95 per cent of the subsidy went for increased food purchases.

The diets of participating families were improved under the program and were better, on the average, than for nonparticipating families with comparable incomes. However, the number of families that participated in the food stamp program was less than one-half of those participating in the direct distribution program in the trial areas, prior to inaugurating the stamp plans. The reasons for this will be seen in our later discussion.

Far and away the largest of our programs to shift the demand for United States farm products is our Public Law 480 program. Under it we sell farm products abroad for foreign currency, which

[8] Direct distribution programs, strictly speaking, should not be included as programs which change the demand for farm products, even though the free food increases the real income of the recipient and, therefore, should have an income effect upon his consumption of other products, including other food. F. V. Waugh in his discussion, *Managing Farm Surpluses* ("Planning Pamphlet No. 117," Washington: National Planning Association, April 1962), classifies direct distribution programs as diversion programs.

[9] *Food and Agriculture—A Program for the 1960's* (Washington: U.S.D.A., Jan. 30, 1952), p. 30.

[10] *The Food Stamp Program, an Initial Evaluation of the Pilot Projects*, AMS-472, Food Distribution Division, Agricultural Marketing Service (Washington: U.S.D.A., April 1962).

usually is loaned to the recipient country, or we make long-term credit sales. If the program operated so that the foreign currency received were valued at its true exchange value and the currency received were used immediately, the program would represent a type of market discrimination program, as previously discussed. However, as long as a fictitiously high value is placed upon the foreign currency so acquired, and most of it is not used and probably will not be by our government to acquire goods and services in the buying country, the program constitutes a massive subsidy program to expand the demand for United States farm exports. This applies especially to shipments under Title I of the program (sales for foreign currency) and under Title IV (long-term loans to importing countries to finance purchase of United States farm products). From the inception of the program in 1954 to December 31, 1961, agreements were signed for the sale for foreign currency of commodities costing Commodity Credit Corporation $10.9 billion and having an export market value of $7.6 billion.[11] Sales of wheat accounted for more than half the total value, and cotton was next in importance. Public Law 480 exports accounted for one-fourth of all farm product exports in value from 1954 through 1960.

In general, subsidized consumption programs, whether domestic or foreign, are essentially one of two types. They increase the consumption of farm products either via the income effect of a cash grant—sometimes a tied grant—or via the income and price effect of reducing the cost of food to the recipient. In both cases, the increase in consumption of farm products is usually less than the expenditure for the subsidy, the difference depending upon the exact form the program takes.[12]

Since straight cash subsidies (or foreign aid) leave the relative expenditures upon food and other goods dependent solely upon the indifference curves of the consuming unit without affecting

[11] *Fifteenth Semi-Annual Report on Public Law 480,* House of Representatives Document No. 385, 87th Congress, 2nd Session (April 9, 1962). The CCC costs include storage and transportation charges.

[12] See Herman Southworth, "The Economics of Public Measures to Subsidize Food Consumption," *Journal of Farm Economics,* 34 (Feb. 1945), for a discussion of impact of different subsidy programs upon expenditures for food and other goods.

the relative prices of the goods, this form of subsidy will allow the recipient to reach a higher indifference curve from a given grant than will a program that specifically subsidizes the consumption of food (or food from a particular country). On the other hand, a program that specifically subsidizes food, because it changes the relative price of food, will result in the recipient achieving a somewhat lower indifference curve than under a cash grant and, of course, will result in a greater increase in the consumption of food. The extent of this difference depends upon the particular subsidy program used.

This can be illustrated by Figure 7. In that figure, let lines *a*,

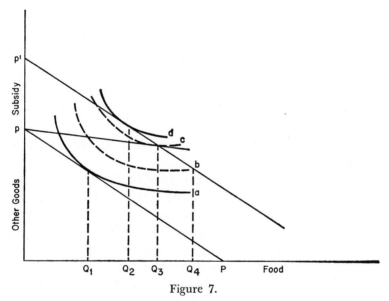

Figure 7.

The effects of various forms of food subsidies upon food consumption and the recipients' satisfaction.

b, c, and *d* represent the indifference map of the recipient (person or country) for food and all other goods, and let line *pp* represent the relative prices of these goods in the market. A decision is made to offer the recipient a subsidy of *pp′*. Prior to the subsidy, quantity Q_1 of food was being consumed by the recipient.

If the subsidy were a cash grant (dollar aid), the recipient would be able to move to indifference curve *d*. Food consumption would increase from Q_1 to Q_2, but much of the subsidy would go for other goods. This is what happens under general welfare programs and foreign aid.

If the subsidy were in the form of a reduced price for food that had an equivalent value to the cash subsidy (using the market value of food), food consumption would increase from Q_1 to Q_3, but the highest indifference curve the recipient could reach would be c, which is above a but below d. Most food stamp plans and sales for foreign currency are of this nature in that they represent price reductions for food.

Programs which involve frozen expenditures require the recipient to buy the "normal" amount of food and then offer a subsidy to induce additional expenditures. Some food stamp plans are of this variety, and a strict interpretation of Public Law 480 would make it so. Under such a program food consumption increases to Q_4, but the highest indifference curve that can be attained by the recipient is b. This is still above curve a, but much less so than under a cash subsidy program or a program that subsidizes food prices.

Under a tied consumption program there will be a selectivity among the participants, as there has been in the trial food stamp plan and in the Public Law 480 program. In the food stamp plans, where the stamps were sold for some specified percentage of the participant's income, families who had spent more than average proportions of their income gained and participated, whereas families who had spent less than the average proportion of their income for food would not gain and did not participate.

Similar results appear in the foreign disposal program. The major participants have been the very poor countries, whereas countries that have been spending fewer of their import dollars for food have not participated extensively. The usual justification for foreign aid in this form is that by such a program the recipient country gets more total aid than it would otherwise receive. Perhaps so, but a straight subsidy of much less than pp′ would make the recipient as well off as does the larger subsidy in the form of food. Therefore, the use of the food subsidy must be justified by the interest in producers' welfare and not by claims that we are providing the equivalent value to the recipients.

It can be shown that if resource allocation is the major value concerned, a cash grant will achieve it, whereas the other forms of subsidy depart from the optimum. The reason that any of the programs other than the cash subsidy program represent a departure from optimum resource allocation is obvious from Figure 7. Each of the highest points attainable on the recipients' indifference surface is a point where the marginal rates of substitution in consumption differ from the relative product prices.

If improving the income of farm producers is the major concern, then a tied subsidy program is a *more* effective way of achieving it. Therefore, a subsidy program to deal with our farm problems involves two questions. First, is any subsidy program an effective way to deal with the problems? Second, if so, what form of subsidy program should be used? Both basically are value problems.

Let us discuss the second question first. Is maximizing the recipients' utility and total resource allocation more important than producers' income? Given the nature of our political processes and the groups which are effective in farm policy, it is clear that those with a preference for improving producers' incomes are more directly involved and are more effective than are those with a major concern regarding total resource use or consumer utility. This is particularly true for foreign aid programs, so that it is to be expected that farm policy makers in Congress are much more likely to authorize expenditures for export sales of farm products for foreign currency than to grant an additional equivalent expenditure to the country in the form of dollars. For the same reason farm congressmen are more likely to provide expenditures for a food stamp plan than for a general cash subsidy to families on relief, part of which would be spent on food.

For poor people and poor countries, where the marginal value of additional food relative to other goods is high, these special programs offer enough of a preferred position so that they will be readily acceptable. If, however, the marginal value of additional food to other goods is low, then very large costs will be incurred to achieve modest increases in consumption.

FOOD SUBSIDIES AND INSTABILITY

Let us return to the first question—is a food subsidy program an effective policy to deal with the instability problem? It offers some help in dealing with two of the sources of instability, those arising from changes in nonfarm income and employment and those arising from unplanned changes in output.

A food stamp plan was inaugurated in the late 1930's as a method of increasing food consumption among low-income families. It is not a satisfactory substitute for general policies to maintain full employment, for it does nothing to restore the losses in real output arising from unemployment. Therefore, a subsidy either of cash or food to unemployed persons rests on equity considerations which are dependent upon our values relating to sharing our abundance with the less fortunate.

Given the decision that some subsidy will be granted the unemployed, what considerations enter the choice between cash and food subsidies? Actually, several may be involved. First, the inelastic demand for farm products means that the burden of a general shift in demand is heavier upon the producers of farm products than upon others. Therefore, subsidies which concentrate on expanding the demand for food during recessions might be justified. Second, food is a necessity, and some have a preference for limiting welfare programs to necessities, wherever possible. On the other side, food subsidy programs generally are not the most efficient way to make income transfers to farmers, because most of the subsidy goes for marketing services for farm products and to production expenses for producing the farm products. Moreover, the distortion in consumption mentioned earlier is involved.

Primarily because of the last two points, most of our programs to deal with cyclical changes in employment and income have been of the cash transfer variety, in the form of unemployment compensation, public welfare assistance, social security, etc. It has been estimated that federal, state, and local expenditures for income transfer programs in cash amounted to about $15.8 billion in 1957.[13] As pointed out in Chapter 5, these, plus other built-in

[13] L. W. Witt, "Potentials of New Markets for Agricultural Products," a manuscript prepared for the Committee for Economic Development (Oct. 30, 1960).

stabilizers, appear to have substantially reduced the impact of cyclical changes in nonfarm employment upon farm prices and incomes. This fact, together with the relative ineffectiveness of a food subsidy program in raising farm income, means there will be little pressure from farm groups for major expansion of such programs. The expansion that occurs will be due primarily to desires to improve the well-being of the recipients.

Subsidized consumption programs also could be used to deal with problems of income instability arising from unplanned changes in output. To do so, however, requires either a very large expenditure to achieve the necessary increase in demand for a particular product or a very restrictive program tying the subsidy to the specific commodity. These problems, together with a presumed preference of consumers for stable consumption, make a subsidized consumption program less desirable than one of the several alternatives, such as direct distribution programs, to deal with the problem of unplanned changes in output.

DEMAND EXPANSION AND THE DISEQUILIBRIUM PROBLEM

The food subsidy programs, as pointed out in Chapter 2, offer a promising major policy goal. They simultaneously offer the attainment of values relating to equal economic opportunity to farmers, income distribution related to production, and sharing our abundance with the less fortunate and, in the case of foreign programs, offer the attainment of values relating to world economic growth, and world political stability.

Let us start with the first issue—will food subsidy programs make a significant contribution to the disequilibrium income problem in agriculture? The answer is reasonably clear for domestic demand expansion programs, but, unfortunately, similar answers are not available regarding foreign demand expansion programs.

A University of Minnesota study examined the costs and potentials of various policies to expand the domestic demand for farm products.[14] The researchers' conclusions were that any de-

[14] John Wetmore, Martin Abel, Elmer Learn, and Willard Cochrane, *Policies for Expanding the Demand for Farm Food Products in the United States,* Technical Bulletin 231 (St. Paul: University of Minnesota Agricultural Experiment Station, April 1959).

mand expansion program sufficient to increase food consumption by an amount equal to the annual surplus accumulation in the late 1950's would be prohibitively expensive. What they failed to say was that such a program still would not have provided equilibrium returns to productive resources in agriculture, but only would have prevented stock accumulation at below equilibrium earnings.

The authors concluded that domestic demand expansion programs were limited in their ability to provide a solution to the "surplus" problem, but that they would be useful supplements to other programs because of their dual achievement of improved consumer welfare and modest improvement in farm income.

Unfortunately, the same thorough analysis of the potential costs and benefits (both to farmers and recipients) is not available for our foreign demand expansion programs. Costs are obscured because we have no rational way of estimating the true value of the foreign currency received in the program. Unlike our domestic food subsidy programs, we cannot say what the actual net budget expenditures for these foreign programs are. A number of studies have suggested that our present foreign currency accumulations already are excessive and that the future accumulations might have a negative value in terms of relations with the countries involved. Schultz has estimated that the real value of the accumulated foreign currencies is very low and that thus the net cost of these demand expansion programs is quite high.[15]

Actually, the policy of subsidizing the export demand for food via foreign currency sales ought to be considered in two parts—one dealing with sales of existing stocks accumulated under past price-support programs, and the other dealing with proposals to expand the program to include foreign currency sales of farm products from current production.

Subsidized sales of farm products from accumulated stocks are relatively easy to justify. These stocks, or at least major portions of them, have no positive net value to the United States. In fact, given the high storage costs involved in holding them, their value, once acquired, may be negative. Thus, as long as the positive

[15] T. W. Schultz, *op. cit.*

value of these products to the recipient countries exceeds the cost of transporting them, there is a gain by such sales.

This reasoning only applies to net sales from accumulated stocks and should not be extended to cover gross sales or sales directly from current production. In recent years, the program has operated in part by making Public Law 480 exports from current production; the argument is that otherwise this production would enter Commodity Credit Corporation stocks while an equivalent amount was exported from old stocks, requiring additional storage and handling charges.

This kind of program provides an illusion that disappearance is balanced with current output at market prices. As long as the currency received is carried on our books at grossly-inflated values which will never be realized, it appears that our export program is sustaining farm prices and income at relatively modest budget costs. It also appears that we are providing large quantities of foreign aid to the recipient countries in the form of food.

Actually, the value to the receiving countries of the foreign aid involved can only be measured accurately by knowing how much aid in dollars recipient countries would be willing to forego in order to receive the aid in surplus commodities. There is no way of judging this value, but it is certainly much less than the dollar value currently attributed to such exports, for the products involved probably would be available to these countries at lower prices than the export prices now attached to our exports for foreign currency.

The figures for Public Law 480 exports actually are confused by two elements in them. The first is the difference between Commodity Credit Corporation costs and estimated export value of the commodities concerned. From July 1954 through December 1961, this amounted to slightly over $3.3 billion, and much of this difference represented a subsidy to United States producers for the difference between domestic support price and export market price, but this cost is not charged to price and income supports in the federal budget. Instead, it is included as the cost of foreign assistance programs in the agricultural budget.

Actual shipments under Title I through December 1961 had

an export market value of $5.0 billion, and the local currencies delivered to the United States Treasury were slightly under this amount. As of September 30, 1961, allocations had been made for $5.1 billion of local currency, and more than $3.3 billion of these allocations were loans or grants to foreign governments. Since it is unrealistic to assume these will be repaid—nor would we probably desire it—one-half or more of the export value of these shipments must be considered as subsidies to the recipient country to expand their demand for United States farm products.

Representatives of the recipient countries assert that such subsidies are valuable to them in maintaining the food intake of their population and in furthering their economic development.[16] Some economists argue that such programs retard the internal development of agriculture in the underdeveloped countries and, therefore, are not in the long-run interest of either world economic development or stability. However, this issue deserves special and extended study that is not yet available, and until it is I would assume that these programs do make a positive contribution of some magnitude to the economy of the recipient countries.

Therefore, let us return to the question of whether this program to expand the foreign demand for United States farm products is an effective way to increase farm income and offers a useful solution to the disequilibrium problem in United States agriculture. Such a demand expansion program can increase the demand for United States farm products and, therefore, will mitigate to some extent the income effects of the resource problem in United States agriculture. The ultimate cost to the Treasury, however, is almost certain to prove much higher than is now recorded, and, therefore, the use of foreign food subsidies as a method of improving the income of American farmers will involve a high cost per dollar of additional farm income generated by the program.

However, recognizing that our subsidized sales of farm products to underdeveloped nations represent other than the optimum way of providing aid to these nations and something less than the optimum way of improving returns to productive factors in agri-

[16] S. R. Sen, "Import and Implications of Foreign Surplus Disposal on Underdeveloped Economies—The Indian Perspective," *Journal of Farm Economics,* 42 (Dec. 1960).

culture, it still may be that, given our political system, these foreign currency sales represent—up to some point—the best achievement possible of several values involved. Those instrumental in policy decisions regarding foreign aid and farm policy will provide more *real* foreign aid if part of it is in food subsidies, which also improve farm income, than would be provided if the foreign aid were exclusively in dollars. This is the justification for the program used privately by some officials who recognize that it falls short of the desired optimum on both counts.

However, there is some point beyond which either the increased farm income per dollar of subsidy is so small, or the distortion of the recipients' preference between United States farm products and other goods is so great, that further expansion of the program will halt. It will halt either because the Congress will refuse to appropriate the additional funds or because the recipient countries refuse to sign further agreements. The former rather than the latter is most likely to be the determining factor, especially if the true cost of these sales becomes evident.

Demand expansion programs alone, either domestic or foreign, cannot provide economic solutions to the basic problem of disequilibrium in agriculture. They can, at considerable expense, improve earnings of the resources producing farm products, while at the same time improving the well-being of the recipient. In so doing, they maintain market prices somewhat above levels that would exist in their absence. This raises the marginal value product of resources and will induce additional inputs of those resources for which the new marginal value product exceeds acquisition cost, and an increase in output—or at least output higher than might otherwise be maintained—will result. Thus demand expansion programs, while improving the earnings of the "fixed" resources in agriculture, will cause some additional resources to be malallocated to the production of farm products.[17]

Despite their obvious inability to provide a permanent solution to the disequilibrium problem in agriculture, demand expansion programs have a great appeal as a method of reducing the

---

[17] This only applies to programs which affect the demand from current production. Programs which subsidize net consumption from government stocks do not affect current resource allocation.

impact of the disequilibrium upon earnings in agriculture. Part of the appeal and support is because the programs offer attainment of other values relating to sharing our abundance, economic growth, and political stability. Part of their appeal is because these demand expansion programs maximize the incomes of those who produce and sell farm production inputs, market farm products, and are generally dependent upon the continued high resource use in agriculture. Since these farm-related groups and farmers virtually dominate the political scene in areas which are represented by those controlling farm policy in Congress, it is not surprising that there is continued support and sometimes insistence on the part of the congressional agricultural committees for continuation and expansion of these demand expansion programs—especially the export sales programs.

Moreover, demand expansion policies have a great appeal to nonfarm groups and help to maintain support for total price and income programs in agriculture. This was pointed out by Mr. Santangelo, the only urban representative on the House Sub-Committee on Agricultural Appropriations. He said: [18]

I have before me a newspaper article from *The New York Times* dated Tuesday, yesterday, in which the Secretary of Agriculture warns the farmers of an urban revolt, and saying that they may become disenchanted with all of the high-cost programs, and if they don't wake up, there may be a little difficulty with the urban representatives, and so I say if you don't have these sweeteners like the school-lunch program and the food stamp plan, which affect the cities as well as they do the rural areas, if you don't have the Public Law 480 which has aspects of foreign aid which many of the people from the city are interested in, you might encounter a great deal of difficulty in passing some of your farm programs which you do not now have.

Summary and Implications of Policies Dealing with the Demand for Farm Products

Policies dealing with the demand for farm products take three general forms—the provision of a completely elastic aggregate demand via price supports, market discrimination programs, and

[18] *Department of Agriculture Appropriations for 1963: Hearings,* Part I, p. 107.

demand expansion programs. All three types were developed to deal with short-run stability problems in agriculture, or what were believed to be short-run stability problems.

None of the programs influencing the demand for farm products can appreciably improve the poverty problem in agriculture. Programs that influence demand improve farm income directly in proportion to the total output of the producer. Neither price supports, market discrimination programs, nor subsidized consumption programs provide much help to those individuals whose productivity is low.

Price-support programs at appropriate support levels can be effective in dealing with stability problems arising from unplanned fluctuations in output, as can market discrimination programs. Both can be of some value in dealing with the internal instability problems inherent in the structure of agriculture that produce short-run "cobweb" cycles in production and prices. Neither is particularly well adapted to dealing with shifts in aggregate demand arising from shifts in aggregate employment and income. Demand expansion programs can be of value in dealing with shifts in demand due to cycles in employment and income, but they are not particularly effective in dealing with either unplanned changes in output or with the internal cyclical fluctuations in agriculture.

The complete inability of a price-support program to deal with the equilibrium problem in agriculture has been amply demonstrated over the past decade. Its failure is evidenced in chronic stock accumulation, high storage costs, and excessively high program costs despite the continuation of resource returns in agriculture well below equilibrium levels.

The failure of the price-support program has caused us to go back into the use of market discrimination and demand expansion policies. However, it is clear that in order for market discrimination policies to increase farm incomes above market-clearing levels, the right to produce for the primary market will have to be allocated or rationed among producers. For export products this involves import controls of some type. Moreover, the additional income streams accruing to producing for the primary market will be capitalized into the value of these production rights, so that over time the returns to factors producing the product will not exceed their returns in alternative production.

Market discrimination programs of the above type offer some clear advantage over unlimited price supports in terms of resource allocation. They offer income advantages to producers over market-clearing prices, although these advantages will accrue primarily to those producers initially acquiring production rights in the primary market. Except as the lower secondary market price reduces resources used in agriculture, market discrimination programs do nothing to reduce the basic disequilibrium resource use in agriculture. They are income transfer programs which will increase income flows to agriculture without any increase in real national product.

Demand expansion programs, both domestic and foreign, also have become major policies in recent years. Originally conceived as a method of dealing with short-run shifts in demand, they are now being expanded as a method of dealing with the disequilibrium problem in agriculture. Domestic policies include school lunch programs, milk programs, and the food stamp plan. By far the largest of our demand expansion policies are our export sales of farm products for foreign currencies and our long-term loans for export sales. All of these programs are attempts to increase the demand for United States farm products via subsidies. The quantities of products involved in the domestic demand expansion programs have been small, but major quantities of products have moved abroad under the Public Law 480 program. Unfortunately, the accounting procedures under the latter program make it impossible to determine the actual subsidy involved in the program, so that its cost and benefits are only guesses.

Demand expansion programs at best can provide slightly higher incomes in agriculture, and this only at very high cost. However, they win widespread support because of their real and alleged benefits to recipients, and because continued high farm output is of immediate interest to most of the agriculturally related industries.

All of these policies dealing with the demand for farm products are in accord with important values underlying our farm policy. They distribute income according to the individual producer's contribution to output; they avoid interference with the individual producer's operation of his business; and they provide income to farmers higher than would be realized in the absence of such programs. These, together with other value satisfaction offered by some of them, mean that the political support for such programs has been and will continue to be strong. However, none of these policies deals directly with the resource allocation problem in agriculture, and all in varying degrees involve less than optimum resource allocation in the economy. None of them alone or in combination can provide a complete solution to the disequilibrium problem in agriculture. It is for these reasons that other policies have been proposed or tried.

Chapter 12

Policies to Control Farm Output

The evidence of substantially lower factor returns in agriculture, and the obviously high cost of attempting to maintain farm income via unlimited price supports in such a situation, has led to an increased interest in some form of output control in agriculture. The rationale underlying this approach runs as follows: Without intervention the output of agriculture would be so high that market-clearing price levels would provide returns below equivalent returns to comparable resources elsewhere for most of the resources engaged in producing farm products. Since the demand for most individual farm products and for farm products in the aggregate is inelastic, a reduction in output will increase gross revenue to producers.

Given this economic rationale, there have been a variety of attempts at output control in agriculture. These have largely been confined to attempts to control farm output via the control of a single input—land. The failure of these attempts—or limited success, depending upon the criteria used to measure success—has led to proposals to move to direct controls over output or marketings as a solution to the problem of low returns in agriculture. Let us first discuss some of the experiences of the control

296

programs that have operated and then discuss the possibilities and problems of a comprehensive program of "supply management."

Controlling Farm Output by Controlling Land Inputs

CONTROLLING INDIVIDUAL CROP OUTPUT

Most of the attempts to control farm output have been through the use of acreage allotments and marketing quotas upon individual crops. Acreage allotments are merely devices whereby a producer of a crop who exceeds his allotted acreage is denied the benefits of price supports. Since virtually all of the price-support operations have been carried out by reducing market supplies, the market price has tended to stay close to the support price, and the penalty for failing to comply with acreage allotments, therefore, has been small.

Marketing quotas, as they have been defined by law up to 1962, are a device to impose a penalty upon producers who exceed their acreage allotments. Thus, an individual's marketing quota has been defined as the output produced upon his acreage allotment, the result of translating the national marketing quota into acreage on the basis of "normal" yields. Individuals who exceed their marketing quotas are subject to civil penalties amounting to a high proportion of the market price.

Acreage allotments and marketing quotas came into usage during the 1930's when the low earnings in agriculture were visualized largely as arising from temporary declines in demand. They have been applied to only a relatively few crops, and for these they have not been used continuously,[1] although they have been used for several major crops in every year since 1954.

Controlling farm output by controlling the land input for a few commodities has had two problems. First, it has been difficult to reduce the output of the controlled crop, and second, acreage allotments on a few crops have no effect upon total farm output.

The inability of acreage reductions to control the output of the specific crop rests largely upon the fact that land is only one

[1] For a summary of these programs see Murray R. Benedict and Oscar A. Stine, *Agricultural Commodity Programs* (New York: Twentieth Century Fund, 1956).

input, and not a major one at that for most crops. There are other inputs which are substitutes for land in crop production. Moreover, for most of these substitutes—fertilizers, irrigation, improved seed, insecticide, etc.—their marginal value product already exceeds their acquisition cost at recent price levels. Therefore, with acreage allotments and unlimited price supports there is a powerful dual incentive to use these new inputs to maintain or increase crop output on the reduced acreage.

The effects of the substitution of other inputs for land can be seen in virtually every crop for which output control by acreage reduction has been attempted. In 1952, 78.6 million acres were seeded to wheat and 71.1 million acres were harvested. The yield per seeded acre was 16.6 bushels and the total output was 1.31 billion bushels. Acreage allotments reduced the acreage seeded to wheat to 54.9 million acres in 1960, but the yield per seeded acre was 24.6 bushels, and total output was 1.35 billion bushels. A combination of selecting the best land, fertilizer, improved seed, summer fallow, and other improved practices has meant that despite a reduction in planted acreage of 30 per cent, approximately the same output was produced under allotment.

The failure of acreage allotments to reduce wheat output to levels of current disappearance can be blamed partially upon a provision of the law establishing a minimum national acreage allotment of 55 million acres. This, together with the maintenance of a market price which made the increased use of new output-increasing practices profitable, has meant that wheat output has steadily exceeded disappearance and huge surplus stocks were accumulated by Commodity Credit Corporation.

Wheat is not the only crop in which acreage reductions have not been very effective in reducing the output of the controlled crop. In 1953, the last year prior to acreage allotments and marketing quotas for cotton, 16.5 million bales were produced from a harvested acreage of 24.3 million acres. In 1960, 14.4 million bales were harvested from 15.5 million acres.

In 1961, a special feed-grain program was used to reduce feed-grain output, under which farmers were paid for idling land which had been used for feed grain the previous two years. The program resulted in a decline of 18 per cent in the acreage of corn for grain and of 29 per cent in grain sorghum. However, the yield per acre of corn and sorghum each rose 13 per cent over the previous high of 1960. The output of corn was reduced only 7 per cent from the preceding year and that of grain sorghum 22 per cent. The high cost of achieving this modest reduction in feed-grain output via a voluntary acreage retirement program was a major factor in the 1962 decision of the Administration to seek legislation authorizing compulsory land-retirement programs to control future feed-grain output.

The substitution of other inputs for land has been recorded for virtually all crops for which output control has been attempted via acreage allotments. It has been necessary to drastically reduce acreage in order to achieve a reduction in crop output at the support prices. When minimum national acreage allotments have been fixed by law, crop output has exceeded disappearance at support price levels, resulting in stock accumulation and attendant high program cost. Even where there have been no prescribed minimum national allotments, political pressures often have prevented a reduction of acreage rapidly enough to prevent surplus accumulation and high program costs.

A notable exception, always cited by the proponents of output control programs, has been the tobacco program. The major types of tobacco have been under acreage allotment in most years since 1938. Prior to the mid-1950's, per capita tobacco consumption was increasing. Despite the steady rise in yields under the allotment program, it was possible to prevent stock accumulation without drastically reducing the total acreage allotment. However, beginning about 1953, the per capita consumption of cigarettes began to decline and total stocks of the tobaccos used in their manufacture began to rise sharply. In order to maintain the record of keeping production in line with disappearance, thus avoiding heavy price-support losses, it was necessary to drastically reduce the acreage of tobacco under the allotment program. These cuts were accepted by the producers who continued to approve the marketing quotas, even though the quotas reduced harvested acreage from 1.8 million acres in 1951 and 1952 to 1.1 million acres in 1958. Penalties for overplanting allotments were increased sharply to make the new lower allotments effective, and the minimum individual allotment level was reduced to .5 acre.

The existence of a minimum allotment level of .5 acre (originally the minimum was higher) has meant that the major burden of the acreage reductions fell upon producers whose allotments were above the minimum level. This has progressed to the point where in 1959 about three-fourths of all allotments were one acre or less (Table 1). It is difficult to believe that even in this labor-intensive crop there are not some economies of scale up to an acreage well above these very small acreages and that the extreme fractionating of acreage has not resulted in production costs for tobacco higher than they would be otherwise.

Table 1

Burley Tobacco Allotments, 1944 and 1959

Size of Allotment (acres)	1944		1959	
	Number of Allotments	Per cent of Total	Number of Allotments	Per cent of Total
0.50 or less	8,881	3.52	85,888	28.31
0.51 to 1	93,626	37.14	137,360	45.28
1.01 to 2	74,302	29.48	49,047	16.17
2.01 to 3	26,641	11.36	16,284	5.37
3.01 to 4	13,883	5.51	6,096	2.01
4.01 to 5	11,577	4.59	3,230	1.06
5.01 to 10	15,380	6.10	4,258	1.40
10.01 to 20	4,454	1.77	980	.32
20.01 to 50	1,182	.47	202	.07
50.01 or over	143	.06	15	.01
Total	252,069	100.00	303,361	100.00

Source: *Hearings Before the Committee on Agriculture and Forestry, United States Senate, 87th Congress, 2nd Session on S.2786* (Washington: U. S. Govt. Printing Office, 1962), p. 423.

Earlier analysis (1952) indicates that the tobacco control program has increased the income of tobacco producers.[2] The control program has achieved this by maintaining the relative price of tobacco in the face of technological advance that reduced the real cost of production.

The fact that acreage allotments for tobacco maintained in-

[2] Glenn L. Johnson, *Burley Tobacco Control Programs*, Bulletin 580 (Lexington: Kentucky Agricultural Experiment Station, Feb. 1952).

come for resources producing tobacco at levels that were generally above the income from alternative crops meant that the right to a tobacco allotment was of value. The additional income accruing to the production control program has been capitalized into the value of the land to which the tobacco allotment is tied. A study of the capitalized value of flue-cured tobacco allotments in areas in Virginia and North Carolina indicates that depending upon other conditions, an acre of allotment was worth up to $2,500 in 1957.[3]

The factor that appears to have determined the capitalized value of the tobacco allotment is the extent of the difference between the marginal returns to the fixed asset (labor) in producing tobacco and the returns in the next best alternative crop or industry. Where the salvage value of labor outside of agriculture, or in another crop, equaled or exceeded the expected returns for that labor in tobacco production, the acreage allotments had no apparent capitalized value. In other words, where labor is not "trapped" in agriculture or has a high salvage value in an alternative crop, production rights for a controlled crop do not tend to acquire a capitalized value. Approximately the same results are found for wheat acreage allotments. In the Great Plains, where the salvage value of the operator's labor in other crops or outside agriculture is low, wheat acreage allotments have been bid into land values. However, in Michigan, where the salvage value of the operator's labor is higher, both in alternative crops and outside agriculture, wheat acreage allotments apparently have no capitalized value.

Returning to the tobacco program, what has been the effect of the program upon returns to resources engaged in producing tobacco? Unfortunately, statistics that measure accurately the marginal returns of the various inputs are not available, but those that are available suggest that real labor returns have not risen at all under the program.[4] The United States Department of

---

[3] Frank H. Maier, James L. Hedrick, and W. L. Gibson, Jr., *The Sale Value of Flue-Cured Tobacco Allotments*, Technical Bulletin No. 148 (Blacksburg: Virginia Polytechnic Institute Agricultural Experiment Station, April 1960).

[4] *Farm Costs and Returns*, Agricultural Information Bulletin No. 230 (Washington: U.S.D.A., June 1960), p. 49.

Agriculture shows that on a typical Kentucky Bluegrass tobacco-livestock farm gross farm income rose from $5,468 in 1947–49 to $6,372 in 1958. Net income rose from $3,334 to $3,486. However, if one allows for a charge for capital (including the capitalized value of the allotments in the land values), the return to operator and family labor fell from $2,549 to $1,940, or from $.91 to $.69 per hour. Of course, these labor returns are residual figures that should be used cautiously, but they are indicative of the labor returns that could be expected under a program of this type.

The experience under 25 years of the tobacco control program would appear about as follows: (1) the price support and control program has stabilized income from the crop and increased producers' incomes somewhat over what would have prevailed in its absence; (2) this has been done with relatively little cost to the federal government; (3) the income streams derived from the program have been capitalized into the value of the land having the tobacco allotments; (4) the returns to human effort in tobacco production are not higher than elsewhere in agriculture, nor have they increased appreciably over time; and (5) the main beneficiaries of the program have been those initially acquiring the allotments under the program.

To date, our attempts to control individual crop output by controlling the land input have ranged from tolerable to disastrous. In virtually all cases, the result has been the rapid rise in the use of land substitutes, which have increased yields per acre and required continued reductions in acreage allotments. This has led to continued reductions in the acreage per farm of the controlled crop, sometimes to the point where the acreage is too small for the efficient use of machinery and operator labor. Equity problems have arisen regarding the distribution of allotments and the burden of sharing reductions in allotments. These and other problems have led many to suggest the abandonment of the use of acreage as a method of production control and the use of quantity controls over marketing as an alternative.

LAND INPUTS AND TOTAL FARM OUTPUT

The acreage allotment and marketing quota programs that were used in the postwar period did not restrict the use of land that had been removed from the controlled crop. As a result, the excess production of some of the controlled crops merely was transferred to other crops not having acreage allotments.

A United States Department of Agriculture study of the effect of acreage allotments upon agriculture had this to say: [5]

Under the acreage-allotment programs, farmers were free to put the land diverted from allotment crops to other uses. In both 1954 and 1955, farmers used most of the diverted acreage for other harvested crops; only a small percentage was used for pasture and fallow. From 1953 to 1955, when both the planted and harvested acreage of the 4 allotment crops decreased by nearly 29 million acres, the acreage of other field crops increased by about 27 million acres.

Most of the diverted land was used for 7 crops—oats, barley, sorghum, soybeans, flaxseed, rye, and hay. For these crops, the percentage changes in harvested acreage, production, and yield from 1953 to 1955 were:

	Harvested Acreage (Per Cent)	Total Production (Per Cent)	Yield (Per Cent)
Oats	+4	+30	+25
Barley	+66	+61	−3
Grain sorghums	+105	+113	+4
Soybeans for beans	+26	+38	+9
Flaxseed	+10	+11	+1
Rye	+49	+61	+8
All tame hay	+3	+7	+3

Better weather and the use of more intensive cultural practices were the two main reasons for the higher yields of these 7 crops in 1955. In addition, much of the land that was shifted from allotment crops to these crops was more productive than the land normally used for these nonallotment crops.

Two independent studies of the control programs in other areas reported about the same results.[6] In general, farmers used

[5] *Effects of Acreage-Allotment Programs,* Production Research Report No. 3 (Washington: Agricultural Research Service, U.S.D.A., June 1956), p. 6.

[6] G. E. Brandow and E. W. Learn, *Effects of 1954 Acreage Reductions on Crop Production in Southern Pennsylvania,* Progress Report No. 128 (State College: Pennsylvania State University Agricultural Experiment Station, Dec. 1954); and Dale E. Hathaway, "The Effects of Agricultural Production Controls in 1954 on Four Michigan Farming Areas," *Quarterly Bulletin of the Michigan Agricultural Experiment Station,* East Lansing, 37 (May 1955), pp. 565–73.

the land diverted from crops under acreage allotment to produce feed grains and forage. Some reduction in the output of the controlled crops was achieved, but the output of livestock was increased as a result of the additional feed output and lower feed prices.

The greatest diversion that occurred under the acreage allotment programs was from wheat to feed grains. Another United States Department of Agriculture study showed: [7]

The Two Plains regions and the Mountain region had the largest diversion of wheatland to feed grains. From 1952–53 to 1957–58, the acreage of wheat harvested in these three regions decreased by 9 million acres. This reduction was more than offset by an increase of 12 million acres of feed grains.

The feed grains produced upon this diverted acreage amounted to just about the equivalent of the additions to Commodity Credit Corporation feed-grain stocks in the years following the reduction in wheat acreage.

Thus the record is fairly clear regarding the use of acreage allotment programs to restrict the land devoted to a few crops. If the acreage reductions are large enough, the output of the individual crops can be reduced, but unless restrictions are placed upon the use of the diverted acres, total agricultural production will not be reduced. Therefore, the very best that can be achieved by the use of acreage allotments on individual crops is the diversion of the impact of the disequilibrium from the producers of the controlled crops to the producers of other products.

However, total farm income may be increased by such diversions. If the elasticity of demand is higher for the products which receive the additional output than for the controlled crops, total gross and net farm income will be increased by the production controls on a few crops. Thus the price supports and production controls limited to wheat, cotton, rice, tobacco, and peanuts which were sufficient to restrict production to market-clearing quantities were estimated to increase net farm income by about 10 per cent

[7] Raymond P. Christensen, Sherman E. Johnson, and Ross V. Baughman, *Production Prospects for Wheat, Feed, and Livestock, 1960–65*, ARS 43–115, Agricultural Research Service (Washington: U.S.D.A., Dec. 1959), p. 22.

over a program of no controls nor supports on any farm products.[8] The higher total net income was due to a rise in the income from the controlled crops and a decline in the income of other commodities where output was increased when resources were diverted from the controlled crops. Therefore, selective crop controls involve a redistribution of income within agriculture even though they may increase total income, and those farmers whose income will be reduced are not likely to favor them.

Acreage allotment programs for individual crops bring other problems also. The acreage allotments, particularly if enforced by marketing quotas, tend to restrict the individual farmer's flexibility in managing his farm and are opposed as being restrictions upon the individual operator's freedom. What is perhaps more important is that different farms in different areas vary in their ability to adjust to the restrictions upon the land used for an individual crop.

In some areas and on some farms, practices are possible that will increase yields and offset the allotments. Some farms have soil and climatic conditions such that good alternative crops are available. However, for some farms the alternatives are poor and adjustment to the allotments is difficult. As an example, under the wheat program, low-cost wheat-producing areas in Western Kansas received the same percentage cuts in allotments, had fewer alternative crops, and were less able to offset the acreage reductions.[9] This area, which would have been in the relatively most favorable position in the absence of the acreage allotments was thus at a relative disadvantage to other producing areas under the allotments.

These and other problems led directly to the attempts to use general land-retirement programs as a method of reducing farm output. In 1956, the Soil Bank program was authorized. Part of the program was aimed at the retirement of land from the supported crops in which output exceeded disappearance and surplus stocks were accumulating rapidly. Another part of the program

[8] See *Economic Policies for Agriculture in the 1960's, op. cit.,* p. 39.

[9] James O. Bray and Dale A. Knight, *Wheat Allotments in Central and Western Kansas: Effects and Possibilities,* Agricultural Economic Report No. 75 (Manhattan: Kansas Agricultural Experiment Station, Oct. 1956).

was aimed at the retirement of cropland from production for a period of years via rental agreements. Under the latter program, it was possible for entire farms to be placed in the *Conservation Reserve,* as the program was called, and the owner of the land received payments for keeping the land out of crop production.

Unfortunate administrative regulations reduced substantially any expectations of reduced output under the Acreage Reserve program, which reduced the acreage of the major controlled crops. Possibly some reduction in their output was achieved, but that phase of the program became more of an income transfer than an output control program.

The general land-retirement program of the Conservation Reserve is generally credited with having some effect upon total farm output. Under it, cropland acreage was reduced by about 6.4 million acres in 1957; 9.9 million in 1958; 22.4 million in 1959; and 28.6 million in 1960. Estimates vary as to what the output would have been on the retired acreage, but the conclusion was that the budget cost of land retirement was less than the loss that would have been incurred on price-supported commodities that would have been acquired in the absence of the program.

The American Farm Bureau has recommended a voluntary land-retirement program as its major proposal to deal with the disequilibrium problem in agriculture. It recommends a program that would withdraw whole farms from production on a bid basis. Acreage allotments for wheat would be ended, and the price support for wheat would be set at a level equivalent to its feed value in relationship to corn. They also recommend that the support level for corn be the average price for the three preceding crop years. Thus all of the disequilibrium in resources in agriculture would have to be absorbed by the voluntary land-retirement program.

A voluntary land-retirement program essentially is a program whereby the government offers farmers a rental value for land high enough so that sufficient resources will be removed from agriculture to balance output with disappearance at some price level. What kind of price level can be maintained and at what cost by such a program?

One analysis was made of the probable extent and cost of a land-retirement program sufficient to maintain farm prices and incomes at 1959–60 levels without surplus stock accumulation.[10] It suggested that about 59 million acres of cropland would have to be withdrawn from production and that the annual rental cost would run to about $1.5 billion annually. Costs would be lower if whole farms were contracted and higher if parts of farms were withdrawn from production.[11]

Despite the possibilities of substitution of other inputs for land, at any given price level there is some point at which such substitution is no longer profitable and total output will be reduced if enough land is retired. Obviously, the higher the price that is attempted to be maintained under the program, the more profitable substitution of other inputs will be and the greater the quantity of land that will have to be retired to achieve a given reduction in output.

The retirement of entire farms tends to reduce the substitution of other inputs for land, because some of the other inputs associated with the land that is retired usually also are withdrawn from production. It was for this very reason that there was substantial nonfarm opposition—from merchants, machinery dealers, and the sellers of other inputs used in agricultural production—to whole-farm retirement under the Soil Bank program in areas where land retirement was extensive.[12] These farm-associated businesses found that land retirement substantially reduced the local demand for services of the associated nonfarm inputs, and the political pressures from these sources were sufficient to cause Congress to end the retirement of whole farms.

The political reaction to the program is typified by Senator Mundt of South Dakota who, in commenting on the Farm Bureau's land-retirement program during the 1962 Senate hearings, said: [13]

---

[10] *Economic Policies for Agriculture in the 1960's, op. cit.*, Part II, pp. 21–32.

[11] Costs of a land-retirement program also vary depending upon whether the retirement is spread uniformly or concentrated, etc. See J. Carroll Bottum, John O. Dunbar, Richard L. Kohls, Donald L. Vogelsong, Gene McMurty, and Sidney E. Morgan, *Land Retirement and Farm Policy*, Research Bulletin 704 (Lafayette: Purdue University Agricultural Experiment Station, Sept. 1961).

[12] See Bottum, et al., *ibid.*, p. 60 and 61.

[13] *Food and Agriculture Act of 1962*, Hearings Before the Committee on Agriculture and Forestry, United States Senate, 87th Congress, 2nd Session on S. 2786 (Washington: U. S. Govt. Printing Office, 1962), pp. 367–368.

It seems to me that your proposal as presented ignores a very realistic situation, that you are absolutely destroying the overall economy of certain rural communities and certain states, certainly in South Dakota. For some reason or other we could never induce you fellows to face up to that and come up with some other program or some other scheme whereby you can take out the most productive land without dispossessing the farm of its farmer and the town of its customers.

Voluntary land-retirement programs on the whole-farm basis tend to draw most of the land from farms with low physical productivity, and where the operator due to advanced age is marginal in terms of physical capability.[14] It also attracted land where the operator was working off the farm or had prospects of doing so. Thus the program was concentrated heavily in certain areas or types of farms where the marginal value product of the resources in agriculture were low or the salvage value of the operators' labor was high in other occupations. It was this heavy concentration in certain areas that resulted in the protests from the local communities which were affected adversely.

The economic effects of a land-retirement program are to reduce the marginal value product of labor and capital in agriculture and to increase the marginal value product of land.[15] If the lower marginal value product for labor puts its value in agriculture below its salvage value outside agriculture, labor would leave agriculture. Some capital would also be withdrawn. A major effect of a land-retirement program is to increase the price of land.

Land-retirement programs, either voluntary or otherwise, represent a movement away from the optimum use of the economy's resources. Such a program removes a resource from agricultural

14 Senator Mundt also objected to the fact that big programs discriminated against areas where the land has low physical productivity (p. 369). He ignored that the higher rent on more productive land would require significantly higher program costs to remove it and that higher payments would be required to idle other more productive resources if the program were spread evenly in all areas.

15 Arnold Paulsen, Earl O. Heady, Walter R. Butcher, and Ross V. Bauman, *Potential Effect of Soil Bank and Corn Allotment Programs on Income and Resource Use, Southern Iowa,* Production Research Report No. 48, Agricultural Research Service, U.S.D.A. in Cooperation with the Center for Agricultural and Economic Adjustment and Agricultural and Home Economics Experiment Station, Iowa State University (Washington, D. C.: May 1961), pp. 21–23.

production that has little or no productive use elsewhere in the economy and, by distorting the marginal value productivity of the resources in agriculture, encourages the increased use of other inputs which have a productive value elsewhere. Thus, real output in the economy would be lower than it might be in the absence of the land-retirement program. Moreover, such programs will, if anything, reduce the returns to human effort in agriculture, even though total income to agricultural resources might be increased if the output is successfully reduced. The major benefits of a land-retirement program will go to the owners of farm land.

In light of these effects, why do farm organizations and some economists who profess a concern with efficiency in farm programs argue that a voluntary (or non-voluntary) land-retirement program is a desirable method of dealing with the disequilibrium in agriculture? Part of the answer lies in the fact that members of the major farm organizations tend to be landowners, who would obtain both higher incomes and capital gains from the programs. Farm operators who are landowners are concerned primarily with their total net income, not with their marginal returns upon their various owned inputs. Therefore, their interest in a land-retirement program is understandable. The economists' reasons for favoring such programs is not clear.

A second reason for the support for a voluntary land-retirement program is its relative freedom from government interference with the individual farm operator. He can participate if it appears profitable and benefit from its overall effects, even if he decides not to participate. A voluntary land-retirement program, especially for entire farms, is relatively easy to administer, largely because it is voluntary in nature. Also, under a successful land-retirement program, income would be received through the market, and income would be related to production or at least would appear to be.

Therefore, a voluntary land-retirement program is consistent with many of the values important in farm policy. It might achieve higher income for farm people (at least landowners); it would preserve the freedom of the individual farmer to participate or not and to manage his farm as he preferred; and it would distribute income among farmers in relationship to their output of farm products. At the same time, a land-retirement program reduces the efficiency of resource allocation within agriculture and between agriculture and the rest of the economy. While it might achieve some improvement in the incomes of many farmers, it will do so only at the cost of considerable economic loss to the economy as a whole, and it will not provide a solution for the basic problem of low returns to human effort in farming.

A compulsory land-retirement program has the same economic effects and weaknesses of a voluntary program in terms of resource use. It does, however, avoid the high budget cost of a voluntary program, which will require sharply rising payment rates in order to remove sufficient land to appreciably affect output. The shift from a voluntary to a compulsory land-retirement program affecting all producers involves some loss of freedom of choice to individual producers and will thus be opposed by some farmers.

In general, our experience suggests that a voluntary land-retirement program of a magnitude sufficient to appreciably improve farm income will not receive continued approval of nonfarm groups, because of both the high budget cost and obvious malallocation of resources that result. This is especially true of programs under which the land retirement is heavily concentrated so that the burden of adjustment falls heavily upon certain areas and communities. Therefore, despite its continued favor with many farm groups, the full-scale use of a voluntary land-retirement program seems unlikely. This likelihood is heightened by the fact that the programs must be approved by representatives of the areas which would be adversely affected.

For similar reasons, plus some additional ones, it is equally unlikely that a non-voluntary land-retirement program sufficient to appreciably reduce the disequilibrium output in agriculture will be approved. The resource allocation problems would be the same or greater, even though the budget costs would be reduced. Many farmers would oppose such a program.

All in all, neither the economic nor political potential of land retirement as a method of reducing total farm output appears highly promising. Experience has shown that land, which makes up only 15 per cent of total inputs in United States agriculture and is declining in importance, offers at best a poor way of controlling farm output.

Controlling Farm Output by Reducing Other Inputs

The discovery that research on new production techniques and information programs to hasten their adoption constitute a productive input in agriculture has caused some economists and farm leaders to suggest that the production of these techniques be slowed or halted. By this is meant that public expenditures for research and extension work on agricultural production techniques should be drastically reduced.[16]

A policy that reduces public expenditures for research and education in agricultural production techniques has two great weaknesses. First, it would not be particularly effective at this point in time, and second, the real cost of such a policy to the economy might be rather high.[17]

The reason for the probable ineffectiveness is that much of the development and dissemination of information about improved production techniques in agriculture is now done by the private sector of the economy. Undoubtedly, abolition of agricultural experiment stations would slow this, or at least increase its cost, but to be really effective would require the ending of all basic research—both public and private—for improved agricultural techniques can come from departments of chemistry and botany as well as from departments of farm crops and animal husbandry.

The more fundamental question is the cost to the economy of foregoing expenditures for research upon new production methods. Loomis and Barton have estimated that it would have cost the economy an additional $9.6 billion annually to produce our 1957 output of farm products with resources having a productivity of 1940 levels and $16.3 billion more annually to produce the 1957 output with resources having a productivity of 1910 levels.[18]

[16] See Willard W. Cochrane, "Some Reflections Upon Supply Control," *Journal of Farm Economics*, **41** (Nov. 1959), p. 713 n for such a view.

[17] Both points are recognized in Earl O. Heady, "Public Purpose in Agricultural Research and Education," *Journal of Farm Economics*, **43** (Aug. 1961), pp. 566–81.

[18] Ralph A. Loomis and Glen T. Barton, *Productivity of Agriculture, United States, 1870–1958*, Technical Bulletin 1238, Agricultural Research Service (Washington: U.S.D.A., April 1961), p. 54.

This probably overstates the savings involved, but, in any case, they clearly are large.

The economy only benefits from such savings if, when new and more productive resources enter agriculture, some of the existing resources leave to produce other goods and services. If many resources are "trapped" in agriculture, most of the potential gains from the new resources are lost, for the net result of their entry is lower farm prices and higher than desired output of farm products. Thus while policies to promote the discovery and adoption of new techniques may offer very high returns to the economy, much of the potential gains from such a policy are lost unless there is attention to the problem of transferring the excessive resources from agriculture to other productive uses.

Our public policies in general, and especially for agriculture, have been to maintain high expenditures for research and information on new production techniques. There is evidence that such expenditures have contributed significantly to our national economic growth. We have not, however, recognized that resource immobility can dissipate an important fraction of these benefits or that in industries such as agriculture, the cost of such growth is great upon the individuals in the industry. To forego the gains from such growth would be costly to our economy; therefore, the search for measures that will redistribute its burden somewhat in line with its benefits must continue.[19]

There are other publicly-supported output-increasing expenditures in agriculture for which no similar justification exists. These are the public subsidies for reclamation projects, and fertilizer, lime, tiling, and irrigation under the guise of agricultural conservation. A very high proportion of these expenditures go for inputs which increase farm output in the short run and will sustain the increase in the long run. During the decade prior to 1958 more than one-half of the approximately $250 million annual Agricultural Conservation Payments went to subsidize practices which would immediately increase farm output.[20] In the Corn

[19] See T. W. Schultz, "A Policy to Redistribute Losses from Economic Progress," *Journal of Farm Economics,* 43 (Aug. 1961), pp. 554–65.

[20] This and the immediately following data are taken from an unpublished research paper prepared for the author by Melvin L. Cotner, Graduate Student at Michigan State University.

Belt, about 60 per cent of the practices were of a nature that immediately increased farm output (fertilizer, drainage, and irrigation), and in Michigan, more than three-fourths of the payments went for these practices.

These programs reduce the cost of these output-increasing practices (inputs) to farmers so that their marginal value product *to the farmer* exceeds their net cost and increased use is warranted. These inputs increase total farm output and further reduce the returns to existing resources in agriculture. Some of the previous resources may leave agriculture, but they may be resources which have a lower value to the economy than the subsidized inputs would have if they had been used elsewhere. The programs result in allocations of resources to agriculture where they have a marginal value product substantially below their true cost to the economy, and the programs, therefore, represent a substantial malallocation of resources.

The best that can be said for the programs is that they are income redistribution programs. Income is transferred from nonparticipants to participants and from the economy at large to the nonfarm producers of the subsidized inputs. It is this latter group that provides much of the political pressure for a continuation of these "conservation" programs, just as politicians and local businessmen are the main proponents of reclamation projects.

It is inconsistent, and somewhat surprising, that policy makers and farm organizations with concerns about the disequilibrium resource use in agriculture continue to support these reclamation and pseudo-conservation programs. Such programs are inconsistent with virtually all of the values related to farm price and income policy and, therefore, attest to the strength of values relating to conservation and to the political power of a relatively small group of beneficiaries.

Proposals have been made, but not seriously received, that would limit the use of other inputs in agriculture, usually by the application of a tax that would raise the price and thus reduce its use. However, the substitutability of the various inputs in agriculture brings widespread recognition of the difficulties in this or any other attempt to control total farm output via the restriction of a single input.

Direct Control over Farm Output

The obvious difficulties of achieving a reduction in farm output through controlling the land input has led to the recommendation of a direct supply control program for agriculture. Certainly the strongest advocate of such an approach is Willard W. Cochrane.[21]

The rationale put forth by Cochrane is much as discussed earlier—the inelastic demand for farm products, increases in output, and disequilibrium levels of prices and earnings in agriculture.

The supply control program as set forth by Cochrane has four general principles:

1. Congress would determine the *fair* price for farm products, presumably a price that would provide income equality or "equal economic opportunity" for farmers.
2. Sales quotas would be set for each farm product at levels that would clear the market at these predetermined fair prices. Quotas would be for final products and not for intermediate products.
3. Each farmer would receive a prorate share of the national quota based upon his historical record of production. Once the program was in operation, it would be illegal to market products included in the program without a covering quota certificate.
4. The marketing certificates would be negotiable.

The advantages of such a system are obvious. Income to agriculture could be increased and maintained at some higher level without the major problems of stock accumulation, surplus disposal, or high budget expenditures. Some of the difficulties have been recognized too—the capitalization of the higher income into the certificate values, the problems of administration and control involved, and the problem of transferring marketing rights,[22] but

21 See *Farm Prices, Myth and Reality, op. cit.,* and "Some Further Reflections upon Supply Control," *op. cit.,* pp. 696–717.

22 For a discussion of both advantages and problems see Cochrane, "Some Further Reflections on Supply Control," *op. cit.* and *Economic Policies for Agriculture in the 1960's, op. cit.* Part IV, pp. 49–64.

several problems have not been adequately discussed, and others have not been discussed at all.

SUPPLY CONTROL, RESOURCE USE, AND INPUT PRICES

The initial objective of a supply control program would be to reduce farm output, and the continuing objective would be to maintain lower output levels than would occur in the absence of the program. The first objective implies either that some resources now producing farm products would be unemployed or that physical production efficiency would decline (output/input decline). The second or longer-run objective would imply that some resources that might otherwise be used to produce farm products would not be so used. What are the implications for the short- and long-run input prices and resource use in agriculture?

The application of marketing quotas at levels below the existing farm output will involve a reduction in the resources used in agriculture. Which resources will be unemployed depends upon the supply elasticity of the different resources. Resources "fixed" in agriculture have a supply elasticity close to zero down to the point where their returns in agricultural production are less than their salvage value outside agriculture. The supply elasticity of variable inputs is somewhat higher, and thus the initial impact of the adoption of a supply control program which reduced the absolute level of output would be to reduce the use of such inputs as fertilizer, irrigation, insecticides, etc. Since the salvage value of land outside agriculture is low, the supply elasticity of land is very low and most of it would continue in production. However, the owners of "fixed assets" in the form of operator labor, land, and durable capital, would find some of these assets unemployed. Therefore, they would desire to buy some marketing certificates in order to maintain these assets in use. They would bid for these marketing rights until the *net* marginal return on their fixed assets (marginal value product minus the cost of the marketing certificates) was reduced to the return these assets could obtain outside of agriculture. The equilibrium point in this process would be reached when the net marginal value product of each of the various resources in agricultural production were equal. Specification of the exact point would require knowledge of the marginal physical productivity of resources in agriculture and their supply elasticities over the relevant range.

With a supply control program that actually reduced farm output, the quantity of farm land used would not be reduced. However, the return to land and its value would decline, perhaps sharply. Hired labor use would decline, and operator labor might also decline as the net marginal return of some of it (after considering the opportunity cost of keeping the certificates instead of selling them) fell below its value outside of agriculture. New machinery purchases would decline, and the asset value of existing machinery would decline. The short-run use of variable inputs would decline. The lower farm output thus would be produced on about the existing quantity of farm land, but with somewhat less labor and less purchased inputs. Eventually, the net marginal return to labor and land would be no higher under the program than it would be if there were no program at all. It might even be lower, depending upon the size of the reduction in output and whether, in the absence of a program, the marginal value product of the fixed assets exceeded their salvage values.

A general supply control program, applied to a condition of disequilibrium and excess capacity, would result in a deflation of land values and no significant increases in the returns to human effort in farming, even though the total income to the industry might be increased.[23] The higher income would accrue to the owners of the marketing certificates. Where these were the farm operators and landowners, their net asset position might be improved, but if any certificates were given to tenants, there would be a substantial redistribution of assets between tenants and landlords as the value of land declined and the value of marketing certificates rose. The capitalized value of the negotiable marketing certificates would thus depend largely upon the relationship between the salvage value of the fixed assets in agriculture, especially of labor,

---

[23] Cochrane, *op. cit.*, pp. 704–5 recognized that the certificates would have a capitalized value. However, he mistakenly asserts that the returns to all factors of production would rise, whereas actually in the short-run the real net returns would not rise appreciably and might even fall, although total net income in agriculture would be increased.

and the gross marginal value product of labor in producing farm products at the controlled price level. If the salvage value of labor were close or equal to the gross returns from producing the controlled farm product, then no one would pay for marketing certificates to acquire the right to produce farm products. This apparently was the reason that tobacco quotas acquired no value in some areas. However, if product prices were set high enough to achieve incomes in agriculture equal to nonfarm incomes, the salvage value of farm labor would be obviously lower, and the certificates would have a value. In other words, the higher the price and income goal, the greater the value that the certificates would acquire.

The problem of capitalization of marketing certificates has usually been passed off by acknowledging its inevitability and asserting that it makes little difference. If, as discussed in Chapter 11, the marketing certificates that acquired capitalized value were rights to newly created income streams, this might be more nearly the case. If, however, they are substitutes for other programs which have influenced asset values (such as acreage allotments and price supports), then the capitalization and who receives it makes a great deal of difference. Farm people are rightly interested in more than their current income, for most of them own physical assets involved in agricultural production. The effects of programs upon the value of these owned assets may be as important as their effects upon current income. Therefore, the capitalization problem is a major consideration in the application of strict output controls.

The ultimate effects of a general supply control program of the type described is the same whether you begin it from a price-support program with acreage allotments and land retirement such as we have had in the recent past, or whether you begin it from a position of market-clearing "free" prices. In the former case, you will deflate returns to fixed resources from current levels to market-clearing levels, and, in the latter, the returns to these "fixed assets" will never rise appreciably above these levels.

What does such a program imply for the efficiency of resource use within agriculture and between agriculture and the nonfarm economy? Since the resources that will be unemployed are those that have the highest marginal value product elsewhere, such a method of controlling farm output should represent a superior allocation of resources to methods of output control through land retirement. Moreover, as long as the marketing certificates are negotiable, producers with lower costs would use this cost advantage to bid certificates away from higher-cost producers.[24] If, as some suspect, large scale farms have a real cost advantage over smaller family farms, rapid farm consolidation might result because operators of smaller farms would make more selling their marketing certificates and working outside agriculture than they could by farming.

Thus, in terms of static resource allocation there is no reason that a general supply control program of the type advocated by Cochrane would impair resource allocation in the economy, as long as the marketing certificates are freely negotiable. If they are not negotiable, resource allocation could be substantially impaired as Cochrane recognizes.

Practically speaking, no one—including its most ardent proponents—believes that such a general supply program for agriculture would be adopted by all producers. Therefore, if adopted, it would be adopted piecemeal, and its results would be somewhat different. Some resources engaged in producing those crops or products adopting a supply control program would be pushed into the production of other crops, increasing the output of those crops until the marginal value product of some of the resources in farming would be below the salvage value outside agriculture. Owners of fixed assets would bid for the marketing quotas on the controlled crops until the net marginal returns from producing the controlled crops would be the same as in producing noncontrolled crops. This means that the application of the controls to products with a highly inelastic demand, like wheat and milk, would increase the production of products with a higher demand elasticity.[25] Total gross and net income in agriculture would be

[24] This assumes that the cost differences are due to something other than different salvage values for fixed assets.

[25] G. E. Brandow, *Interrelations Among Demands for Farm Products and Implications for Control of Market Supply*, Bulletin 680 (University Park: The Pennsylvania State University, College of Agriculture, Agricultural Experiment Station, August 1961).

increased; the income of producers of the controlled crops would be increased; and the income of existing producers of noncontrolled crops would be reduced. It is probable that producers of uncontrolled crops might be forced to adopt a control program in self defense.

LONGER-RUN IMPLICATIONS OF SUPPLY CONTROL

The short-run problems of static resource allocation are probably less important than the long-run changes in technology and production methods. What effect would a comprehensive supply control program have upon these?

It has been argued that stable prices and good incomes under a comprehensive supply control program will increase the rate of adoption of technology.[26]

To the extent that the new methods were cost-reducing by increasing output (fertilizer, hybrid corn, irrigation), they would require an outmovement of existing resources since total output could not be expanded. This would be accomplished by the adopters of the changes using the expected (or realized) benefits of the technology to bid away the marketing certificates held by other producers. Where the technology was cost-reducing without affecting a change in physical output (a machine that does the same work, but costs much less to design and manufacture), the early adopters would benefit, and they would again have an incentive to bid some certificates away from nonadopters. Therefore, the ultimate benefits of the new technology would accrue largely to the owners of the marketing certificates and not to consumers in the form of lower product prices as they would in the absence of intervention in the market. This would be parallel to the tobacco situation where the major benefits of technology have accrued to the owners of land having tobacco allotments.

Some of the proponents of a comprehensive supply control program do not recognize that there is nothing in the program that will maintain the size of the agricultural population or that will maintain the continued excessive quantities of resources in agriculture. It is recognized by some groups that furnish inputs to agriculture, and supply control is vigorously opposed by them

26 Cochrane, *op. cit.*, pp. 712–13.

for this reason. It is likely that merchants in small towns heavily dependent upon farm people for trade would find the comprehensive supply control program had the same or worse effects on their business as the Soil Bank, and they undoubtedly would be equally opposed if they realized its implications.

A valid question is whether farm people should be asked to bear the burden of rapid increases in productivity, when the nature of the industry is such that it results in chronic low returns for their efforts. Increases in productivity that mark economic progress are much easier to absorb in an industry where the demand for the product is growing rapidly, so that the adjustment can be made by reducing the relative labor input *while the absolute input remains steady or rises.* Agriculture is not such an industry and, therefore, if we insist that the maximum possible gains in productivity be achieved, equity considerations demand that some attention be given to the costs of these gains to farm people. Comprehensive supply control would not do this, except that it would allow the initial owners of certificates to capture gains from technology.

The foregoing discussion is in terms of a static labor force in agriculture and does not take into account the normal departures from the farm labor force due to death and retirement. What would be the value and disposition of the marketing certificates belonging to such individuals? If potential new entrants to the controlled, stabilized agriculture were able to accurately forecast their expected gross marginal returns from resources committed to farming, they would enter only if their net earnings after purchasing the marketing certificates would be equal to their opportunity costs in other occupations. The stability of the program should enable potential entrants to avoid errors in earning expectations from the sources that now cause overcommitment of resources to farming, so that, given a long enough period, the real returns to factors in agriculture should equal the real returns to factors elsewhere in the economy. At this point, the real price of farm products would be above the true equilibrium price by the amount necessary to cover the capitalized value of the marketing certificates; the resources employed in agriculture would be less than the optimum quantity; and resources producing farm products would be earning an equilibrium return. Thus in the very long run, after all of the present labor and durable capital in agriculture was replaced by another generation and another group of durables, the economy would be operating at less than maximum output (in terms of consumer satisfaction) because farm products would be overpriced. Nor is it possible to solve this problem by merely lowering the relative price of farm products, for this will merely deflate the value of the "fixed assets" then in agriculture and not the price of the marketing certificates.

TECHNOLOGY UNDER LIMITED SUPPLY CONTROL

No one believes that comprehensive supply control, even if tried, would be applied to all products, especially if a vote of approval by the affected producers is required. What then would be the effect of supply control on a few products upon the rate of technological advance in the controlled products and the uncontrolled ones?

As before, the early adopters of technology would attempt to acquire more marketing certificates so as to increase output. However, the productive resources displaced from the controlled crop would move into the next most profitable alternative, which probably would be in agriculture. The owners of the resources producing the uncontrolled products would thus find their returns lowered to the point where the employment of some resources outside of agriculture would be more profitable, and eventually some of these resources would leave farming. Thus a limited supply control program with negotiable marketing certificates would intensify the problems of resource adjustment for the uncontrolled products, because they essentially would be absorbing the resource adjustments for the controlled crops in addition to those for the products they produce.

THE IMPLICATIONS OF NEGOTIABILITY

The maintenance of internal efficiency in resource allocation in agriculture requires that the marketing certificates be made negotiable. In the absence of negotiability, some resources would be unemployed on every farm, with some of the unemployment being taken in the form of unwanted leisure for farm operators who would be unable to find part-time work and who could not sell their marketing certificates and leave agriculture. In the absence of negotiability, the resources unemployed would not be those which have the highest value elsewhere in the economy, and most of the potential gain to the nonfarm economy from such a program (from obtaining higher real output by employing some resources outside agriculture) would be lost. Moreover, nontransferable quotas would substantially reduce the incentive to adopt new practices or other changes that would result in gains to the economy.

Farmers and farm leaders who look with favor upon supply control programs generally do not favor the idea of negotiability of the marketing certificates, and the reason for their suspicion is fairly obvious. Negotiability will drive the real return on their fixed assets down to its salvage value and implies a rather significant redistribution of assets. There is virtually no conceivable way in which the certificates can be distributed other than on the basis of present or recent past output, and this is not necessarily even closely related to the ownership of fixed assets.

Another reason that farmers fear negotiability is because if the movement of the marketing certificates had the effect of drastically reducing local population, the cost of community services for the remaining individuals would rise sharply. Since the community services are paid for through a tax system and the marketing certificates sold in a market, there is no way in which the increased community costs arising from outmigration can be priced into the value of the certificates.

An even greater fear on this matter is found among the nonfarm persons in rural communities whose incomes are dependent upon serving farm people. Such individuals would have the same violent objections to the negotiability of marketing certificates, with the possibilities of wholesale movements of people out of certain agricultural areas, as they had to the whole-farm Soil Bank which had the same effect.

This concern was expressed by Senator Proxmire in the 1962 hearings on the proposed dairy quotas. He said: [27] "You see, this is more than just simply a matter of concern for the farm com-

27 *Op. cit.*, p. 284.

munity. This is a matter of concern for the whole community, for the village, for the area. If they lose their allotments, they are in a very bad situation. The community becomes a ghost town."

It is quite probable that the impacts of such a program upon areas heavily dependent upon agriculture would be much less than anticipated. People would leave agriculture where the salvage value for labor outside the industry is highest, and this would tend to be in areas where they could change occupations without physical migration. It is probable, then, that most of the operator labor that would leave agriculture with the initial application of a supply control program with negotiable certificates would not be in remote areas where community resources or business activity are largely dependent upon the farm population.

Farm people and others, who believe that the family farm adds political and social stability to our society also fear making marketing certificates negotiable because they fear that larger-than-family units are more efficient and would use their cost advantage to bid certificates away from operators of family farms. This, of course, might happen if there are economies of scale beyond the family farm. However, the use of some device to prevent acquisition of quotas by large farms would represent a choice between efficiency in the economy and the assumed social stability attributed to a larger number of independent family farms. Some argue that family farms really are as "efficient." If so, then no such device would be necessary because the transfers would not take place without them. If such prohibitions are necessary, then they are not costless, and the cost should be considered rather than ignored or assumed away.

THE PROBLEM OF INAUGURATING
SUPPLY CONTROL

If a supply control program for agriculture could be inaugurated at a time when the industry was in equilibrium—so that no excessive resources were employed in the industry and all factors were earning their acquisition costs—supply control would present few problems of income and asset redistribution within agriculture. However, under those conditions no one would want or need such a program, so that it is only considered when the disequilibrium is so large that its cost—in terms of farm income or budget cost—is great enough to force drastic political action.

The application of either a comprehensive or limited supply control program involves the distribution of rights to future income flows. Moreover, depending upon how these are distributed, it inevitably will involve a redistribution of asset values for the existing productive assets in agriculture. The distribution and redistribution of present and future assets under such a program is a value problem in which making one person better off will automatically result in another being worse off. For this reason, it is to be expected that a supply control program and the details of its operation will involve major political struggles.

While it need not do so, a supply control program might be a vehicle whereby income and assets in agriculture were redistributed to produce substantially less inequality than now exists. The existing political power structure in agriculture is not dissatisfied with the present income distribution, or at least not enough to attempt to change it toward less inequality, but the present political power structure in agriculture cannot either individually or as a group achieve a comprehensive supply control program without at least the consent, and probably the aid, of nonfarm political groups. Two of these groups, the labor unions and the political parties, have power structures that tend to cause them to favor more equal distribution of incomes than now exist in agriculture, and it is possible that their political support will not be forthcoming for the creation of such assets and income streams unless the distribution thereof is consistent with their values.

It is not clear whether the implications of the necessity of urban approval have been realized by some of the most ardent supporters of supply control programs—who are not necessarily among the poor and disadvantaged in agriculture. It is quite possible, given the present political situation, that some of the supporters of a supply control program would suffer a net loss because of the program, even though the net income to agriculture was increased as a result of it. The issue of whether or not the certificates are negotiable will not affect this situation, for its impact rests largely upon the initial method of distributing marketing certificates and not upon whether the certificates can subsequently be sold.

FREEDOM AND COMPREHENSIVE SUPPLY CONTROL

The greatest opposition of farmers to comprehensive supply control arises not over its implications for efficiency or income distribution, but its implications for the freedom of farm operators. It is asserted that such a program will substantially reduce the freedom of the individual farm operator.

Specifically, such a program would restrict the total quantity of products a farmer could market to the quantity of marketing certificates he owned. If, however, the marketing certificates are negotiable and a market for them established, this would not constitute an absolute amount of products. The quantity that could be sold would depend upon the certificates a farmer could acquire, just as the amount that an individual now can market is dependent upon the inputs he can purchase.

As long as the certificates are negotiable, they merely constitute an additional fixed cost and, therefore, such a program would not constitute a barrier to entry in the industry. The freedom that actually would be restricted is the freedom of the individual to expand *aggregate* output in a competitive market. Such a program would face the individual producer in agriculture with much the situation facing a monopolist with an inelastic demand curve, where every increase in the output of the firm results in a reduction in marginal revenue.

A comprehensive supply control program which did not permit negotiable marketing certificates would indeed constitute a drastic restriction upon the freedom of the individual farm operator. Total individual output would be fixed at the level of the marketing certificates, and entry would be dependent upon one's ability to obtain an allocation of certificates. Such restrictions are not unknown elsewhere in our economy and are accepted as a part of the business, but this neither justifies nor condemns their application in agriculture.

In one way, the freedom of the farm operator under a comprehensive supply control program would be greater than under a program of compulsory acreage allotments. A supply control program will allow the individual producer to combine the inputs under his control in the best possible way so as to maximize his income under this total marketing quota. An acreage allotment program involves both interference with internal resource allocation and some restriction on the ability to expand total output, whereas a program which controlled marketings would involve only the latter.

Supply Control and Instability

Supply control is not a useful policy tool to deal with the problems of stability in agriculture arising from shifts in aggregate demand due to changes in employment and income, nor is it a useful solution to the problems of fluctuations in income arising from unplanned changes in output due to weather. It would, of course, reduce the uncertainty and instability arising from the internal instability of production cycles in agriculture.

A supply control program would require some kind of storage program for storable products, and the storage program would absorb the income shock of declines in demand. However, if chronic stock accumulation is to be avoided, production in some future period would have to be reduced, and thus the adverse shifts in demand would be reflected in producers' income sooner or later.

Unfortunately, under such a program, producers probably would pressure for marketings consistently at the full-employment level of demand, with some kind of extraordinary programs to dispose of surpluses that failed to clear the market during periods of slackened demand. Thus, while the program could and probably would be operated so that producers' incomes would not suffer as the result of declines in nonfarm employment and income, such a program would do so at the expense of the nonfarm public and would not constitute a substitute for a program that maintained demand and employment.

Not only would a supply control program be ineffective in dealing with unplanned changes in farm output, but such changes would be a serious problem for an effective supply control program. This is why a supply control program would require a storage and price-support program if it were to be effective, and it would be the storage program, not the supply control program, which would provide protection to farmers' incomes from unplanned changes in output. A storage program can perform this function as well in the absence of supply control as with it.

The relative price stability (some might prefer to call it rigidity) between farm products that would be achieved under a comprehensive supply control program should improve the internal resource allocation in agriculture. Assuming that the relative prices are consistent with the relative utilities of consumers for the different farm products, much of the inefficiency of resource allocation that now arises from the instability of relative prices in agriculture would be removed. Here again the economy would gain by the release of resources from agriculture to the production of other goods and services, assuming that the marketing certificates were negotiable and that alternative employment for the resources was available.

Supply Control and the Poverty Problem

Supply control has never been put forth seriously as a solution to the poverty problem in agriculture. In fact, at the very best, it would be neutral in this regard, and quite possibly it would have a regressive effect upon the income position of the very poor in agriculture.

Assuming that marketing rights under a supply control program would be distributed among farmers on the basis of their recent past production, it would be about neutral for some of the very low-income people in agriculture and would clearly lower the income of others.

Incomes would be reduced to hired farm laborers and older farm operators partially or largely dependent for their income upon renting their land. It was pointed out earlier that the effects of a supply control program not tied to land would be to reduce the real net returns to those factors having the least elastic supply function. This would mean that labor returns and land rents would take most of the initial brunt of unemploying some resources from agriculture.

The impact of such a program, regardless of whether or not the marketing certificates were transferable, would be to reduce the wage rates of hired labor (assuming their alternative opportunities outside of agriculture are limited). Attempts to help hired laborers by the imposition of a minimum wage would merely unemploy them without improving their employment opportunities elsewhere. Since this group has virtually no political power, either within or outside agriculture, it is unlikely that they would receive any substantial consideration in the formulation of a supply control program.

Older farm operators and retired farm operators who have invested their savings in farm land and are largely dependent upon the rental income from this land also would have their income and assets reduced. This is assuming that bona fide tenants (who vote—at least in the Midwest) would receive part of the marketing certificates and the benefits therefrom. Of course, supply control that operates through land retirement would increase the income and assets of individuals dependent upon the ownership of farm land and would work to the disadvantage of tenants, hired farm workers, and sharecroppers. The relative influence of landowners in farm organizations may explain why most farm organizations push for output controls operating via land inputs rather than for general controls over marketing.

Those low-income farm operators who would receive a proportional share of the benefits of a supply control program would have their income level improved by such a program, but they would still be among the low-income group in our society. Given their present low productivity and output, some fractional increase in price for that output would not provide a solution to their basic underlying problem of too few productive assets. Moreover, the number of such farmers is still so large that a policy which attempted to correct the skewed distribution of physical and human assets in agriculture via the distribution of marketing rights probably would reduce substantially the efficiency of resource use in agriculture without solving the basic problems of low productivity.

Summary and Implications

Farmers and their leaders have long believed that their bargaining power in product markets is limited by their inability to control aggregate output. Some form of output control is the major idea behind several of the farm policy proposals of recent years. The inelasticity of demand for farm products, individually and in the aggregate, makes the idea of controlling farm output an appealing solution to the disequilibrium problem in agriculture. Attempts have been made at such controls for individual crops and for total output. To date, these attempts have been something less than successful, partially because they have concentrated on reducing the land input—for which there are ample substitutes—and partially because the control programs have not been actively pursued to their ultimate end.

Output controls, regardless of the method pursued, will result in the unemployment of some of the resources engaged in producing farm products. Land retirement removes an input that has little or no productive value elsewhere in the economy and, therefore, constitutes a serious malallocation of total resources in the economy in both the short and long run. Moreover, the benefits of land-retirement programs will accrue to landowners, and the returns to labor in agriculture will not be increased by a land-retirement program. In fact, labor returns will be reduced by such a program to the salvage value of labor outside of agriculture. Voluntary land retirement is expensive in terms of budget costs, tends to be self-defeating, and tends to be heavily concentrated in a few areas. Compulsory land retirement represents the same or greater malallocation of resources, and involves substantial restrictions upon the freedom of individual operators, but the budget costs of the program would be less. Thus there are significant political barriers to either a voluntary or compulsory land-retirement program large enough to reduce farm output to the level of current disappearance.

A comprehensive supply control program that limited marketings of farm products to some predetermined level would also unemploy some resources from agricultural production. Since those unemployed resources would be those with the highest value elsewhere in the economy, the implications of such a program for resource use would be better than a land-retirement program. However, all of the income stream arising from the program would be capitalized into the value of the marketing certificates if they were negotiable, and the marginal returns to the labor now in agriculture would not be improved. The income of those owning the marketing rights would be protected and increased, partially at the expense of those owning resources whose asset value would be reduced by the program.

Over a period of time long enough so that the present owners of resources in agriculture are replaced by another generation, the returns to resources producing farm products should be comparable to those elsewhere in the economy under a comprehensive supply control program. Such a program should not affect the rate of adoption of new technology, but the benefits of the technology will accrue primarily to the owners of the marketing certificates rather than to the consumers of farm products. However, since the resources used to produce the needed farm output would be reduced, the economy would gain increased total real output as a result of the employment of some resources elsewhere.

It is unlikely that it will be politically possible to obtain either a land retirement or marketing control program sufficiently restrictive to deal effectively with the disequilibrium problem in United States agriculture. Major issues of resource use, freedom, and income and asset distribution are involved. The use of compulsory controls over farm output, either via land retirement or otherwise, involves major distribution problems within agriculture. Given the commodity and area fractionization of the agricultural committees in Congress, it is unlikely that the internal political forces in agriculture can resolve them. The direction that would be taken if they are resolved by political forces in the nonfarm economy is difficult to determine.

Chapter 13

Compensation and

Tax Policies

Most United States farm policies to deal with the income problems in agriculture have attempted either to influence the demand
for farm products or to reduce farm output. Price support and
storage programs to maintain the price of farm products have resulted in stock accumulation, in large auxiliary costs for storage,
and in very large budget costs for the improvement in farm income. Demand expansion programs are expensive in terms of the
improvement in farm income achieved. Policies that have attempted to control farm output via land retirement have distorted
resource use and are not especially effective. General controls over
farm marketings have not been tried, but they would result in
serious administrative problems and substantial reallocation of
income within agriculture.

The serious problem of resource allocation that arises under
most price support and production control programs has led many
economists to conclude that the problem of maintaining equitable
income in agriculture ought to be separated from the problems of
resource allocation. They suggest some kind of direct policy to
deal with the problem of farmers' income that does not interfere
with either the production of or the demand for farm products.

The programs that have been proposed include direct government payments to farmers, income insurance, and modification of the tax structure.

Direct Payments

Contrary to popular opinion, direct payments to farmers were not devised by Secretary of Agriculture Brannan in 1949 when he included them as one of the support methods in his controversial Brannan Plan. Direct payments were proposed and written into law in the 1930's as "parity payments" and were used on several commodities in the 1930's.

In 1945, the American Farm Economic Association held a contest for the best essays on farm price policy. Virtually all of the 18 winning essays included a recommendation that income aid to farmers, if any, should be achieved through the use of direct government payments to farmers.[1] T. W. Schultz advocated compensatory payments in his 1945 book, *Agriculture in an Unstable Economy*,[2] as did D. Gale Johnson in his *Forward Prices for Agriculture*.[3] Brandow [4] recommended a version of direct payments as did Galbraith in 1955.[5] Thus many economists concerned with farm policy have, at one time or another, recommended the use of direct payments as a solution to "the farm problem."

Despite all of the intellectual power favoring them, direct payments, as such, have not been regarded favorably by practicing policy makers. The reason for the strong political opposition to the use of such a program will be discussed after some of the economic implications are discussed.

---

[1] William H. Nicholls and D. Gale Johnson, "The Farm Price Policy Awards, 1945: A Typical Digest of the Winning Essays," *Journal of Farm Economics*, **28** (Feb. 1946), see especially pp. 273 and 276.

[2] (New York: McGraw-Hill, 1945.)

[3] (Chicago: The University of Chicago Press, 1947.)

[4] G. E. Brandow, "A Modified Compensatory Price Program for Agriculture," *Journal of Farm Economics*, **37** (Nov. 1955).

[5] J. K. Galbraith, "Farm Policy: The Current Position," *Journal of Farm Economics*, **37** (May 1955).

THE ECONOMIC IMPLICATIONS OF DIRECT
PAYMENTS

The idea of "direct" or "compensatory" payments is simple. Under such a policy, the market for farm products is allowed to clear, and the income of producers is maintained at some predetermined level by making direct payments from the Treasury for the difference between the market price and some predetermined target price or income.

The economic appeal of such a policy is obvious. There are no problems of stock accumulation or export subsidies. Consumers are able to consume the entire farm output, and consumers' prices are lower than under a support or control program. Whereas the incidence of a production control program falls upon consumers, the cost of a direct payment program is distributed according to the general federal tax burden. Farmers are free to combine resources on their farms in the way they prefer, without the interference of acreage allotments or production controls.

However, a direct payment program would do little or nothing about the problem of excessive resources devoted to the production of farm products. In fact, if the payments were made on total output, the program might act as a powerful incentive to increase output where the marginal returns (from the market plus payments) on certain products exceeded the cost of the additional input. Thus an unlimited direct payment program probably would involve either a steadily-rising public expenditure to maintain farmers' incomes or require some form of production control program.

However, Brandow has shown how a direct payment program could avoid these problems by assigning individual quotas to producers and making the payment upon some portion of these quotas.[6] Under his scheme, the marginal price that faced producers would be the market price, so that the payments would not constitute an incentive to increase output unless the additional output were profitable at market prices. He also would limit payments on livestock to original producers in order to

6 G. E. Brandow, *op. cit.*, and *Economic Policies for the 1960's, op. cit.*, pp. 65–74.

avoid making excessive payments where value-added was low.[7] Another way of handling this problem would be to require persons who purchased feed or livestock to transfer an equivalent quantity of the certificates for which payments were to be made to the seller of the grain or the feeding stock, so that feeders would only obtain payments upon the value added in their feeding operation.

Such a program would not have the economic results that are predicted by most of its opponents. It would not "stimulate production, increase unit costs, depress market prices" as charged by the Farm Bureau.[8] Since the payments would go to individuals, it might, however, tend to maintain more farm operators in farming than would market-clearing prices in its absence, for operators' incomes in agriculture would be maintained at some higher level, thus requiring a higher salvage value elsewhere to attract them from the industry. However, as long as the income in agriculture was not increased by the payments to levels above other industries, so that additional labor was attracted to farming, this probably would not represent a serious resource allocation problem. Since a limited payment program would not attract an excessive quantity of other productive resources into farming, as does any program which maintains market prices, it would provide better resource allocation than most alternatives, including land retirement.

DIRECT PAYMENTS AND DISEQUILIBRIUM

The widespread endorsement of direct payments by economists was by and large by those who assumed that the income problems in commercial agriculture were temporary or, in other words, that with full employment there would not be a chronic disequilibrium in resource use and income in United States agriculture. Direct payments were recommended as the most desirable way of handling low incomes in agriculture arising from declines in nonfarm demand during depressions. Most proposals contained a cut-off point for the direct payments when some level of "full" employment was regained.

[7] *Ibid.*, p. 70.
[8] *Farm Bureau Policies for 1962*, p. 11.

The use of direct payments in a situation of a large and chronic disequilibrium in agriculture is a somewhat different matter. Given the present resources producing farm products and the inelastic demand for farm products, the Treasury cost of a payments program to maintain income in agriculture would be very high if income were to be maintained at anything approaching recent levels. If income levels were appreciably lower, there would be a substantial decline in the income of farm people and a substantial downward revaluation of assets in agriculture.

Brandow has estimated that an unlimited direct payment program to maintain farm income at 1959 levels would require an annual expenditure of $5.5 billion in the early 1960's.[9] Moreover, the annual cost would increase over time with such a program, as farm output increased in response to the program.

A direct payment program which limited the maximum payment per farm operator to $2,500 annually and which limited payments to 80 per cent of the operators' base production would cost much less, partially because farm income would be lower. Brandow estimated that such a program might cost about $2.2 billion annually, but that the net income of farm operators from farming would be substantially less than under the existing price-support program, although it would be above market-clearing levels by the amount of the payment. Asset values in agriculture probably would decline appreciably under such a program.

This highlights one of the greatest economic problems of using direct payments to deal with the disequilibrium problem in agriculture. Essentially, the payments program does not attempt to deal with the disequilibrium in resources engaged in agriculture, for it merely is a policy to prevent the impact of the excessive resources from falling completely upon farm incomes. Thus, like price supports or subsidized consumption programs, a direct payment program is not a positive policy to deal with the basic problem, but is a policy to mitigate some of its symptoms. With a direct payment the economy would still have a lower total income than it might attain by transferring some resources from producing farm products to other goods and services, and taxpayers would bear the burden of a major income transfer program.

9 G. E. Brandow, *Economic Policies for the 1960's, op. cit.*, p. 68.

Even so, a direct payment program probably is preferable to a loan and storage program or a consumer subsidy program, as far as most consumers and taxpayers are concerned. At least, most of the budget expenditures would go to farmers and not for storage and interest costs on accumulated stocks, and consumers, both at home and abroad, would benefit from the lower product prices.

Two additional points need to be made regarding direct payment programs. It has been stated that direct payment programs constitute unfair competition, pitting our Treasury against foreign producers. This might be valid if one is discussing an unlimited program covering all output, but it would not be a valid criticism of a limited program of the type Brandow has proposed. Under it, producers would receive only the market price for the last 20 or 25 per cent of their production, and their output would not exceed what it would be without a program—unless the payments extended to such a large portion of output that part of exports were covered. In fact, it would appear to be none of our foreign competitors' business as to the level at which we choose to maintain our farmers' income, as long as our products are not sold abroad with an export subsidy or at a price which fails to cover the marginal cost of producing the exports. Therefore, a payment program limited to quantities consumed domestically would appear to be much more consistent with our international trade policy than is our present policy of export subsidies.

A second fallacy is the assertion that limited direct payments constitute a subsidy to consumers. This rests upon the assumption that payments are made on output to the point where some of the output has a marginal cost of production that exceeds its price. Under a payment program which limited payments to some fixed portion of a past production, this would not occur.

One of the appealing features of a direct payment program to many nonfarm groups is the very fact that it would not automatically result in a substantial reduction in farm output or a significant displacement of farm people. The prospect of continued high output of farm products, together with a reasonable level of farm income, is appealing to groups that sell farm inputs, market farm products, or are dependent upon farmers for sales of consumption items. Processors of United States farm products also often favor the use of payments because their raw materials cost would be lowered. This would improve the competitive position of processed United States farm products both at home and abroad, and this appeals greatly to cotton mills, among others.

Therefore, despite its probable high budget cost, a program of direct payments receives a good deal of support from many sources as a method of living with, if not solving, the disequilibrium problem in United States agriculture. It would avoid stock accumulation, expand consumption, be consistent with our foreign trade policy, and protect the income of farmers. It would offer little or no positive inducement to reduce the quantity of resources producing farm products. However, all of the demand manipulation programs offer continued inducements to expand the resources producing farm products, and production control programs either remove the wrong resources or, in the case of quantity controls, force them out by unemploying them.

DIRECT PAYMENTS AND INSTABILITY

Direct payments were conceived largely to deal with shifts in demand arising from shifts in nonfarm employment and income. They are useful in this context since they would allow an uninterrupted flow of products to market. This would allow consumers to consume the same quantity of farm products during a depression without a substantial reduction in the income of farmers.

A direct payment program is less well adapted to deal with the instability of farm prices and incomes that arise from unplanned shifts in farm output. A direct payment program would allow wide shifts in consumption and prices with varying crop size and would not provide the utility to consumers of a storage program which stabilized consumption from year to year. For products which are not storable, however, a direct payment program would stabilize farmers' incomes in the face of varying output.

The use of direct payments as a policy to stablize farm income for the producers of crops with a highly inelastic demand, such as potatoes or dry beans, will result in very high program costs in years of large crops, and direct payments will continue one of the major problems facing the producers of such crops. Relative price instability is one of the major reasons for erroneous resource allocation within agriculture, for it makes it difficult for farmers to allocate the resources at their disposal among products in the best fashion. Direct payments would do nothing to solve this problem and might even worsen it. Thus, direct payments on feed grains, without a stabilizing storage program, could prove to be a major destabilizing factor in livestock production because livestock producers would face a relatively stable product demand and highly unstable input prices. The net result might be the introduction of even greater cyclical changes in livestock production and prices than in the past.

In general, direct payments would be a useful policy device for dealing with certain of the stability problems in agriculture. Shifts in domestic demand, output fluctuations in nonstorable products with a relatively elastic demand, and some of the internal instability problems of agriculture could be handled by price guarantees implemented with direct payments. As long as the average price level for these guarantees did not exceed the expected average price for a normal crop under full employment, the program cost would not be excessively high. When such a program is used to maintain income guarantees well above the average expected market price as a method of dealing with the disequilibrium problem, then the program costs will mount rapidly as the Brandow estimates show.

THE POLITICAL BLOCK TO DIRECT PAYMENTS

No one has ever suggested that a payments program would be of any great import in dealing with the poverty problem in agriculture. It, like all of the other programs where benefits are related to current or past output, would do little or nothing to improve the well-being of those persons whose productivity in agriculture is low. However, a direct payment program would appear to offer significant economic advantages over past, present, or contemplated alternative programs to deal with some of the disequilibrium problems and with certain stability problems in agriculture. Despite these apparent advantages, direct payments are rarely used. How does one explain this phenomena?

The failure to use direct payments lies with the values of farm people and their leaders and the extraordinary veto power that farm groups and certain individual congressmen can exert over farm policies under the committee system in Congress.

The values involved are that income ought to be earned in the market and that the price of farm products should be high enough in the market so that farmers will be able to attain "equal income opportunity" without direct subsidies. The concept involved is something of a "fair price" concept which Cochrane rightly discusses as a concept of importance to farm people.[10] The Grange resolutions mention this idea by saying: [11] "Americans have both a moral and economic obligation to pay an American price for United States farm products which they use or consume."

The Farm Bureau resolutions combine a similar idea with other value-loaded concepts by saying: [12] "Payment programs would socialize the production and distribution of food and fiber by having consumers pay a part of the cost through taxes—rather than full value at the store."

The concept of a "fair" price in the market is a particularly frustrating one to economists because, unlike many of the value concepts of importance to farm policy, it cannot be given analytical content by the familiar tools of analysis. Economists can discuss "efficiency," or at least a limited concept of it, and ideas like "welfare" and "equal opportunity" if they are expressed in money terms, but the concept of a "fair" price cannot be expressed in the same terms.

The opposition to direct payments rests not only upon the value that income ought to be obtained via a "fair" price in the market, but it also is dependent upon some rather practical political considerations. Demand expansion, price support, and production control programs all make some portion of the income transfers to farmers through the market in the form of higher product prices. Direct payments would place both the total and the individual income transfer involved clearly in the open and

[10] W. W. Cochrane, "Some Further Reflections upon Supply Control," *op. cit.,* p. 701.

[11] *1960 Summary of Legislative Policies and Programs of the National Grange, op. cit.,* p. 9.

[12] *Farm Bureau Policies for 1962, op. cit.,* p. 11.

as the Farm Bureau says, "would make farmers dependent upon Congressional Appropriations."

Now, of course, farmers are dependent upon Congressional approval and appropriations for other programs as well. But, the other programs disguise or cloud the real cost of the programs to the rest of the economy. It is entirely possible that the legislators representing nonfarm constituents would oppose income transfer programs of the recent magnitude if they and their voters knew the actual costs involved.

An even more likely occurrence is that under a direct payment program there would be some upper limit upon the payments to a single farm operator, probably at some level that would prohibit payments to larger than family-size farms. It would be too much to expect that the Congress would approve "welfare" payments running into six figures or more to the owners or operators of very large farms whose income may well compare favorably with the upper 5 per cent of the nonfarm population. However, an upper limit on payments would be inconsistent with the value that incomes should be distributed within agriculture according to output.

Thus, direct payments probably would lead to a reduction in achievement of two important values in agriculture: that "fair" incomes should be received from "fair" prices *in the market* and that income should be related to one's contribution to total output. What is of major importance is that an upper limit on payments would deny the second value (and income) to those farmers who are most influential in congressional policy.

It happens that the chairmen of the powerful agricultural committees and the very inflential Chairman of the Subcommittee on Agricultural Appropriations of the House Committee on Appropriations are adamantly opposed to the use of direct payments for major farm commodities. Their opposition may be due to the highly-skewed income distribution in Southern agriculture and their dependence upon the more prosperous farmers (who would be hit by the probable payment limitations) for support and advice. Their opposition may be due to the high budget cost that such a program would entail and the possibility that the income transfer would be reduced in size if it were to become obvious. Or their opposition may be due to their personal sharing of the values related to obtaining income in the market and having it distributed according to one's contribution to output.

This opposition was expressed openly by Mr. Whitten in the 1962 appropriations hearings. He said: [13]

Based on my experience on this committee I have always warned against—speaking only for myself—compensatory payments.

I take the view that appropriations to cover compensatory payments to any sizable extent would not be forthcoming through the Congress. If you had such a program, it is my belief that there would be limitations to it that would become so restrictive that in effect you would not have any program.

Whatever the reason for their opposition, there is no question as to its existence. When this is coupled with the intense opposition of the Farm Bureau leadership to direct payments, it becomes virtually impossible to obtain legislation or appropriations to authorize a direct payment program, even if such a policy were desired by other groups including many farmers. Some observers believe the failure of the agricultural committees to approve the administration program in 1961 was because the legislation would have permitted the use of direct payments where they are appropriate.

Despite their values relating to fair prices and income distribution, farmer opinion surveys have shown that many farmers are not opposed to the use of direct payments, especially upon perishable products.[14] Regardless of the preferences of some farmers and many nonfarm groups for the use of direct payments program for certain commodities, the particular processes by which farm policy is made enable a few individuals to effectively prevent the adoption of such a program. Anyone believing that the processes of policy formation are neutral in their program selectivity can correct this misimpression by investigating the fate of most proposals for direct payments.

[13] *U.S.D.A. Appropriations for 1963: Hearings*, Part I, p. 96.
[14] See Dale E. Hathaway and L. W. Witt, "Farm Policy: Whose Valuation," *Journal of Farm Economics*, 34 (Aug. 1952) and the periodic surveys of farmers' opinions on policy issues published in *Wallaces' Farmer*.

A major breakthrough of this political barrier occurred in the final passage of the Food and Agriculture Act of 1962. After a prolonged political battle in each House, somewhat different versions of legislation were sent to a conference committee. The bill that finally resulted from the conference committee and was approved by the Congress contained a form of direct payments for two major commodities—the 1963 crop wheat and feed grains. Neither of the two versions that was sent to conference contained this provision!

The particular version of payments authorized was "payment-in-kind" to eligible producers. Since the payment-in-kind is in the form of certificates, negotiable in cash as well as in commodities, it constitutes a direct payment. There is a major distinction, however, in that direct appropriations are not required for CCC redemption of payment-in-kind certificates. This bypasses the opposition of the powerful House Subcommittee on agricultural appropriations. And, of course, having been introduced in conference committee, the payments did not have to be approved by a majority of either of the agricultural committees.

This suggests that the use of this policy device is dependent upon the political processes through which it must pass. Only time will tell whether the 1962 experience will make this device politically more acceptable in the future.

Income Insurance for Farmers

Boris Swerling has proposed an income insurance program for farmers as a substitute for all price support, production control, and other farm price and income proposals.[15] While the proposal has been generally disregarded by policy makers and undoubtedly will continue to be, it was highly enough regarded by his peers to be awarded the American Farm Economic Association Award for the best published research in 1961. Therefore, it deserves analytical attention which it has not yet received.

---

[15] B. C. Swerling, "Income Protection for Farmers: A Possible Approach," *Journal of Political Economy*, 47 (April 1959); and "Positive Policies for American Agriculture," *Goals and Values in Agricultural Policy* (Ames: Iowa State University Press, 1961).

The proposal is appealing in its simplicity, because it avoids all of the obvious economic difficulties inherent in commodity price supports, demand expansion programs, and production controls. To quote: [16]

The measure attempts to apply standard principles of social insurance, along the following lines:

1. As with unemployment insurance, benefits would be related to the income experience of the individual farm operator during the recent past.
2. Social security practices would be followed in establishing an upper limit on the amount of insured income, and there would accordingly be a modest ceiling on the total benefits enjoyed by a particular individual.
3. Benefits would accrue only to growers who suffer an abnormal reduction in income, not to prosperous and distressed individuals indiscriminately.
4. Specifically, a grower would draw benefits if his farm earnings in a given year fell more than, say, 25 per cent below the average of the preceding 5 years. The maximum base income would be set at $4,800, net equivalent to some $15,000, gross.
5. The right to benefits would attach to the person, not to farm land or to the farm enterprise, and would accordingly not be transferable.
6. Benefits would not be conditional upon the production of particular commodities or even upon continued employment in agriculture.
7. Benefits would be scaled downward as off-farm sources of income rose, but at the same time contingent protection would be afforded to persons shifting from farming to other occupations.
8. The plan would be contributory and compulsory, but the federal government would subsidize the program by making premium payments on some matching basis.

Actually, the income insurance program is a form of direct payments in which the payments are based upon past income experience rather than upon commodity price levels and the payments are attached to individuals rather than commodity output. In this case, the payments are based upon 75 per cent of the aver-

[16] Boris Swerling, "Positive Policies for American Agriculture," *Goals and Values in Agricultural Policy, op. cit.,* pp. 312–13.

age income of the five previous years (up to $4,800 income annually). The contributory feature adds an element of forced savings to the program, but this is more a matter of fiscal ethics on the part of the originator than a matter of importance.

INCOME INSURANCE AND DISEQUILIBRIUM

The author of the proposal specifically questions whether a disequilibrium in resource use in agriculture exists and, in fact, suggests that farmers' real income position is underestimated and that the true facts would show the incomes of farmers to be quite good.[17] Admittedly, the income level of the 800,000 or so most productive commercial farms is good, as was shown in Chapter 2, but even on these farms the returns to human effort in farming are low compared to returns for comparable effort elsewhere. Real or alleged capital gains do not change this fact, and besides if capital gains are to be discussed, we should include those of wealth-holders in the nonfarm economy. Despite Swerling's assertions to the contrary, there has been and continues to be a substantial disequilibrium in United States agriculture, with too many resources producing farm products and some of them obtaining very low returns as a result.

An income insurance program of the type proposed would do little or nothing either to improve resource allocation in agriculture or to hasten the outmovement of excessive resources, although allowing the payments to continue for those leaving agriculture would avoid "locking in" people to obtain benefits. Once the initial transition to market prices was completed, it would offer no improvement in either resource allocation or farmers' income beyond that offered by any program of market-clearing prices.

Even the transition cushion that would be offered by such a program is limited. In Table 1, the net incomes of two types of commercial farms reported by the United States Department of Agriculture are shown. The Northern Plains cattle ranch is shown, because it has the highest coefficient of variation in income of any type of farm reported in these United States Department

17 *Ibid.*, pp. 314–15.

of Agriculture statistics. The small cotton farm was chosen, because it has the lowest capital investment of any of the farms reported, and the program was proposed as a "social insurance" program with welfare implications.

Table 1

Net Income and Program Benefits Under an Income Insurance Program

	CATTLE RANCH—NORTHERN PLAINS			COTTON FARM—DELTA (SMALL)		
	Reported Net Income	Average of Past 5 Years	Program Benefit	Reported Net Income	5 Year Average	Program Benefit
	(1)	(2)	(3)	(4)	(5)	(6)
			DOLLARS			
1947	7,955	4,468	0	1,877	*	†
1948	7,824	4,464	0	2,379	*	†
1949	3,024	4,578	410	1,515	1,709	†
1950	5,087	4,359	0	1,877	1,756	0
1951	9,804	4,445	0	1,619	1,883	0
1952	6,470	4,445	0	1,964	1,853	0
1953	4,303	4,445	0	2,072	1,871	0
1954	3,765	4,701	0	1,736	1,809	0
1955	2,830	4,494	542	2,334	1,854	0
1956	2,140	4,100	935	1,975	1,945	0
1957	4,163	3,568	0	1,437	2,016	81
1958	6,423	3,540	0	1,372	1,910	61
1959	5,162	3,747	0	1,996	1,770	0
1960	4,980	3,954	0	1,759	1,882	0

* Data not available.
† Data not available but probably zero in view of the later experience.

Source: Cols. I + 4, Costs and Returns on Commercial Farms, Long-Term Study, 1930–57, Statistical Bulletin No. 297, Economic Research Service (Washington: U. S. D. A., Dec. 1961). Cols. 2 and 5 computed from data in Col. I. Cols. 3 and 6, benefit payments assuming that payments are made when net income falls below 75 per cent of previous 5-year average and that payments bring income up to 75 per cent of the average.

Using the income insurance program that has been suggested (with a $4,800 upper limit on income insured), the higher income farm would *receive benefits in only three years*, even though its net income declined from $9,804 in 1951 to $2,140 in 1956—with a decline in every successive year. If you assumed that from 1956 on, the net income remained at $2,000 annually (because other programs were ended), a payment of $191 in 1957 would have been the only additional payment.[18] Over the 14 years covered by the statistics, the program benefits for the cattle ranch would have averaged 2.5 per cent of net income and for the cotton farm less than 1 per cent of net income.

The principle of social insurance just does not help those engaged in an industry in disequilibrium. It is true that workers temporarily unemployed from an industry because of cyclical fluctuations in demand are helped by unemployment insurance, but the coal miners in West Virginia and the auto workers in Michigan who exhausted their unemployment compensation in 1954 and were never rehired find little comfort in the aid that unemployment insurance gives workers who were temporarily unemployed in 1961. The same would hold true for a farm program that based its assistance in each year upon the experience over a short period of preceding years. Thus, it is clear that the income insurance scheme as proposed would offer no longer-run solution at all to the disequilibrium problem in United States agriculture, and it would offer virtually no cushion to the short-run adjustment to a market-clearing price level.

INCOME INSURANCE AND INSTABILITY

The income insurance program was not aimed at dealing with the disequilibrium problem, and it is, therefore, not surprising that it would provide little help to that situation. It was devised to deal with instability in agriculture. In the words of its author: [19] "Income variability—whether the result of natural hazards, changing market circumstances or special commodity cycles—does remain a real hazard of commercial agriculture, and public policy can reasonably seek to moderate its impact upon the individual farmer."

---

[18] In his *Journal of Political Economy* article, Swerling shows the number of farms that would receive payments under his scheme. However, he shows neither the distribution nor absolute amount of the payments. He shows 34 farms would have received payments out of a possible 300 cases (25 farms times 12 years), so my example of 3 payments out of 26 cases is reasonable for a small sample. It is unlikely that most of the payments on other farms would have been as large as I have shown, because the average income level is lower and the variability less for most farms than for the cattle ranch.

[19] *Ibid.*, p. 315.

However, as it turns out, the proposal as put forth would offer only modest help in this area. A reference to the preceding Table 1 shows that because of the cut-off limit on covered income, a farm operator with a very high variance in income would only receive benefit payments in three of the thirteen years covered by the data. If his average income substantially exceeded the $4,800 base limit, it would be virtually impossible to collect benefits under such a program. The only beneficiaries under such a program would be those with low average incomes and extremely high variance in income. About the only persons that come to mind in this regard would be small fruit farmers. The data for the small cotton farm show that under the proposal the operator would have received a modest benefit payment despite sharp declines in income.

Of course, the weakness that hardly anyone would ever receive a benefit payment could be partially remedied by removing the upper limit on covered income and increasing the percentage of coverage. The limits, however, were those imposed by the author of the program, and they had the avowed purpose of avoiding over-generous coverage or protection of the fortunes of higher-income farmers. These goals were met! If the income cut-off were removed and the coverage raised, the program would become another direct payment program based upon income rather than commodity prices and one with several appealing features.

The inclusion of income from all sources would recognize that many farm operators actually are more dependent upon nonfarm income than upon the production of farm products, and it would prevent subsidization of the income of such persons. The attaching of the payments to individuals rather than farm output should increase appreciably the outmovement of people from farming to other occupations, and such a program would provide a cushion during the transition. If the program were not extended to new entrants, it would have a terminal point—a feature which is not obvious in any form of commodity support. However, the program undoubtedly would face the same political opposition from farm groups as do other direct payment programs, even if its rates were adjusted to levels where substantial benefits would be received.

Certain other weaknesses of the income insurance approach to the stability problems in agriculture could not be overcome by tinkering with the rates and levels in the program. The problem of fluctuating supplies and their uneven distribution over time would not be solved, nor would the problem of uncertain prices facing producers. These problems, as in any direct payment program, would remain.

The Use of Taxation Policies to Stabilize Farm Incomes

The instability of farm income from one year to the next not only is disconcerting to farmers personally, but it also results in their incurring a substantially greater federal income tax liability than would persons with the same average income received in equal annual increments. This is shown in Table 2 where the tax liability from a fluctuating income is compared with that from a steady income of the same average size.

Table 2

Federal Income Tax Liability with Two Income Distributions Over Time *

	Unstable Income	Federal Income Tax	Stable Income	Federal Income Tax
1954	$ 3,765	$ 200	$ 4,209	$ 281
1955	2,830	31	4,209	281
1956	2,140	0	4,209	281
1957	4,163	272	4,209	281
1958	6,423	805	4,209	281
1959	5,162	552	4,209	281
1960	4,980	516	4,209	281
Total	$29,463	$2,376	$29,463	$1,686

* Assuming a joint return with 2 dependents and 1961 tax rates.

The farm income data used is the data for the hypothetical Northern Plains cattle ranch in the previous table. It shows that the unstable farm income would have incurred income tax obligations that exceeded those for the same average stable income by 41 per cent. The reason for this disparity is the personal exemption and the progressive structure of our federal tax system. It would not be difficult to put forth a situation in which the disparity is even greater by merely increasing the average level of the fluctuating income and the variance around the average.

On the face of it, there is little consistency in a government policy to improve returns to commercial agriculture and a federal tax policy which puts such a heavy penalty upon farmers who are subject to large year-to-year fluctuations in income.

The present federal income tax law allows a net income loss to be carried back three years or forward five years to be applied to other years' net income. However, on most commercial farms, net income losses are not particularly common, although large fluctuations in net income (after depreciation) are relatively common. Carry-back and carry-forward provisions are not of help unless actual losses are incurred.

Several suggestions have been made that would enable farmers with fluctuating incomes to avoid the higher incidence of federal income taxes because of unstable incomes. One suggestion involves the purchase of savings certificates from years of high income which would then be declared as income in subsequent years of low incomes.[20] In essence, the scheme is a modified form of forced savings because the government would hold the saved income until the earner declared it as income by cashing the certificates in some subsequent year. While this scheme would stabilize realized farm income after taxes from year to year, it would require a cumbersome and complex record system to administer it. It is an unduly complex way of avoiding the inequitable tax burdens upon persons having fluctuating incomes.

There is no reason that a system of forced savings needs to be imposed upon farmers. No evidence suggests that farmers have an unduly high propensity to consume or that the capital market cannot handle most year-to-year fluctuations in income that remain if the proper price stabilization policies are operative. Therefore, the major problem would appear to be the inequitable income tax burden resulting from fluctuating incomes.

The American Farm Bureau has recommended that individ-

20 E. Lloyd Barber, "Modifying the Federal Income Tax to Promote Greater Stability of Farm Income," *Journal of Farm Economics*, **30** (May 1948).

uals and unincorporated businesses be allowed to defer depreciation from years when they are unable to receive the full tax benefits to years of higher income. They also recommend that unused
personal exemptions be allowed to be carried forward or backward as business losses are now.

The extent to which these devices would reduce the tax liability for farmers with fluctuating incomes would depend upon
several factors. The deferred depreciation would be of greatest
value to farmers whose expenses were heavily weighted with de-
preciable investments. The tax savings would be greatest for those
with the highest income and with the greatest income variance.
The carry-over provision on personal exemption would provide
the greatest benefits to those with large families and highly variable incomes.

The carry-over provision for personal exemptions is hard to
justify on economic grounds. Congress has granted certain levels
of personal income tax exemptions that have no particular economic rationale, and there would appear to be little justification
for allowing farmers or others with variable income to apply these
exemptions as a method of reducing tax liabilities.

On the other hand, there would appear to be an economic
justification for allowing depreciation allowances to be shifted to
years in which income is high. Depreciation on capital is a legiti-
mate business expense, and the equipment involved is necessary
for the production of income. It would appear justified to allow
business expense (depreciation) to be taken so as to produce the
same net income after taxes that would be obtained if the individual were engaged in an industry where his capital produced a
stable net income. This would have some of the same effect that
income averaging would have, although the latter would have an
even greater effect upon reducing tax liabilities on fluctuating
incomes.

None of these tax devices will reduce the actual fluctuations
in net farm income. They would reduce somewhat the inequities
that arise in our tax system that now substantially penalize farmers who have highly variable incomes.

General Summary and Conclusions

Two devices, compensatory payments and income insurance, have been suggested as ways of getting away from the difficulties inherent in commodity price supports and production controls. Neither would strike at the basic problem of disequilibrium in agriculture. Direct payments would deal with the income side of the problem via large budget expenditures, but such a program would not encourage a significant reallocation of resources from the production of farm products to other goods and services. The use of limited direct payments would, however, end the incentive offered by price supports and production controls for the addition of more resources to the production of farm products.

Income insurance based on recent history would be of little value in dealing with the disequilibrium problem in agriculture, either in terms of farm income or in terms of improving resource use. It, like direct payments, would reduce the incentive to additional output by allowing market-clearing prices to prevail.

Direct payments are a way of handling the problems of income instability, especially that arising from shifts in demand. Income insurance could do the same if it were properly adjusted. The benefits to farmers in terms of protection would be directly related to the costs, for income insurance becomes direct payments if it is noncontributory and guarantees some fixed income level.

There is strong political opposition from some individuals and groups against the use of direct payments. These arise from the fear that nonfarm people would not tolerate the income transfers if they become readily apparent as they would under such programs. Some persons also object to having income distributed outside the market and feel that limitations would be placed upon payments which would discriminate against higher-income farmers.

The advantages of some form of payments over our past programs cause many groups to favor their use. This is especially true for nonfarm groups who are concerned with the international complications of our present programs and who object to the steadily mounting cost of surplus stock accumulation. They believe that at least consumers should enjoy the benefits of high consumption and lower food costs in return for our high farm program expenditures. The political power of these groups in farm policy is gaining slowly. However, it may be some time before it is enough to bring the adoption of such a program for a major commodity.

Chapter 14

Programs Outside Agriculture

Both reasoning and experience indicate that the major economic problems of United States agriculture cannot be solved entirely within the industry. The low returns to resources in agriculture, especially to human effort, are the result of a combination of economic circumstances in agriculture relating to the demand and supply conditions in the industry and the immobility of resources out of farming once they have been committed. The cost of dealing with this problem by manipulating the demand side is so large as to virtually rule it from consideration. Dealing with the problem on the supply side will require a reduction in the resources producing farm products. This reduction in resources, and the way in which it is accomplished, has important implications both for total output of the economy and for the welfare of farm people and the communities in which they live. Increasingly important decisions will be made that affect resource movements from agriculture, and they will be made by a president and congressmen from the large urban centers, who are little impressed by the quality of farm living and rural communities where they have never campaigned, let alone lived.

Resource mobility is more dependent upon governmental policies outside of agriculture than upon what generally is regarded as farm policy. Policies outside agriculture can influence the well-being of agriculture and can operate either as substantial complements to policies within agriculture that attempt to improve the welfare of farm people, or as deterrents to adjustments which will improve the well-being of farmers. This chapter will discuss some of the important policies that are not directly related to farm price and income policy, but which are crucial to the maintenance of a successful farm income policy in a political democracy.

The Crucial Importance of Full Employment

The vital role of full employment in the economy in a solution to our farm problems seems so obvious to many as to hardly warrant mention. Yet, it must not be obvious to many farm people and their spokesmen, for they are often in the forefront of those opposing public policies to expand employment. In this opposition they are often joined by the business groups in small towns, who somehow seem to feel that the benefits of full employment accrue solely to large industrialized urban areas.

Full employment is a necessary condition for a solution of each of the farm problems—disequilibrium returns in agriculture, instability, and poverty. As we shall see, however, it is a necessary but not sufficient condition for at least the first and third.

Full employment is an especially crucial condition for a solution to the disequilibrium problem. The low returns for human effort in farming must be attributed in large part to the "trapping" of excess labor in agriculture because of the low salvage value of this labor outside of agriculture. The salvage value of labor outside of agriculture is a function of the earnings available to a farmer outside of farming and the cost of obtaining these earnings. These earnings are a function of the wage rate in jobs which might be available to farmers and of the expected probability of obtaining employment at those wages. The fact that nonfarm work pays considerably better than farming holds little appeal to the farmer who also knows that there are many unemployed nonfarm workers, many of whom have both the qualifications and desire to take one of those jobs if they became available.

Moreover, when many of the unemployed have previous work experience in similar jobs, the farmer knows that the probability of his getting the job is somewhat below that of the other job seeker.

There is ample evidence that the salvage value of labor outside of agriculture rises rapidly with reductions in the nonfarm unemployment level. All of the available evidence suggests that this is of much greater importance than either the absolute or relative level of farm income, for outmovement from agriculture has been most rapid during some periods of greatest absolute and relative prosperity in agriculture.

As long as there is substantial unemployment in the nonfarm economy, a removal of resources from agriculture will not significantly increase national output. Neither soil bank nor supply control, which remove people from agriculture, will produce better resource allocation or higher national income if the resources are paid to accept unwanted leisure or forced to accept unemployment. In fact, part of the adverse reaction to the soil bank in some areas came from nonfarm workers who objected because farmers left their farms and undercut the local labor market for unskilled or semi-skilled labor. A full-employment economy would have prevented or reduced this reaction.

Full employment is an essential in an economy that expects to achieve the maximum possible gains in income from technical change, changes in organization, scale, or other sources. Such changes all involve the transferring of resources from employment in one sector or industry to alternative employment. In a full-employment economy, these changes are relatively painless for most individuals and industries because they involve a relative decline in growth or employment rather than an absolute decline. Thus, the prospect of higher income merely attracts new resources into the expanding areas of employment without a decline in the absolute income level of the existing resources.

However, for some industries the changes in the economic structure are so rapid that absolute declines in factor returns occur for existing factors committed to the industry experiencing the change. Where, as in agriculture, very large absolute declines in income are required to achieve significant reductions in the resources used, the costs of such changes in resource use also are very large. These costs are borne largely by the individual resource owner and not by the society at large that benefits from the changes in resource use.[1] Nonfarm unemployment substantially increases the reductions in income necessary to induce resource mobility and may make the costs so high as to be politically unacceptable.

Farm people have had the political power to force the general public to bear some of this cost in the form of extensive commodity price supports, soil banks, and subsidized consumption programs. Since they have permanent price-support legislation on the books, they have been able, through the congressional committee system, to prevent nonfarm groups from forcing more of the costs of these adjustments upon the owners of farm resources via compulsory land retirement without payments, comprehensive supply controls, or lower price supports. A full-employment economy that increased substantially the nonfarm value of labor and other resources now in agriculture would reduce the losses that would be experienced by farm people if they left farming.

This is not to say that people who have left farming in past years have experienced losses relative to what their position would have been had they stayed in farming. However, most of the group that left did not come from productive commercial farms. Blank found that farmers who had held off-farm jobs and returned to agriculture had lower incomes in 1955 than those farmers who had never worked off the farm.[2] The difference was especially pronounced for those who had taken off-farm employment following World War II and after the age of 35. He concluded that these were persons who tried to leave agriculture and were unsuccessful, because they were marginal in the nonfarm labor market during periods of unemployment. Therefore, these individuals probably took an absolute loss over time by acting on the belief that their earnings would be higher outside of agriculture than in it.

The major loss experienced by either those remaining in agri-

---

[1] This point is clearly made by T. W. Schultz in his "A Policy to Redistribute Losses from Economic Progress," *Journal of Farm Economics*, 43, No. 3 (Aug. 1961).

[2] Blank, *OASI Data of the Farm Labor Force, op. cit.*, pp. 201–12.

culture or leaving after farming for some time is the wide difference between original expected earnings and earnings actually
realized. It is impossible to believe that the preference for farming is so great among farm-reared people that they entered farming with the clear expectation that they would never make more
than one-half the income that people with comparable abilities
would earn in the nonfarm economy. Instead most people enter
farming with the belief that they will obtain incomes equivalent
(in real money and satisfaction) to nonfarm incomes. When this
turns out to be untrue, they often find that the nonfarm jobs
available to them offer little income improvement over their present situation and usually involve a lower social status.[3]

The Purdue studies were made in 1958 and 1960, both years
of substantial nonfarm unemployment. They suggest that at the
time the salvage value of labor outside of agriculture was not appreciably above its earnings in agriculture, which, of course, were
heavily dependent upon government programs. Full employment
would be one of the necessary conditions to bring the expected
income from leaving farming above the income from farming for
many persons in agriculture.

While the desirability and the necessity for full employment
is seen by virtually everyone, the United States has discovered that
our international position can place severe restraints upon the
domestic policies which may be actively pursued to achieve this
desirable goal.[4] One of the common prescriptions to expand domestic employment is via the reduction of short-term interest rates
which stimulate investment. However, during the last decade
the United States has become the international banker, with the
dollar the international currency. A reduction in short-term interest rates now stimulates a sufficient outward movement of short-
term capital to threaten the gold reserves that back our currency.

3 Philip G. Olson, *Job Mobility and Migration in a High Income Rural Community*, Research Bulletin No. 708 (Lafayette: Purdue University Agricultural Experiment Station, Nov. 1960); and R. D. Geshwind and V. W. Ruttan, *Job Mobility and
Migration in a Low Income Rural Community*, Research Bulletin No. 730 (Lafayette:
Purdue University Agricultural Experiment Station, Sept. 1961).

4 See the interesting papers by Harry G. Johnson, *Canada in a Changing World
Economy*, Allen B. Plaunt Memorial Lectures, Carleton University (Feb. 15 and
17, 1962), University of Chicago.

In addition, full employment tends to induce price rises that reduce our commodity exports and stimulate commodity imports. These shifts, together with our extensive foreign military and economic aid programs, have resulted in large deficits in our balance-of-payments sufficient to become a major continuing policy concern.

Thus, the tight-employment economy that would be necessary to appreciably reduce the large gap between the acquisition cost and salvage value of excess labor now "trapped" in United States agriculture may be effectively blocked by other national and international policy considerations. We feel that our foreign assistance programs are vital to our and the free world's security and that to remedy our balance-of-payments problem by reducing this aid is impossible. At the same time, we feel we must protect the reserve position of our currency, and we show no predilection for abandoning our fixed exchange rate. As long as these international policies dominate our thinking, there is only modest hope of attaining a sufficiently low level of unemployment to reduce appreciably the disequilibrium problem of agriculture.

Labor Mobility as a Solution to the Farm Problems

The maintenance of full employment is a necessary condition to achieve a reduction in the gap between acquisition costs and salvage value for labor in agriculture. But, is it a sufficient condition and, if not, what would be required to bring the returns to human effort in farming up to the point where they would be within a politically and socially tolerable distance of nonfarm returns?

On the face of it, the problem appears deceptively simple. If the salvage value of labor now engaged in agriculture could be increased to approximately the level that similar human resources are getting elsewhere in the economy, then there would be a major shift from employment in agriculture to other industries. Assuming this situation can be maintained, then any new productive resources would enter farming only if they could receive comparable incomes (including money and satisfaction), and they would leave if earnings in farming fell below comparable levels. Thus, the real world would approach the theoretical world of perfect competition which underlies economists' models of optimum resource adjustment. As we shall see, there are still several gaps between this ideal and reality.

The maintenance of full employment would not suffice to bring the salvage value of labor presently in agriculture up to its acquisition cost. Even if every person now in agriculture could get a nonfarm job at the wage rates paid nonfarm counterparts in education, ambition, and abilities, a gap would still remain. Farm people, by the nature of their occupation, are scattered geographically, with a very large portion of them considerably removed from major centers of employment. This means that their expected earnings from the alternative employment must be discounted by the costs of commuting or migrating to the place of nonfarm employment. For single persons the cost of physical migration may be modest, but for married couples with families it is not, as many college professors can attest. Moreover, there is evidence that physical migration fails to take place despite the existence of income differentials far in excess of those required to cover moving costs.

One of the reasons for this phenomenon is the continued existence of uncertainty regarding employment, which causes the potential migrant to discount the expected nonfarm earnings. This is particularly true if the potential migrant realizes that the unemployment tends to be concentrated among the less skilled, the young, and the new entrant to the urban labor market. As many immigrants to our wealthy industrial states have found, unemployment compensation and even local welfare are dependent upon a minimum qualifying period, and life can be difficult, even in high-wage areas, if one hasn't the work experience to qualify for unemployment compensation.

Another factor reducing mobility, even in periods of full employment, is lack of accurate information about nonfarm employment opportunities, especially in areas so remote as to require physical migration. The few available studies show that most information regarding distant employment opportunities comes by word of mouth from relatives, friends, and acquaintances.[5] Our Federal-State Employment Service is primarily a local employment service in that information about employment opportunities outside the local labor market area is not available to a job seeker. What is worse, the Farm Placement Service does not even make local nonfarm jobs known to potentially qualified farm workers because of the real or implied political retaliation that would come from farmers-employers. However, a Kansas study reported that former farmers said they would not have left farming sooner even if they had known of nonfarm employment opportunities.[6]

In general, even in a full-employment economy, there are substantial impediments to the sufficient outmovement of labor from agriculture to achieve and maintain earnings in agriculture close to those in the nonfarm economy.

Given the age structure of the farm population, a substantial reduction in the agricultural labor force could be achieved by merely diverting the potential new entrants from agriculture to other occupations (Table 1). Forty-three per cent of the farm population was under 20 years of age in 1961. If a major portion of this group entered nonfarm occupations, the persons employed in agriculture would decline sharply over the next decade merely as a result of the age structure and without the necessity of a change in their occupation. Unfortunately, there are three serious problems in achieving this goal. The problems are: (1) the lower level of formal education of rural youth; (2) the lower quality of education of most farm youth; and (3) the rapidly rising number of new entrants to the nonfarm labor force.

The median years of school completed by the rural farm pop-

5 See Eldon D. Smith, "Nonfarm Employment Information for Rural People," *Journal of Farm Economics,* 38, No. 3 (Aug. 1956); W. F. Porter and W. H. Metzler, *Availability for Employment of Rural People in the Upper Monongahela Valley, West Virginia,* Bulletin 391 (Morgantown: West Virginia Agricultural Experiment Station, June 1956); William H. Metzler and J. L. Charlton, *Employment and Underemployment of Rural People in the Ozarks,* Bulletin 604 (Fayetteville: Arkansas Agricultural Experiment Station, Nov. 1958).

6 John A. Schnittker and Gerald P. Owens, *Farm to City Migration: Perspective and Problems,* Agricultural Economics Report No. 84 (Manhattan: Kansas Agricultural Experiment Station, Sept. 1959).

Table 1

Farm Population by Age and Sex: April 1961

Age	Total	Male	Female
		Thousands	
All ages	14,803	7,711	7,092
Under 14 years	4,505	2,287	2,218
14 years and over	10,298	5,424	4,874
14 to 19 years	1,867	1,035	832
20 to 24 years	741	403	338
25 to 44 years	2,979	1,478	1,501
45 to 64 years	3,342	1,777	1,565
65 years and over	1,369	731	638
Per cent Distribution			
All ages	100.0	100.0	100.0
Under 14 years	30.4	29.7	31.3
14 years and over	69.6	70.3	68.7
14 to 19 years	12.6	13.4	11.7
20 to 24 years	5.0	5.2	4.8
25 to 44 years	20.1	19.2	21.1
45 to 64 years	22.6	23.0	22.1
65 years and over	9.2	9.5	9.0

Source: Table 2, *Farm Population*, Series Census—ERS (P-27), No. 31 U. S. Dept. of Commerce, Bureau of the Census (Washington: U.S.D.A., Economic Research Service, March 14, 1962).

ulation is lower than for the nonfarm population in virtually every state and community. This is in part due to the higher proportion of older persons in the farm population, but it is true even when corrections are made for age differences. What is more important for our purpose is that the years of school completed by the younger group in the farm population falls off rapidly (Table 2). This decline begins at about age 14 and rises rapidly among the older youth.[7]

The problem of school "drop-outs" is closely related to the

[7] Part of the decline at the college age level is because the 1960 Census defined college students by where they were living while going to college and not where their parents lived. Hardly any farm youth can live at home and go to college, whereas this is not uncommon in urban areas. Therefore, farm youth attending college generally are counted in the urban population.

Table 2

Per Cent of Males Enrolled in School by Residence, 1960

| | | PLACE OF RESIDENCE | |
Age	Total	Urban	Rural Nonfarm	Rural Farm
5 years	64.1	74.1	58.0	33.7
6 years	97.8	98.8	98.0	92.7
7 to 9 years	99.6	99.6	99.7	99.7
10 to 13 years	99.4	99.5	99.5	98.6
14 to 15 years	97.9	98.0	98.3	96.3
16 to 17 years	84.5	85.1	85.4	79.7
18 to 19 years	47.8	51.4	46.8	33.5
20 to 21 years	27.1	31.1	20.8	18.8

Source: Bureau of the Census, U. S. Dept. of Commerce, Washington, D. C.

occupation and unemployment experience of the labor force.[8] Persons not completing school tended to be concentrated in the unskilled occupations, had lower incomes, and made up a disproportionate share of the unemployed. This problem is becoming increasingly acute as technological change in the nonfarm economy puts an increasing premium upon formal education.

The reasons for the failure of rural youths to attain as much education as their nonfarm counterparts are many and varied. One is the cost of education. Lack of funds is a major reason given for failure to attend college by high school graduates from farm families. In addition, the opportunity cost of not working after reaching age 15 or so is higher on farms than in cities and may be especially high for low-income farm families. Cultural values in rural communities and farm families also put less value upon education than do many other groups in society. These, plus the greater social adjustments usually involved in leaving a rural area to attend college, result in a lower proportion of farm high school

[8] See Arnold Katz, *Educational Attainment of Workers, 1959*, Special Labor Force Report No. 1 (Bureau of Labor Statistics, U. S. Dept of Labor, February 1960); and Sophia Cooper, *Employment of June 1960 High School Graduates*, Special Labor Force Report No. 15, *op. cit.*, May 1961.

graduates entering college and a lower proportion of those who enter college finishing.

Unfortunately, even those completing the same number of years of school in many rural areas receive much poorer quality education than their nonfarm counterparts. Statistics for rural schools show that the average annual expenditures per pupil for instruction are lower, that the proportion of qualified teachers is lower, and that school size often is below the minimum necessary to maintain certain basic facilities necessary for an adequate modern education.[9] Raup reports that in Minnesota 20 per cent of the public high schools find themselves unable to offer the minimum level of mathematics required for entrance into college freshman algebra courses.[10]

What is perhaps more disconcerting is the ample evidence of serious malallocation of public education funds in our rural areas. This malallocation is in the expenditure of funds for vocational education. Even though it is apparent to everyone that the absolute level of agricultural employment must decline and the relative level must decline even more, 44.5 per cent of all vocational education funds in the United States are spent for agricultural training. In the twenty states where agricultural income makes up the highest proportion of state income, 18 of the 20 states spend more than half of their vocational training funds upon vocational agriculture.

Thus, farm youth are handicapped in competing for nonfarm jobs in several ways. In general, because of economic pressures and other reasons, they get fewer years of school on the average. The formal education that they obtain is often of lower quality because of less adequate teachers and facilities. In many rural high schools, the only vocational training available to them is in agriculture, which further instills in them values for an occupation where they all cannot hope to enter and prosper and often gives them illusions regarding the economic prospects in the industry.

[9] *Statistics of Public School Systems in 101 of the Most Rural Counties 1955–56,* Circular No. 529 (Washington: U. S. Dept. of Health, Education, and Welfare, 1958).

[10] Philip M. Raup, "Economic Aspects of Population Decline in Rural Communities," *Labor Mobility and Population in Agriculture* (Ames: Iowa State University Press, 1961), p. 101.

These handicaps might not be crucial to the success of farm youth seeking nonfarm employment if they were entering a labor market where demand was high and qualified entrants scarce. Millions of farm people successfully left agriculture in the period 1940–55 when the nonfarm demand for labor was high and the number of new entrants low because of the decline in birth rates in the 1920's and 1930's. However, the situation that faces rural people seeking nonfarm employment will be drastically changed for the foreseeable future. New entrants to the labor force started to increase rapidly about 1960 as the wartime babies reached working age, and the increase will continue at least through 1970 (Table 3). The bulk of these new entrants will be born and raised in urban communities, will have gone to urban schools, and will be there locally when and if new job opportunities become available.

Table 3

Young Persons Reaching Age 18 Annually, 1950, 1955, and Projected 1960 to 1970

Year (July 1)	Number (millions)
1950	2.2
1955	2.2
1960	2.6
1961	2.9
1962	2.8
1963	2.8
1964	2.8
1965	3.8
1966	3.6
1967	3.6
1968	3.6
1969	3.7
1970	3.8

Source: Bureau of the Census, U. S. Dept. of Commerce.

Farm people will be at an even greater disadvantage because the job mix in the nonfarm economy has been turning away from and is expected to continue to turn away from those nonfarm occupation groups which farm people have tended to enter. Farm-nonfarm migrants have been found in disproportionately high numbers as operatives, nonfarm laborers, and farm laborers. They were found less often than expected (if their nonfarm jobs were distributed the same as all migrants) as managers and proprietors, professional and technical workers, sales and clerical workers, and craftsmen and foremen.[11] Expectations now are that these occupations that farm-nonfarm migrants have tended to enter will be those that show the greatest relative decline or least absolute growth over the coming decade (Table 4). This is completely consistent with the findings of Schnittker and Owens,[12] who reported that a survey of personnel managers found that farmers were considered good capable employees in jobs requiring unskilled labor or semi-skilled labor, but not in skilled labor or white-collar work.

Table 4

Employment by Occupation Groups, 1960 and Projected 1970

Occupation Group	1960 Millions	1970 Millions
Professional and technical	7.4	10.4
Managers and proprietors	7.1	8.8
Clerical and sales	13.9	17.6
Craftsmen	8.7	10.6
Operators	12.5	14.8
Laborers, other than farm	3.8	3.8
Services	8.1	10.1
Farm managers, and farm laborers	5.9	4.9

Source: U. S. Dept. of Labor.

It is possible to argue that the preparation and encouragement of new entrants to the labor force in rural areas is not a matter of concern for public policy. Some may hold that if farm youth prefer to drop out of school, or if rural people refuse to provide good schools, then they should expect to experience difficulty in competing in the labor market and lower earnings. Such an attitude, however, is inconsistent with concern regarding excess labor

11 Larry Sjaastad, "Occupational Structure and Migration Patterns," *Labor Mobility and Population in Agriculture, op. cit.,* p. 23.
12 *Op. cit.,* p. 31.

devoted to farming. Every new entrant to agriculture who enters because his nonfarm opportunities are poor represents the same potential waste of resources as does a person already in the industry who might be producing a significantly higher product elsewhere in the economy. There probably are few expenditures in the economy where the returns, in terms of higher future national income, will be greater than they would be from the allocation of adequate educational and vocational training resources to reduce the excessive allocation of rural youth to an agricultural industry where many of them will inevitably become "trapped" with low earnings in the production of products with low value to the economy.

More than full employment will be required in order to raise and hold the salvage value of labor in agriculture even close to the returns to labor elsewhere in the economy. The cost of labor transfer and the inadequate preparation of many farm people for nonfarm employment in the growing occupations mean that public policies would be required to reduce these impediments to labor mobility. The Manpower Training Act of 1962 was one such policy which might prove helpful if applied adequately to excess labor in rural areas. However, this and all other such programs will prove inadequate unless aggregate demand in the economy is expanded sufficiently to provide full employment. Without this, retraining programs will merely serve to upgrade the educational level of the unemployed and underemployed.

THE EFFECTS OF OUTMIGRATION UPON RURAL COMMUNITIES

Most studies of outmigration from agriculture find that those who have migrated generally are satisfied with their change, although many of them would prefer rural living, if all other things were equal. It also is clear that outmigration, which reduces the labor force in agriculture, increases the returns to those remaining in agriculture over what the returns would have been in the absence of a reduction in the farm labor force. These two elements suggest that outmigration as a solution to the farm problems approaches one of those rare situations in which everybody gains. However, a more careful examination of the results of outmigration shows there are many costs which are not reflected in either the national income accounts or the earnings of the individuals directly involved, and that these costs are greater than are generally realized.

Most of rural America was settled prior to the development of the automobile and the hard surface road. A pattern of small towns and villages grew up as trading centers for farm people, and these places were located in terms of the transportation technology of the time in which they were established. The shift to auto and truck transportation alone would have been enough to induce a substantial decline in the number of these rural service towns, as farmers were able to travel further to trade and found that larger centers with a wider range of specialized goods and services were attractive. However, the impact of the new transportation technology upon these towns and villages has been multiplied many-fold by the concurrent farm consolidation and rapid decline in the farm population through outmigration.

One observer has aptly suggested that there are economies of scale in rural service centers as in many other areas of the economy.[13] He suggests that there are four requirements for a rural community to remain viable. They are: (1) a supply area adequate to provide a sufficient volume of farm products necessary to enable the efficient operation of processing and assembly functions; (2) a trade territory large enough to support the provision of producers' supplies and services at a minimum cost; (3) an internal labor market large enough to provide a range of job opportunities sufficient to effectively utilize the local labor force; and (4) a tax base and economic structure sufficient to support an adequate structure of community services such as schools, churches, and public utilities. Not included, but necessary as a parallel to the second point, is the necessity for a population base or trading area large enough to attract specialized consumer services such as doctors, appliance repairmen, communication media, and others.

It is obvious that the technological change both inside and outside of agriculture and the decline in the farm population have resulted in a major portion of the small rural towns not

[13] Philip M. Raup, "Economic Aspects of Population Decline," *op. cit.*

being able to achieve the minimum scale necessary to survive as a viable rural trading center. The result is a sight common to all travelers who leave the major United States highways in farm areas away from the cities. The farm states are dotted with declining towns—complete with empty houses, boarded-up store fronts beside others that have not been remodeled since 1920 and soon will be boarded, and an aged population. Community facilities, such as schools and churches, are inadequate and declining.

Our farm programs have prevented farm people, by and large, from realizing large capital losses on their investments in farm land, equipment, and livestock. Most who have left agriculture have done so without substantial capital losses, and many have even realized capital gains. Federal programs have been devised to clear urban slums, and the property owners in deteriorating city neighborhoods usually are paid handsomely for their property acquired for these purposes. No program and no one has compensated the owners of property in these declining rural towns for the major capital losses they have suffered as a result of major social and economic changes, even though, on balance, they have been perhaps the greatest losers in the economy from such shifts.

The farm people remaining in these rural areas have not escaped the cost of the continuing outmigration. The population decline in these counties has resulted in local schools which are uneconomic in size, so that the per pupil cost is high in relation to the quality of the education offered. School consolidation has resulted in high transportation costs per pupil, amounting in some areas to one-third of the instructional cost per pupil.[14] The declining tax base of the rural towns has meant that an increasing portion of the total school costs must be borne by the surrounding farmland. Thus, the index of farm real estate taxes per acre stood at 613 (1910–14 = 100) in March 1962, more than double the 1947–49 average and up nearly one-third from the 1957–59 average. This item represents far and away the most rapidly rising item in farm costs in the postwar period.

It is ironic that these rural communities, which are now paying so heavily to provide an education that is often inadequate

[14] See *Statistics of Public School Systems in 101 of the Most Rural Counties 1955–56, op. cit.,* Table 3.

for young people who will probably migrate to other areas to earn and spend their productive income, are among the forefront in opposing federal programs that would shift the costs of secondary education to the higher-income urban areas. This shift would be especially important to the plains and mountain states where 62 and 82 per cent, respectively, of the school revenues in rural counties in 1955–56 came from county and local sources.[15] It is a good testimony to rural Southern politicians to note that, in contrast with the above, less than 20 per cent of the revenues for schools in the most rural counties in the South came from county and local sources in 1955–56.[16] Rural Southerners can afford to oppose federal aid to education, because they have successfully tapped the tax stream of the higher-income cities in their states.

Not all, or perhaps not even the greatest, of the impacts of outmigration are economic. There are social and political impacts which are discernible but unmeasurable. As one sociologist has so clearly described it: [17]

In fact probably one of the most significant impacts of population decline on the community is its snowballing effect; decline generates further decline. The process is quite apparent: as population declines the community finds it an increasing burden to add new services and provide new amenities offered by a dynamic technology and creative culture. As it lags in the march toward bigger and better stores, schools, churches, and banks, a retrenchment of goals takes place. No longer are community leaders encouraged to make it the greatest little town in the countryside. The emphasis turns to holding the line, making do with facilities and personnel as they are; the community stresses preservation of values, and glories in its past, while others dream of a greater tomorrow. In time its lag becomes apparent as retiring doctors are not replaced, store fronts become out-dated, and the community's general appearance engenders memories of an earlier decade.

The most debilitating of all in this process appears to be pessimism generated concerning the declining community's future. It is this pessimism which constricts investment of finances, manpower, and enthusiastic leadership. Those with savings invest it elsewhere lest it

15 *Ibid.,* Table C.
16 *Ibid.*
17 Marvin J. Taves, "Consequences of Population Loss in Rural Communities," *Labor Mobility and Population in Agriculture, op. cit.,* pp. 107–21.

depreciate with the decline of their town; those with children sacrifice to educate them for jobs elsewhere in the larger society, and those with free time fail to be inspired to apply it to community improvement. This self-generating decline is often halted only after the community has fallen well behind. Even then the thought is for maintaining the community for the present, not for building for the future. At this stage it begins to die with the passing of each of its business and social leaders; it becomes a village of old merchants, old houses, old people, a fading village which will weather and slowly crumble unless it finds a leadership which rekindles optimism.

In general, these are the areas and the populations that are overrepresented in our federal and state legislatures, especially the latter. Given the age and economic structures of these communities and the problems they face, it is not surprising that representatives of such areas may oppose increased public expenditures for foreign aid, urban renewal, transportation and school aid to large cities, and the like. Reapportionment may reduce the influence of such areas in our political processes, but it will not reduce and may increase the economic and social problems of communities losing population as a result of outmigration from agriculture.

One farm organization has suggested that the clock can be turned back or that most of these social and economic changes might have been averted. When commenting on the 1962 Supreme Court decision relating to the apportionment of seats in state legislatures, it said: [18]

National Farmers Union said in a statement that it agrees with the Court's decision because malapportionment is not fair, but added that it was unfortunate that the issue came up in the first place because there was really no need for the tremendous rural to urban population shift that caused the malapportionment.

NFU said that enactment of good farm programs and an effective rural development program would get more people back on the land and reapportionment would not be such a problem.

[18] National Farmers Union, *Washington Newsletter*, Vol. 9, No. 11 (April 6, 1962), p. 2.

While this kind of statement appears unrealistic, it is equally unrealistic to ignore the very great social and economic cost that outmigration has forced upon most rural communities or to assume that all of the gains in national income and welfare from the reduction in the agricultural labor force is net gain.

THE PROBLEMS OF RECIPIENTS OF FARM-CITY MIGRATION

Urban businessmen, and the financial interests which support them, have great enthusiasm for rapid population growth in their community, because such growth increases business and the wealth of the owners of business capital, at least in the short run. Most of the rural-urban migrants have adjusted satisfactorily to their new surroundings and have become productive contributors to their new communities. However, many migrants have experienced difficulty in adjusting, especially when their inadequate skills and education make them marginal members of the labor force subject to chronic unemployment or when their skin color prevents their attaining adequate housing regardless of economic circumstances. Nearly every major city can document that new farm-nonfarm migrants account for a significant portion of the cities' crime, welfare payments, and delinquency, just as the earlier generations of migrants from other countries did in previous decades.

The new migrants are fertile as well as economically productive, and every city that has experienced an immigration has found the pressures for new schools great and the expense high. But being young and in the lower income brackets, the new migrants own little taxable property, so that the burden of the provision of the schools falls heavily upon the previous property owners, who are not necessarily the businessmen who benefit greatly from the expanding population.[19] The combination of increasing population, social problems, and taxes increases the

19 Roger Burnight, *Suburban Migration and the Cost of Education*, Connecticut Population Reports No. 2, Progress Report No. 15 (Storrs: Agricultural Experiment Station, Sept. 1956), shows that previous residents in eight Connecticut towns paid costs per child attending school ranging from 21 to 84 per cent more than did new migrants.

"flight to the suburbs" of the higher-income groups, leaving our central cities with impossible problems—a declining tax base and a below-average population in terms of income. The result is an inevitable demand for public action at the federal level to solve the local problems of slum clearance, welfare programs, and urban transportation. With the rapid rise in political power of the large cities, such programs will be forthcoming.

It would be ridiculous to assert that all of the problems of our urban areas are the result of migrants from farms. However, it is equally as ridiculous to ignore the fact that just as there are economies of scale in small towns there are diseconomies of scale (both in economic costs and social amenities) in cities above a certain size. Part of these diseconomies have been masked by the large federal and state expenditures for expressways and airports. Part have been masked by the decline in leisure inherent in traffic jams, commuting, and otherwise living in areas of high population concentration. Part are only about to be realized by the necessity for large public expenditures for air pollution control, urban transportation, and other problems.

These large losses that may accrue to both areas losing and gaining population through internal migration, largely escape the national income accounts. Our public policies have been primarily of a nature that made people more mobile and capital less so, in that large urban centers where capital is concentrated have received preference in our housing loan policies, business loan policies, and federal income tax structures. Only since 1961, in the Area Development Act, has there been minor recognition of the fact that society might gain in both an economic and social sense by the use of federal policies which induced some capital mobility away from the centers of greatest population concentration rather than to induce further human migration into already overcrowded metropolitan areas.

OCCUPATIONAL MIGRATION AND LOCAL INDUSTRIAL DEVELOPMENT

A recognition on the part of the communities losing population of the severe effects of the outmigration upon the community has led to intense competition among communities and states to attract industries which will offer local nonfarm employment to redundant farm population as an alternative to migration. Unfortunately, within the context of a less-than-full-employment economy much of the new industry attracted to one area comes from another area rather than representing total industrial growth.

Theories regarding industrial location choices are numerous, but efforts to pin down why firms chose a particular site turn out to be fewer and the results less conclusive. Despite this lack of knowledge, many communities make a variety of concessions in hopes of attracting new industries to their area.

Wallace studied the impact of these incentives and other factors upon location of industries in Southern Indiana for four years.[20] He found that firms accounting for 17 per cent of the manufacturing jobs created by the new plants were influenced in their site selection by community actions. These community actions were of an economic nature and generally involved a cost of some kind to the community.

Wallace concluded, however, that the community actions were effective in influencing location decisions regarding a specific community after the firm had decided to locate somewhere in the general area. Moreover, there is some suggestion that the economic incentives offered by the communities may have been greater than required in order to attract the industry.

This and similar studies point out that communities which lack the essential overhead capital facilities, in terms of sewerage, water, schools, etc. are automatically ruled out of consideration for plant location. This, of course, highlights the major problems of reversing the decline of communities where the population decline has proceeded to the point of community deterioration.

There is no doubt that local industrial development which offers nonfarm occupations without necessitating change in residence offers an advantage to local agriculture as well as to those

[20] L. T. Wallace, *Factors Affecting Industrial Location in Southern Indiana 1955–58*, Research Bulletin 724 (Lafayette: Purdue University Agricultural Experiment Station, Aug. 1961).

who take the nonfarm jobs.[21] Analysis of part-time farming in Georgia and North Carolina shows that part-time farming, even at relatively low nonfarm wage rates, will result in significant improvements in family income.[22] In most cases, however, a sufficient expansion of capital on the farms would provide the families with approximately the same income level.

There is a significant difference between the two solutions of part-time farming and additional capital per farm. Local industrial development which enables part-time farming *withdraws* resources from agriculture and will reduce aggregate farm output. Adding capital to increase individual farm incomes adds resources to agriculture, expands total output, and probably will result in lower than expected returns for the additional capital. Despite the disdain of farm management economists for part-time farming, it appears that this provides an optimum way of integrating industrial development into local farm communities, especially where farms are small and undercapitalized.

There is no evidence that the recent or prospective patterns of industrial development in the United States are such that they will provide a solution to the disequilibrium problem in agriculture. Even with full employment, the pattern of industrial location would be such, barring positive public policies to change it, to require substantial outmigration from the major commercial farming areas. These areas are located so far from the major population concentrations that there is little or no possibility of sustained industrial growth sufficient to provide local employment for excess labor in agriculture. This does not mean, however, that positive policies to further the decentralization of industry

21 See W. H. Nicholls, *op. cit.;* Fletcher E. Riggs, *Income Levels in the Upper Tennessee Valley: A Comparative Analysis,* T58-1AE, Division of Agricultural Relations (Knoxville: Tennessee Valley Authority, Sept. 1957); and Paul H. Price, Alvin L. Bertrand, and Harold W. Osborne, *The Effects of Industrialization on Rural Louisiana: A Study of Plant Employees,* Department of Rural Sociology (Baton Rouge: Louisiana Agricultural Experiment Station, Jan. 1958).

22 Fred B. Saunders, *Economic Analysis of Part-Time Farming in Georgia,* Bulletin No. S. 65 (Athens: Georgia Agricultural Experiment Station, Dec. 1959); J. H. Sutherland, C. E. Bishop, and B. A. Hannush, *An Economic Analysis of Farm and Nonfarm Use of Resources on Small Farms in the Southern Piedmont, North Carolina,* Tech. Bul. No. 138 (Raleigh: North Carolina Agricultural Experiment Station, May 1959).

would not have considerable impact upon the problems of providing adequate nonfarm opportunities without migration.

LABOR MOBILITY AND THE LOW-INCOME PROBLEM

Sufficient labor mobility out of agriculture to achieve a sharp reduction in the disequilibrium problem in the industry will be difficult to achieve. It will require full employment and several other factors sufficient to increase the salvage value of labor in commercial agriculture to levels exceeding the earnings of labor on commercial farms. It is doubtful that these can be achieved, although enough may be accomplished to reduce substantially the rate of new entrants into agriculture and, thereby, the labor force in agriculture over a decade or more.

The problem of labor mobility among the very low-income groups in agriculture is of a different nature. Persons on low-income farms and concentrated in low-income areas know they are underemployed and are willing, in fact eager, to find work elsewhere. A West Virginia survey found that 10 per cent of the people interviewed were either looking for work or were available for employment.[23] An Arkansas survey of rural people in the Ozarks found that 12 per cent of the people of working age were available for work.[24] A manpower survey in Kentucky in 1959 found that 42 per cent of the males and 36 per cent of the females over 14 years old would have taken another job if it were available.[25] A similar survey in Sharp County, Arkansas found that 65 per cent of the males and 44 per cent of the females over 14 said they were able and available for work.[26] In all of the cases, most of the people who wanted different employment were in the productive age groups.

Two characteristics of the group were interesting, but prob-

[23] W. F. Porter and W. H. Metzler, *Availability for Employment of Rural People in the Upper Monongahela Valley, West Virginia, op. cit.*

[24] William H. Metzler and J. L. Charlton, *Employment and Underemployment of Rural People in the Ozark Area, op. cit.*

[25] *The Manpower Resources of Adair County, Kentucky* (Division of Employment Service Research and Statistics Service of the Dept. of Economic Security, Frankfort, Kentucky, Mimeograph, no date).

[26] *Experimental Rural Area Program, Part II-C, Sharp County, Economic Base Report* (Little Rock: Arkansas Department of Labor, Employment Security Division, June 1961).

ably not surprising in view of the large migration from such rural areas to northern cities. First, there was almost a universal desire for work other than farming. The reason generally given was "better pay." Second, a very high proportion of the people were willing to move, long distances if necessary, in order to obtain work.

The West Virginia study found that 64 per cent of the persons looking for work were willing to leave home. This percentage varied inversely with age, education, and present level of living. The Metzler and Charlton study also found that more than half of those preferring nonfarm work were willing to leave home, if necessary, to obtain it. The results in Adair County, Kentucky and Sharp County, Arkansas were essentially similar. Most of the people were willing to leave the area to find work.

Obtaining nonfarm employment may prove to be quite a problem for some of these people. All of the studies show that vocational training had been a characteristic of the previous out-migrants, and the willingness to leave was greater among those having vocational training. However, only 15 per cent of those available for work in West Virginia had such training; 4 per cent of those over 14 in the Ozarks had such training; 26 per cent of the males in the Kentucky area had vocational training; and 16 per cent in the Arkansas area had such training. Most of the vocational training of those wanting employment consisted of high school vocational agricultural training for the males and home economics training for the females. There also were a number of men who had received specialized training in the armed forces.

The people in these areas apparently are conscious of their need for further training to enter the nonfarm labor force. In Sharp County, Arkansas, 46 per cent of the persons over 14 indicated an interest in further training. Although 96 per cent of those desiring such training said they were willing to pay for it, only 13 per cent of them had finances to do so.

Previous nonfarm work experience could serve as a substitute for vocational training. However, all of the surveys showed that a high proportion of those interested in jobs had only farm work experience. Most of the nonfarm work experience was as unskilled or semi-skilled workers.

Unfortunately, many of the people in this group lack the formal education that is becoming increasingly important in our economy. In the Ozark study area, 68 per cent of those over 14 had 8 or less years of school, and only 14 per cent had completed high school. In the Kentucky County, 73 per cent of those looking for work had grade school or less, and 12 per cent had completed high school. In Sharp County, about half of the aspirants to the nonfarm labor force had no more than a grade school education.

In the Kentucky study, a number of the job applicants were given a series of tests to measure their aptitudes and abilities. As might be expected, in light of their school backgrounds, vocational training, and work experience, they rated fairly high in potential and very low in terms of being qualified to perform the jobs in which they had an interest.

Thus, unlike many persons engaged in "commercial" agriculture, most of the persons on low-production farms in the low-income areas have no illusions regarding their future prospects in farming. Even though most of them have little off-farm experience and relatively weak backgrounds to fit them for the nonfarm labor market, they are willing and anxious to obtain nonfarm employment, even if a move to an urban area is required. Given the poor educational background and little *useful* vocational training that these individuals have, most of them may prove to be marginal members of the nonfarm labor force in the decades ahead, and they certainly will be so in the absence of full employment. However, the provision of adequate vocational training to such individuals might enable them to become successful participants in the nonfarm labor market, either locally or elsewhere.

Many of these low-production farming areas lack both the natural and human resources to successfully compete in attracting the necessary nonfarm employment opportunities to keep this excess farm population in their local communities. Many of these communities are of the type that are so lacking in community facilities and social overhead capital as to be completely excluded from consideration as sites for industrial expansion. Thus, over time the low-production farm problem has been declining rapidly in numbers and in relative magnitude as the people involved have left the areas in increasing rates to take advantage of better opportunities elsewhere. This trend will continue, and public policy might speed it or ease it, but not reverse it.

Other Programs to Achieve Adjustment

Even with full employment and other programs to facilitate the outmovement of labor from agriculture, it is questionable whether a sufficient adjustment in resource use in agriculture could be achieved to remove the disequilibrium. Critics of the labor force adjustment approach argue that new nonlabor resources will continue to enter agriculture at such a rate that they will more than offset the decline in the labor input, so that output will continue to rise and earnings in agriculture will remain low.

Several other changes in emphasis in public programs might improve the effectiveness of an outmovement of labor. These include price-support programs, resource allocation programs, and our public research and education programs. Many of the excessive resources now "trapped" in agriculture were erroneously committed to farming in the belief they would earn returns comparable to the nonfarm economy. These errors were in part induced by our price-support programs and other public policies.

For more than a decade we have maintained a price policy which supported the market prices of a number of farm products. This, of course, has been to maintain farm income. However, the price and income supports have given some farmers the erroneous impression that such price and income levels can be expected to continue for all of the resources that want to stay in agriculture and for all the new resources that want to enter. Every knowledgeable policy maker in agriculture realizes that further reductions in the farm population and labor force are not only essential to even a partial solution to the disequilibrium problem, but also inevitable. However, the values relating to agriculture and the folkways of farm politics are such that it is unheard of for a national official to even admit this—let alone advocate policies to improve the resource transfers. Instead, every Secretary of Agriculture is obliged, almost as a ritual, to guarantee that under his administration all who might wish to farm will become prosperous. Even the inclusion of a modest program to aid outmovement of labor in the 1962 legislative proposals, brought this reaction from the Farmers Union: [27]

Emphasis on training low-income people to leave farming is a negative approach. What is really needed is much more credit at reasonable rates to enable young people to enter the modern, highly capitalized business of farming and to enable perfectly fine farmers to expand their less than economic operations into units which would return a fair standard of living.

In other words, the solution to too many resources in farming is the addition of more resources which will drive down prices and incomes to present resources even further! Such a statement suggests that an essential element in a solution to the equilibrium problem in agriculture is a frank recognition of the nature of the problem.

One does not have to question public support for farm income in order to question the soundness of constantly encouraging the entry of new resources, both human and otherwise, into farming by the pricing of farm products at above market-clearing levels without barriers to new resource entry. There are numerous ways in which farmers' income can be protected without pricing the marginal output in agriculture at excessive levels. Instead, we have persisted in a policy of commodity pricing which is bound to be at least partially self-defeating.

It is hardly reasonable to expect that politicians will campaign with a promise not to improve farm income if elected, but it does seem reasonable to expect that the public research and educational agencies which serve agriculture might be expected to show somewhat greater forthrightness. Unfortunately, this is not always the case. Economists have known for years that the labor force in agriculture was declining and would continue to do so. Even so, it has not generally been openly discussed in colleges of agriculture because of the hostility of production-oriented colleagues. This has contributed to continuation of programs geared to another age and other needs. Field staffs have been expanded with-

[27] *National Farmers Union Washington Newsletter,* Vol. **8,** No. 40 (Dec. 22, 1961), p. 1.

out regard to either changes in transportation and communication technology or to the number of farmers needing such services.

What is more important is that these institutions have failed to develop realistic programs to deal with or improve the disequilibrium in resource use in farming. Only recently has there been any public discussion by educators of the fact that the prospect for resource earnings in farming are not as bright as elsewhere. Even now, there is only limited discussion of the fact that most farm youth would do well to consider nonfarm alternatives before preparing to enter farming.

There also is little or no research and education regarding the economic level of adoption of new farm practices and forms of organization. Some economic research and information programs might have forestalled the substantial over investment in broilers and turkeys that have occurred in recent years. Instead, farmers were generally told about the short-run income gains that could be expected by the early adoption of the new practices and heavy investments. When product prices declined rapidly following widespread adoption of these ideas, these same public servants were available to advise upon refinancing, more efficient management, and all other sorts of micro-adjustments to a disequilibrium situation. It was unfortunate that no one was available with a discussion of the probable effects of the changes, which might have enabled some farmers to avoid the error of committing themselves to huge investments which were later "trapped" in agriculture.

The agricultural industry in the United States has been largely dependent upon public research and education agencies to develop and disseminate information about new technology and new practices. These organizations have never developed an accompanying research and education program regarding the aggregate impact of these changes or the equilibrium level of their adoption. At present much of the new technology is developed and promoted by private businesses, and it is not in the interest of these businesses to tell farmers that they cannot expect future prices to remain as high after the new output-increasing technology is widely adopted. These companies want to sell feed, seed, fertilizer, and machinery, and while it is in their individual interest to have good research to avoid over-investing in productive facilities that will prove unprofitable, it is not in their interest to do the same for their customers.

In light of the serious disequilibrium in agriculture, an expansion in public research and education regarding the aggregate effects of potential changes in agriculture and the probable equilibrium level after adoption appears warranted. Such research will not always be popular with persons in production-oriented departments of the universities nor will it be acclaimed by the sellers of inputs. Even so, the public is paying heavily for both the production of new information and its dissemination and for the disequilibrium of resources in agriculture. Programs which could, without coercion, produce an improvement in resource use should in these circumstances be both economically justified and consistent with all of the values involved in farm policy.

Nonfarm Policies and Agricultural Stability

Nonfarm business cycles have been an important source of instability for agriculture in the past. However, as pointed out earlier, the impact of these cycles upon the demand for farm products has been reduced significantly by the use of stabilizers and income transfer programs in the nonfarm economy. Regardless of how effective these programs are, they are not substitutes for stable nonfarm employment and price levels, as far as the external stability problems of farmers are concerned. Even though the domestic demand for farm products has been partially stabilized, other problems remain for farmers.

Farm families obtain an increasing share of their income from nonfarm sources. Despite the increased general stability of personal disposable income, the scanty evidence available suggests that farmers' nonfarm income is highly unstable. This may be because they tend to obtain their nonfarm income from highly volatile industries, because they are marginal workers with little seniority and skills; or it may be because many of them do not qualify for the programs that help maintain nonfarm workers' income while unemployed. In any case, programs to stabilize farmers' incomes from nonfarm sources will have to come from outside agriculture as part of general stabilization policy.

Equally important and more difficult may be the stabilization of prices of purchased farm inputs. We appear to have arrived at a position where wage and price increases in basic materials occur almost without regard to demand or existing levels of output. Given the demand and supply conditions in agriculture these cost increases tend to come directly from farmers' income, especially in the absence of unemployment levels sufficient to induce rapid factor mobility from agriculture.

Thus, the basic policy dilemma relating to nonfarm employment levels and price levels is even more complicated. For a variety of political and economic reasons we need to avoid internal inflation to protect our international position. A policy of price stability also protects farmers against cost increases. However, if a relatively high unemployment rate is required to maintain price stability, then the poverty and disequilibrium problems in agriculture are worsened by using this method of attaining price stability.

Summary and Conclusions

The problem of low returns to resources engaged in farming, especially for human effort, requires that either some of these resources be shifted from farming to producing other goods and services, or that these resources continue to receive low earnings, or that some kind of income transfer program be used to maintain the income of resources above what the market would bring them. Either of the last two solutions represents a malallocation of resources in the economy, because total national output would be higher if some of the resources producing farm products were shifted elsewhere.

Several conditions must be met in order for the movement of resources from farming to other industries to represent an improved resource allocation. First, the resources that leave farming must have employment elsewhere producing products which have a higher value to the economy than do the farm products they

are now producing. Second, the cost of movement of the resources must be less than the differences in the net product added by the shift in use. Finally, the social costs of the resource shifts, which often are not directly priced in our economy, must not be so great that they more than offset the gains that are priced in our income accounts.

It is clear that full employment in the nonfarm economy is a necessary condition to reduce the gap between the return to labor in agriculture and the return in other sectors of the economy. However, because of the geographic dispersion of farm people and the relative concentration of nonfarm jobs, even full employment in the nonfarm economy will fall short of raising the salvage value of labor now engaged in producing farm products sufficiently to equate returns between agriculture and other occupations. Full employment and programs to facilitate movement out of agriculture might, however, reduce the gap to a tolerable level.

The farm population now contains a high proportion of young people not yet in the labor force. If these young people can be encouraged to enter nonfarm employment, much of the necessary reduction in the farm work force will be achieved at a minimum cost. Unfortunately, even in the relatively prosperous farming areas, farm-reared youth are less well prepared to compete in the nonfarm labor market than are their urban counterparts. A lower proportion enter and complete college. Those that go to work after high school (or earlier) generally are less well prepared for nonfarm employment since most of the funds for vocational education in rural high schools are spent for instruction in vocational agriculture. Thus, the nation is allocating public funds to train young farm people for an industry already overcrowded; and, in many cases, mistakenly implying to these people that if they are industrious and thrifty, their future in farming is as bright as anywhere.

The outmigration from farming has been little short of phenomenal over the past four decades, especially since 1940. Much of it has involved physical migration, and the cost to the communities losing population has been great. The declining population in those rural areas removed from urban centers has brought decline and decay to many rural villages. The cost of minimal community services, such as schools and churches, has risen sharply for the remaining population and the quality of those services has declined in many areas. The migrants usually have gained by their moves to other areas and occupations, but those remaining in the rural areas and villages have not always gained. It is these problems, which are so often overlooked by economists concentrating on efficient resource use, that are of major concern to politicians from rural areas who see their political power and economic base declining with each passing year. Representatives of these areas will oppose any public policies which will hasten the process of outmigration, whether it is a whole-farm soil bank or a federal training program. Higher national income is no substitute for local prosperity; no one knows better than representatives of areas with declining populations about the impossibility of measuring interpersonal gains and losses.

Occupational change, and probably physical migration, is virtually the only solution for the problems of the young on low-production farms. Both historical evidence and current surveys show that such persons are willing to leave farming and, if necessary, to leave the areas in which they now live. Here again full employment is crucial, for in its absence many of these persons would be marginal in the nonfarm labor market. Despite their willingness to leave farming, many persons on low-production farms will experience difficulty unless there are some positive public policies to provide them with better education and vocational training than they usually have. The Area Redevelopment Act of 1961 and the Manpower Retraining Act of 1962 were modest steps in this direction, but, as yet, they have not been extended to rural areas to any significant degree.

If there is to be resource adjustment in agriculture, farmers need much better information than they have received regarding the probable long-run income position of the industry and regarding the probable aggregate impacts of changes in farming. The public institutions that have provided the basic research for the great technological and organizational changes in farming have not provided parallel information about their probable effects and equilibrium levels of adoption.

Labor mobility in agriculture, by itself, is unlikely to be sufficient to bring returns for human effort in agriculture up to returns elsewhere in the economy. However, in its absence, the disequilibrium problem and the low-production problem in agriculture are insoluble. Therefore, programs which improve resource mobility will continue to be crucial to our living with the farm problems, although they will not be easily solved by such programs.

Chapter 15

The Future of Farm Policy

The exact nature of farm policy a decade or even five years ahead cannot be accurately forecast, for it is contingent upon innumerable items. However, some of the issues and elements that will influence the direction of farm policy in the years ahead can be isolated, and it is these items and their potential impact that will be discussed.

Agricultural Policy in Perspective

The United States has had the experience of more than three decades of federal policies dealing directly with the income problems of agriculture. Despite all of the obvious imperfections in these policies, an overwhelming conclusion remains. By and large, our farm policies have been extraordinarily successful, given the magnitude of the problems with which they have dealt. Their success is a tribute to the amazing resiliency of our economic and political system, neither of which should be underestimated.

The success of our farm policies is apparent in a number of ways. The diet of the average American consumer is excellent, both in quality and variety, and its cost in real terms has declined steadily over time. In thirty years, the farm population has been reduced by one-half or more, releasing former members of the agricultural labor force for the production of other goods and services. The level of living of our farm people, on the average, has risen sharply and far surpasses that of farm people in most other nations. Income of farmers has become more stable, and institutional arrangements to deal with the instability have been improved vastly. There are no major social or class barriers between rural people and the rest of society, unlike much of the world where the term "peasant" carries social as well as economic connotations.

These gains have not come without costs to our society. Some will argue that they have occurred in spite of, rather than because of, our farm policies. To some extent, this may be true, but the fact that our policies have not prevented these changes or even tried to prevent them is most important. Actually, we must conclude that our farm policies have been of a nature to make the great economic and social changes in agriculture bearable, rather than to prevent them. It is likely that our future policies will have the same results, for it is impossible, given the multiple values involved in farm policy, to develop a policy which will provide complete attainment of all of these values.

It should be noted, that contrary to popular opinion, agriculture in the United States is not a declining industry. It is an industry in which output has expanded rapidly, and continued expansion will be necessary as population and income growth continue. It is an industry in which the total productive resources used have expanded and will continue to expand. However, it is an industry in which the addition of new nonlabor resources generally requires a withdrawal of some of the labor force if their incomes are to be maintained. So, it is an industry that is declining in terms of its labor force, but to assert that the industry is declining is erroneous.

Despite the fact that agriculture has been and will continue to be a growing industry in an absolute sense, it will continue to decline in relative importance in the economy. It is this relative decline in both population and economic importance that will influence farm policy in the years ahead.

The Value Structure of American Society Regarding Agriculture

Values may have several roles in influencing preferences among the various policy choices. First, the value structure of society may change. If so, then program preferences will change. Second, the technical possibilities relating to value achievement may change, so that it will require more or less reduction in one aspiration to achieve some additional attainment of another; here again, program preferences will change.

Indications are that the value structure of our society changes slowly, although there is little doubt that the values of our urban society differ from those of our predominantly rural society of earlier decades. It is the professional task of disciplines other than economics to measure these changes, if measurable, and presumably, it is the task of philosophers to evaluate them. Yet, in a democracy this evaluation task is widely shared and is a constant part of the political process.

The rapid change to an urban society appears to be increasing the importance of "efficiency," as used in some economic sense of the allocation of resources to satisfy the current consumer satisfaction as expressed in money terms. Urban societies often appear to be more interested in dollar output than in either beauty or what some would regard as the "good" life. Parks and trees give way to expressways and shopping centers; stately old buildings to enormous slabs of glass, concrete, and steel. Nothing stands in the way of "progress," and progress is measured almost exclusively in terms of dollar value of output. This may be due to less value on these "pleasant" items, or it may be due to the sharply-rising costs that they entail in an urban society.

There is no reason to believe that this high regard for efficiency and progress will not be evident in the farm policies of the future. As the voice of the urban society grows in farm policy, it is likely that the pressures will increase for programs that are more "efficient," both in terms of moving toward increasing total national output and in terms of what is achieved for a given public expenditure.

This latter item, the efficiency of the program in achieving the values underlying it, is likely to be increasingly important in the years ahead. All theoretical considerations aside, there are practical political limitations to the proportion of national income that can be diverted to governmental programs in peace time. The political pressures for public expenditures in urban areas are very great and are rising. Thus there will be a continuing pressure from the urban society for farm programs that place less drain upon the federal budget. Urban people will tolerate, up to some certain point, income transfer programs for agriculture that operate through higher market prices, such as market discrimination programs or production control programs. There is likely to be some limit to their tolerance of the ever-rising costs of unlimited price-support programs, with their high overhead costs and huge disposal losses.

Another attitude that is changing with the shift to an urban industrialized society is that regarding the importance of individual freedom of the proprietor regarding his enterprise. Persons living in areas of high population concentration are used to zoning laws, building codes, traffic regulations, sanitary regulations, work rules, minimum wages, compulsory union membership, social insurance programs, and the like, most of which are restrictions on someone's freedom. However, in a highly-interdependent, closely-related society most people believe that such restrictions are necessary in order for society to function, and they believe that the other values gained are important enough to warrant some of the restriction of individual freedom that is implied by such programs.

Urban people who are used to such restrictions tend to be skeptical or downright suspicious of the strong preference placed by farmers upon freedom to operate their individual enterprises without government or other interference. They feel that farmers want to have their cake and eat it too, and nonfarm people are especially skeptical when a major portion of the cake comes from public funds provided by urban taxpayers. Therefore, there is likely to be increasing pressure from urban people on farmers to use some of the restrictive devices that are commonplace in the nonfarm economy as methods of improving farm income without large budget expenditures.

Another important element in farm policy which may change over time is that relating to local political control and the avoidance of outside political domination. Most urban dwellers are rightfully skeptical of the quality of their own local political organizations and find that national programs often are more responsive to local wishes than are well-entrenched local political machines. Moreover, the use of local political control in the South to perpetuate a social system of racial discrimination and the failure of rural-dominated state legislatures to even recognize urban problems lead many urban people to believe that local political control is merely a façade to perpetuate the power of groups with which they have little sympathy. Therefore, future farm policy is likely to give less weight to local control than in the past. The increasing power of national advisory committees in farm policy is one indication of this trend.

Thus far, the discussion has centered on attitudes in the society at large regarding agriculture. What about the changes in the values of farm people, if any? The improved transportation and communication and the continuing commercialization of farms probably have shifted the value structures of farm people toward those of their urban counterparts. Death, retirement, migration, and the extension service have replaced farmers who believed farming was a way of life with hard-headed businessmen whose concern with efficiency equals or exceeds their nonfarm business counterpart. Farmers' concern regarding the efficiency of total resource use also is great, although generally not great enough to overcome their desire for higher incomes. However, many farmers would prefer programs that maintained their incomes without the large federal expenditures which are politically vulnerable.

Increasingly, farmers' values relating to freedom to manage their individual enterprises appear to be less important to them than are those relating to income. However, farmers and their representatives are not willing to accept compulsory controls over farm output as long as they have other alternatives politically available to them. Whether farmers would approve effective output controls as an alternative to removal of price supports is another matter, but it is a matter about which we shall be uncertain unless and until urban representatives impose the choice upon farmers. Farmers are not going to impose such a choice on themselves.

Farmers' values regarding local political control also may be shifting. Increasingly, they are finding that federal programs can be organized to their advantage, sometimes more easily than can local ones. Working through commodity organizations using hired professionals, farmers find that reduction in national acreage allotments may be easier to block than are individual farm reductions by county committees.

Perhaps above all, the improved communications with urban areas have made farmers increasingly concerned with the attainment of equal economic opportunity for farm people. When urban-rural contacts were impersonal and infrequent, differences in levels of living, education, and material possessions were less important. Now, however, farm wives are conscious of the standards of living of urban families and, where circumstances permit, equal or exceed them. Farm youth are increasingly conscious of the real or imagined handicaps arising from lower incomes. The collective action of nonfarm groups, such as labor unions and large corporations, to improve their incomes, with little apparent concern with the "general welfare," leads farm people to believe more strongly that the earnings in agriculture ought to be equal to those in other occupations and that farmers' claims on society for public policies to obtain higher incomes are justified.

These shifts in values are slow at best, and they may represent a shift in circumstances more than a shift in basic values. Even though they are minor shifts, the impact on farm policy may be great. They suggest: (1) that the demands by farmers for policy action to improve farm income are not likely to subside; (2) that the pressures for programs which make more efficient use of national resources will increase; (3) that future programs may contain more restrictions on farmers' freedom, and if so they may not be rejected; and (4) that future income transfer programs may be less dependent upon large federal expenditures.

Beliefs Regarding Agriculture

One of the fundamental beliefs that has been important to our farm policy has already undergone a significant change, and that change is likely to continue at an increased rate. The belief that a large agricultural population is necessary to provide moral, social, and political stability to our society is not surviving the urbanization of the society. This is to be expected, for how can a predominantly urban society admit that it is dependent upon a way of life which it no longer represents? However strongly some of us may feel that farm life does have values and attributes not found in crowded cities, we are the last generation of urban dwellers likely to think so. Many of the present urban population were farm reared, but in another decade or so, people born and raised in urban areas will be in the majority. They are likely to dismiss the values of rural life as folklore, as do many urban-reared people already. In fact, many farm people also doubt this belief and are somewhat embarrassed when their leaders use it to justify farm policies.

The disappearance of this belief will have important implications for farm policy, related to the increased emphasis on efficiency. Maintaining the size of the farm population and the family farm will decline as a policy goal, and there will be increased emphasis upon programs to improve resource use, even if the farm population is sharply reduced in numbers as a result. This trend is already foreshadowed in the "supply management" approach to farm policy and in the "labor mobility" approach.

Another belief which has provided a good deal of nonfarm support for farm policy is that nonfarm prosperity is dependent upon farm prosperity. The steady decline in the farm population has reduced the importance of its purchasing power as far as consumption goods are concerned, and this is obvious to the nonfarm people who consider it. Equally obvious is the declining proportion of total demand for nonfarm goods and services constituted by the farmers' demand for inputs. As if this were not enough proof, we have seen a major decline in farm income during the postwar period without precipitating a major nonfarm depression.

While nonfarm businesses in predominantly rural areas are still largely dependent upon farm income levels, people in large urban centers are increasingly isolated from any effects that fluctuations in farm income may have. Therefore, some of the strong support of organized labor for farm income programs is slipping away, and it is likely not to return.

The decline in these beliefs about the contribution of agriculture to social and economic stability in our society means that expensive farm programs are going to be more difficult to justify to nonfarm groups as in their interests. This change is important, because this justification has been used to offset some of the adverse effects of farm programs that have been clearly recognized as not always in the interests of nonfarm groups. Farm policy in the future will require justification on a different basis, perhaps on equity grounds, but it will be increasingly difficult to justify programs of the type we have had on the basis of equity.

The Politics of Agriculture

The politics of agriculture as much as any other element will affect the future of farm policy in the United States. The politics involved will be the interaction between the congressional agricultural committees and the executive who, regardless of party, is increasingly dependent upon urban political support and is increasingly concerned with the impingements of farm policy upon other national policies.

The rural interests of our national legislature are now heavily dependent upon the power of the agricultural committees, backed by commodity interest groups, and sometimes buttressed, sometimes bitterly opposed, by the three major farm organizations. It is something of a popular pastime for nearly everyone concerned with farm policy to vent their frustrations upon these agricultural committees or uncooperative members thereof. People forget that these politicians have the almost impossible task of dealing with policies that involve a multitude of competing and conflicting values, in which one group's welfare usually can only be improved at the expense of some other group. They are carrying out the political task of protecting the interests, as they perceive them, of the commodity groups and areas they represent and of agriculture in general. Whether we like the results or not, one of the strengths of our particular brand of democracy is the ability it provides for minority groups to protect their interests against the imposition of political programs which are wholly unacceptable to them. The rural interests in Congress have been doing this for almost a decade now, and this accounts, in part, for the stalemate in policy from one session to the next.

The history of legislative action for most of the past decade is an indication that party discipline will not yet enable the executive to obtain farm programs from the agricultural committees that are considered less desirable than the programs now having permanent legislative status. There was little question that the executive could have obtained passage of its legislative programs in several sessions, if it could get them out of the committees. However, generally the committees changed the legislation prior to releasing it, despite the presence of an overwhelmingly popular Republican president prior to 1960 and a popular and powerful Democratic successor. It was not until 1962, when the party mechanism effectively overrode the committees on the floor of the Senate, that the power of the committees to block change was effectively reduced.

There is little chance that the committee system will be changed drastically, for this is a weapon that cuts two ways, and many urban representatives have seniority on committees where they wield great power and influence. However, over time, the make-up of the committees will change. There was a noticeable shift in the composition of the House beginning in 1963, as a result of redistricting following the 1960 Census. Indications are that by the time the redistricting following the 1970 Census is completed, there will have been substantial reapportionment and realignment of political power between rural and urban areas. Perhaps then, if not before, the nonfarm population will have the political power to extract farm legislation from the agricultural committees which is consistent with urban values and goals.

As long as there is permanent legislation on the books requiring price supports for major farm commodities, those interested in price and income protection for farmers will not have to accept programs which bring about major reductions in the welfare of farmers. Minor program retreats or minor changes to make the programs more attractive to nonfarm groups may be made for reasons of political strategy. Major program changes are not likely to occur which are adverse to the interests of the producers of commodities and areas with major political power in the committees. Thus Congressional farm policy will continue to be a source of chronic frustration to many groups, including farmers.

The same will be true for those responsible for farm policy formation in the executive branch. The Secretary of Agriculture will continue to have pressures from farm-oriented groups to resist programs that will reduce farm income or resources used in agriculture. They will want to maintain high gross farm income. At the same time, other interests in the executive branch will wish to reduce farm program expenditures and to make the programs more consistent with other national policies. Since to please one group will almost always displease the other, the task of the executive is not to be envied either. However, given the changes in total population, it is almost inevitable that the political interests of the executive increasingly will lie with urban interests. The partisan nature of farm policy will become more important, and, as a result, the influence of general farm organizations in the executive decisions probably will decline. Perhaps more accurately, the decline that has been going on for a decade will continue.

Economic Changes Affecting Farm Policy

There is little question that the chronic unemployment level of 5 per cent or more in the United States from 1958 through 1962 reduced the outmovement from agriculture below what it otherwise would have been. Thus, part of our high farm program costs are attributable to our failure in the employment area. Even so, it is difficult to visualize a much more rapid adjustment of the population and labor force than has taken place in agriculture since 1940. The costs of this outmigration have been great indeed to the losing communities, and it is doubtful that either the political or social structure could have borne a much greater rate of movement.

The reduction in the number of low-production farms [1] has proceeded at an almost unbelievable pace. In 1949, there were 1.6 million places classified as farms in this category. In 1959, there were only 349 thousand. Part of the decline was due to a change in definition of a farm, but it appears that more than a million of these low-production farms disappeared in the 1949–59 decade. Barring a major depression, this movement can be expected to continue, and in another decade, much of this poverty problem (in an absolute sense) will have disappeared or, at least, will have been transferred to urban areas.

The extension of social security coverage to farm operators in 1955 will reduce the future number of older farm operators with very low incomes. It probably will make it possible for more older farm operators to retire when they reach age 65 than has been the case in the past. Even if they continue to farm, an increasing proportion of older farmers will no longer be solely dependent upon the income from their farms.

Unfortunately, neither recent trends nor future prospects appear as bright for hired farm workers. The failure of their numbers to decline rapidly and of their earnings to keep pace with other rising incomes suggests that this group constitutes one of the major poverty problems in United States agriculture. Economic policies to deal with their problems will be difficult and will be hotly-debated issues.

In terms of resource use and public expenditures, it is the disequilibrium problem that has claimed the most attention over the last decade. This will continue to be the case in the years ahead. No public policy within agriculture can or will be effective over the next decade in achieving returns to human effort in farming equivalent to those outside of farming. In fact, as long as resources must continue to move out of agriculture, some sort of income differential will be required to induce outmovement or

[1] These are farms where sales are less than $2,500 annually, the operator is under 65, and either worked off the farm less than 100 days or the family income from nonfarm sources was less than from farming.

prevent excessive amounts of new resources from entering. About all that any of the farm programs that have been discussed can hope to achieve is to maintain an income level in farming that is tolerable to farm people while the outmovement continues. Tolerable levels will be defined in a political context, in that many farm people will feel that higher income goals should be maintained via public policies for agriculture, while other groups will feel the cost of the programs that are maintained are too high.

Outmigration of labor alone, even with full employment, will not be sufficient to maintain farm income in the absence of some kind of government intervention. Some gaps between acquisition and salvage value for labor will still exist and will be sufficient to keep returns to human effort in farming below those in other occupations. Continued mistakes will be made in investments in durable capital, in that expectations regarding return on investment will not be realized. The very specialized nature of durable capital in agriculture means that with constant economic and technical change in agriculture there will be a substantial difference between the acquisition cost and salvage value of at least some of the capital.

It is worth noting that net capital investment in farming has declined substantially over the past few years. For the seven years 1947–53, it averaged about $1.9 billion annually. For the seven years 1954–60, it averaged only $332 million or only one-sixth as much. This suggests that farmers are becoming more conscious of the problem of "trapped" investments that produce less than expected returns.

This, together with somewhat lower price supports and a variety of land-retirement programs, has meant that the net intake of agricultural products under the price-support program fell sharply in 1959, 1960, and 1961. In 1959, the net domestic effect of Commodity Credit Corporation takeovers and sales reduced domestic supplies of farm products by only 1 per cent below current output. In 1960, the figure was 1.3 per cent, and when all of the figures are available for 1961, they undoubtedly will show that the net effects of Commodity Credit Corporation feed-grain sales more than offset takeover of other products. This is compared to a net intake averaging 7 per cent of farm output annually from 1952 through 1958. Thus, current output in the period 1959–62 was only slightly above disappearance. Of course, a good deal of the disappearance is dependent upon domestic and export subsidies of one type or another, and output was reduced by special programs.

Program costs have continued to rise each year, not because the current imbalance between output and disappearance is increasing, but because the storage and interest changes and disposal losses are rising on stocks accumulated in past years. If net stock accumulation ends, these costs will decline somewhat, although the other costs—price-support losses, export subsidies, and foreign disposals—may rise. This means that to maintain farm income levels via the methods used in the late 1950's will require annual budget expenditures for price supports and foreign disposal programs of at least $4 billion. Attempts to increase gross farm income via these kinds of programs will raise costs sharply, to perhaps as much as $6 billion annually. Therefore, political realities suggest that farm programs that will achieve appreciably higher net farm income are not likely to be forthcoming.

If total net farm income is maintained at recent levels, it appears that some reduction in the number of commercial farms can be expected. This reduction will arise largely from the failure of new entrants to replace retiring farmers. However, this will not occur at a sufficient rate to bring a reduction in farm output or a significant relative rise in the returns to human effort in agriculture. It should be sufficient, however, to prevent a further worsening of the farmers' position.

If the programs that are operated are such that they do not further inflate land prices (or even deflate them), the capital gains in agriculture that have been common since 1940 will cease, and the real impact of the low returns to labor in agriculture will become obvious to existing and prospective farmers. This may reduce new entrants and hasten outmigration, and it will end the errors of resource commitment that have occurred because of the confusion of increases in equity due to capital gains with real returns to labor.

Thus, while there are no foreseeable economic changes, either inside agriculture or outside, that foreshadow an end to the disequilibrium problem in United States agriculture in the immediate future, there are prospects that it will not further worsen. This may not be pleasant for either politicians or farm people to contemplate, but it is likely to be true, and to suggest otherwise would be to perpetuate and compound the errors of the postwar period.

Economists and Farm Policy

The role of economists in farm policy in the period ahead is, if the future has been correctly judged, likely to continue to be frustrating. Those engaging in policy formulation, either actively or as advisors, tend to underestimate the strengths of the values and beliefs related to positions different than their own and to underestimate the political opposition to what may to them appear a rational program. After several successive defeats, there is a tendency for many to decide that trying to inject some economics into United States farm policy is a hopeless task, probably not worth accomplishing.

Does it make any difference if economists concern themselves with farm policy? In fact, does the direction of farm policy in our rich country make any difference at all? The answer to the second question still appears to be yes, and, because it is, the answer to the first also is yes.

However rich, we cannot as a nation afford to do without economic change and progress in our agriculture. Because we are rich we cannot afford, in a political democracy, to ignore the very high cost that this change and progress forces farm people to bear. This means that we must continue to have progress and change in agriculture and that we must, if for no other reason than equity, have public policies to make these changes tolerable to farm people.

Given the need for policies, economists have a major role to perform in evaluating how policies may contribute most to the attainment of the values underlying these policies. If they wish to express preferences among values and work for particular policies, they can contribute here too, but their contribution in so doing is not unique, whereas, it is in other areas. Perhaps as great a contribution as any may still be made by the development of better facts about agriculture—the income distribution, factor returns, factor mobility, and the contributions of various factors to increased output and progress. Improved facts about agriculture might do as much as changes in values to smooth the course of future farm policy.

Farm policy by nature will never be wholly satisfying to those involved. It will contain some elements of the free market and some attempts at output control. It will contain some elements of demand expansion and some of market discrimination. It will contain some programs to improve resource mobility from agriculture. The resulting policies will contain too little of some of these elements to suit some groups and too much to suit others. Efficient resource use will be patently disregarded according to some views, and it will receive entirely too much attention according to others. Farm policy must be a pluralistic policy designed to achieve a number of values, and, therefore, it will always be diverse, diffuse, and involve much more than economics. Like it or not, so is the real world.

Index

Abel, Martin E., 71, 287.

Acquisition cost, defined, 111; relation to equilibrium in agriculture, 117; and salvage value, adjustment to differences under different situations, 115, 116; and salvage value, effect of cyclical fluctuations in nonfarm employment on, 121; and salvage value, factors affecting durable assets, 118, 119; and salvage value for human effort in agriculture, 120, 121; and salvage value of flow inputs, 123; and salvage value of land, 122; and salvage value of nondurable inputs, 123.

Acreage allotments and freedom, 305.

Acreage allotments for tobacco, 300; effects of, 300, 301.

Acreage reduction, effectiveness in controlling output, 298, 299.

Acreage Reserve Program, 306.

Agricultural Advisory Commission, problems of, 208.

Agricultural Conservation Payments, 312.

Agricultural exports, 88.

Agricultural policies, success of, 386, 387.

Agricultural treadmill, and farm income, 109; and new technology, 108.

American Farm Bureau Federation, as a farm organization, 221–6; attitude toward the Area Redevelopment program, 252, 253; attitude toward the Cooperative Extension Service in farm policy education, 214; attitude toward direct payments, 334; attitude toward Farmer Committees, 211, 212; attitude toward proposed solutions to the poverty problem, 251; background, 223; beliefs on distribution of economic power, 14; beliefs regarding competitive market, 11, 12, 13, 14; beliefs regarding distribution of political control in government, 13; beliefs regarding economic opportunity, 17, 18; beliefs regarding economic organization, 11–14; beliefs regarding rewards as related to productive contribution, 11; and commodity groups, 224; difficulties in adjusting to change in the political structure, 234; land-retirement program, 306, 307; membership, 1961, 221; and partisan politics, 223, 226; recommendation to defer depreciation, 349–50; regarding the family farm as a policy goal, 65; regarding freedom as a goal of farm policy, 74; regarding parity as a policy goal, 66, 67; regarding parity price and parity income as a policy goal, 66; relation to Farm Bloc, 187–8; short-run

401